CHAOS IN THE BOX

By the same author

THE ILLUSTRATED HISTORY OF FOOTBALL (2016)

THE ILLUSTRATED HISTORY OF FOOTBALL:
HALL OF FAME (2017)

GOALLESS DRAWS (2018)

CHAOS IN THE BOX

CHRONICLES FROM MODERN FOOTBALL

DAVID SQUIRES

First published by Guardian Faber in 2024
Guardian Faber is an imprint of Faber & Faber Ltd,
The Bindery, 51 Hatton Garden
London EC1N 8HN

Guardian is a registered trade mark of
Guardian News & Media Ltd,
Kings Place, 90 York Way, London N1 9GU

Typeset by Faber & Faber Ltd
Printed and bound by CPI Group (UK) Ltd, Croydon CR0 4YY

A CIP record for this book
is available from the British Library

ISBN 978–1–783–35283–8

2 4 6 8 10 9 7 5 3 1

For Sarah

CONTENTS

INTRODUCTION

The six-year period covered by this book has witnessed wars, a global plague, more UK prime ministers than I can be arsed to google and the death of one head of the British royal family (at the time of writing). It has also been a tumultuous time for football. Guys, *two* different teams won the Premier League.

My job each Tuesday is to deliver a cartoon summary of the week's football stories for the woke, anti-growth extremists at the *Guardian*, and I present here the choicest cuts of the strips I didn't *completely* hate.

People often stop me in the street and breathlessly plead with me to reveal the secrets of The Artistic Process. Criminally, I've never been asked to share the details of my daily routine for a glossy Sunday supplement, thus providing conclusive evidence that I'm being silenced by the MAINSTREAM MEDIA (if you ignore the fact this volume is a compilation of cartoons for a national newspaper).

You, however, have been good enough to receive this book from someone who vaguely knows you like football, so my reward is to let you peek inside the artist's studio as you inevitably sit reading this on the toilet, perched above your own mess as you flick through my last six years of toil. You're welcome. x

3.00 a.m.: I am awoken by my personal trainer, Claude, with a single crow's egg and a conical flask of marrow juice. Claude then explains the latest internet memes to me as I complete five hundred finger press-ups to prepare my hand for the creative exertions ahead. He also reads the direct messages from people pretending not to understand my A-League cartoons, some feigning genuine anger and disappointment – a long-running in-joke I've enjoyed with My Public.

5.00 a.m.: A leap into the plunge pool. I can't swim (Speedo allergy), so this really starts the day with a jolt of adrenalin. Once Claude has massaged my heart back into action, it's ablutions time! A single, rigid sausage of waste is evacuated, retrieved, labelled and stored, lest it fall into the hands of my enemies (unlucky, the *Telegraph*'s 'Matt'!).

7.00 a.m.: Eyelids pinned back, I sit in front of a vast wall of televisions and consume every football match that has occurred during my four hours of sleep. This is followed by the first of a half-hourly scroll of the various social media timelines: Lars von Trier critiquing Wotsits for LADbible on Facebook; some spicy takes, formerly known as white supremacist race hate, on X, formerly known as Twitter; and a gallery of artwork by beautiful people on Instagram who are better at drawing than me and have filtered their lifestyles in such a way as to make me feel like I live in a service station needle bin by comparison. Self-esteem crushed, I'm ready to attack the day!

9:00 a.m.: To my drawing board. The quill. The parchment. The ergonomic throne. An ambient mood is set with a deep-focus audio compilation of an incomprehensibly popular YouTuber screaming at a football awards ceremony, which is surprisingly soothing if you imagine he's being violated by a polar bear.

I attempt to decipher the notes I've compiled over the last week: 'Crown Prince Mohammed bin Salman crossbar challenge'; 'Pochettino Rubik's cube'; 'Buy more crow eggs'. A rich bounty of satirical treasure.

Neurological synapses sparkle, comedic equations dart across my vision, I squint at a waterfall of neon digits like on *The Matrix*, before inevitably deciding just to do another cartoon about Roy Hodgson.

12.00 p.m.: Lunch in gaseous form. An infusion of cheese-and-pickle sandwiches and a lungful of Wotsits (nice one, Lars von).

Recharged, I plough through some more work, before my favourite chore of the day: family time (2.00–2.12 p.m.). Once that shit's out of the way, it's back to the old LOL factory. (Please don't tell anyone I call it the LOL factory.)

3:00 p.m.: Pickleball session with Mark Wahlberg, Stormzy and Jake Humphrey.

5:00 p.m.: Once my sketch is complete, it's time to add some flesh to the bones of my latest masterpiece with the mechanical assistance of a rusty contraption of pipes, cogs and dials. It's expensive to run and prone to frequent malfunction, but Adobe Photoshop remains the market leader for creatives who can't be bothered to learn the basics of a new software program.

7.00 p.m.: There follows the weekly sparring session with the lawyers, who crush the blossom of my creativity in their grey fists by arguing that my joke about ███████████ being a ██████ is 'definitely libellous', blah, blah, blah. Eventually, I am forced to concede defeat when Claude advises that even I can't afford a lengthy legal battle with ███████████. Mercifully, the legal team at Faber aren't scared of the truth.

11.00 p.m.: The cartoon is uploaded to the internet. Exhausted from another day of bringing joy and dated cultural references to the world, I retire to my oxygen chamber. Claude dutifully █████s me to sleep as I soak in the glowing online feedback, which usually takes the form of a load of shit puns and some classic banter about not understanding at least three panels.

2018–19:
MOU'S POLEMICAL ROMANCE

The season began in a post-World Cup glow, with football re-energised after a holiday in Vladimir Putin's Russia. Despite all the pre-tournament fears about holding the tournament in an authoritarian state, it turned out that everyone was super-friendly when the eyes of the world were on them – especially if you didn't think about the fate of the protesters who were dragged off the pitch during the final. Sure, hindsight's a wonderful thing, but who could have predicted that spending a month cosying up to Vlad would age like a fine yoghurt?

Manchester United manager José Mourinho had spent the tournament enjoying the hospitality of *Russia Today*, but he then embarked upon a pre-season tour of the US with all the enthusiasm of a teenager forced to go on holiday with his stupid loser family. In a series of increasingly moody press conferences, he moped about United's transfer business, grumbled that, if he was a fan, he 'wouldn't spend my money to see these teams' and dug out Anthony Martial for being absent while attending the birth of his child. Fair's fair, you can always have more boring kids, but how many times in life do you get to play *the* San Jose Earthquakes?

Sure, I hammered the joke of Mourinho acting like an emo kid, like the great man himself berating a female club doctor for doing her job, but it was becoming obvious that he wouldn't be slamming the doors at Old Trafford for much longer. José's three-year employment lifespan is similar to that of a hummingbird, and there he was, flapping his arms and emitting a constant whine, while admittedly looking pretty damn handsome in the colourful plumage of the Adidas training apparel.

Despite Emo Mou being a popular character, it was a relief when Manchester United finally pulled the plug, especially because I'd almost exhausted the Wikipedia entry for 'Emo artists'. Needless to say, the Lowry Hotel's surliest long-term resident had the last laugh, getting fired ten minutes after I'd filed that week's cartoon. It really was an . . . All Time Low.

The vibes were more positive at Arsenal. Unai Emery had replaced Arsène Wenger, who was waved on his way as fondly as the 'WENGER OUT' signs that had become a global internet phenomenon. There was no chance that the new coach would be reduced to a lazy meme based on the way he pronounced his 'V's.

There was a new dawn at Chelsea, too, with the tobacco-chewing Maurizio Sarri taking the reins with his big old banana fingers. The campaign started brightly, but his authority disintegrated as the season burned down to its dog-end, as evidenced by Kepa Arrizabalaga's refusal to be substituted during the League Cup final against Manchester City. The furious Sarri was the width of a Rizla paper away from stropping out of Wembley, but he stuck it out until May before slumping away in disgrace, Chelsea having only finished third and lifting a European trophy.

A fresh young buck was being lined up as Maurizio's replacement: Frank Lampard. His 'Frank Lampard's Derby County' team were locked in a Championship promotion battle with Leeds United, managed by some foreign bloke called Marcelo Bielsa, who didn't even have any GCSEs. The two fell out when one of Bielsa's coaching staff was caught spying on a Frank Lampard's Derby County training session.

In terms of comic potential, it was a story bettered only by Crystal Palace goalkeeper Wayne Hennessey claiming he'd been waving to a friend in a restaurant when a photograph was taken that appeared to show him giving a Nazi salute. The one time I've had a cartoon completely spiked by the legal department was when I depicted Hennessey's night out, featuring a series of unfortunate events that, caught in the moment, looked like hate crimes (e.g. goose-stepping over a bread roll, ordering a stacked flamin' burger that looked like a burning cross, getting a pointy white napkin blown onto his face by a hand dryer).

I'm not sure where to drop this – and presumably neither did they – but in April, someone left a sex toy in the Old Trafford dugout.

Liverpool amassed 97 points but still ended as runners-up to Manchester City. The two sides matched each other win for win during a tense run-in, until City struck a decisive blow at the start of a mad week that reminded you why you love this crazy, unpredictable game that inevitably ends with Pep Guardiola tossing another piece of silverware into Sheikh Mansour's Scrooge McDuck-style trophy pool. Vincent Kompany smashed in a late long-range winner against Leicester before the words 'Don't shoot' could escape Pep's throat, virtually assuring them of the title.

The next evening, in the Champions League, Liverpool overcame a 3–0 first-leg deficit to both figuratively and literally clip Lionel Messi's Barcelona round the ear with an unforgettable 4–0 win.

Yet more drama was to follow on Wednesday, when Lucas Moura scored in the 96th minute to send Tottenham – *Tottenham* – through to the final at Ajax's expense, the Dutch side having led 3–0 on aggregate after 35 minutes of the second leg. That was an evening of high drama that couldn't even be ruined by a weird cutaway to a gurning Peter Walton on BT Sport.

Liverpool went on to win the all-Premier League final, which everyone agreed was a great advert for the Eredivisie.

THERE WERE A FEW DAYS THERE WHEN THERE WAS **LITERALLY NO FOOTBALL**. HOLLOW-EYED SUPPORTERS WERE FORCED TO SURVIVE ON THE THIN GRUEL OF:

THE OVERSEAS PRE-SEASON THIRD KIT SHOWCASE.

A NATIONWIDE SELECTION OF LOWER-LEAGUE FIXTURES.

FITBA.

THANKFULLY, **PROPER FOOTBALL** IS BACK, WITH THE RETURN OF **THE EREDIVISIE!!** ALSO BACK IS THE PREMIER LEAGUE, WHICH LIVERPOOL WON ON SUNDAY WITH A 4-0 WIN AGAINST A WEST HAM TEAM AS RESOLUTE AS JACK WILSHERE'S KNEE LIGAMENTS. IT WAS ALL TOO MUCH FOR ONE YOUNG LIVERPOOL FAN:

Thank you, Mo; I wasn't even born the last time we won the league!

No... ...one... ...was...!!

~POP~

AT LEAST JÜRGEN KLOPP COULD BE RELIED UPON TO KEEP HIS COMPOSURE.

Here, lads, has anyone seen my shower ge... oh.

A LOT HAS CHANGED OVER THE SUMMER, NOT LEAST AT ARSENAL. UNAI EMERY'S TEAM ARE NO LONGER PUSHOVERS, AS DEMONSTRATED BY PETR ČECH NEARLY PASSING THE BALL INTO HIS OWN NET AND FRENCH EXCHANGE STUDENTS APPARENTLY BEING PICKED TO ANCHOR THE MIDFIELD.

Guys, this is Jean-Paul. He is 15-years old and lives in a house in La Rochelle. He has one sister and likes the babyfoot and partnering the Granit Xhaka.

ČECH REACTED ANGRILY WHEN THE TWITTER ACCOUNT OF BAYER LEVERKUSEN MADE A JOKE ABOUT HIS MISTAKE. **LIGHTEN UP, PETR**; EVERYONE KNOWS THAT SOCIAL MEDIA OFFICIAL ACCOUNT BANTZ IS EXCELLENT AND IN NO WAY MAKES YOU FANTASISE ABOUT THE DAY THAT THE MACHINES FINALLY RISE UP AND CRUSH HUMANITY!

This will CAP off a good day lol...

Gah, if anything this is worse.

CHELSEA GAVE A DEBUT TO THE WORLD'S MOST EXPENSIVE GOALKEEPER, KEPA ARRIZABALAGA. NEW BOSS MAURIZIO SARRI SEEMED SLIGHTLY UNDERWHELMED BY THE SIGNING; PERHAPS HE'D HAVE BEEN MORE ENTHUSIASTIC IF KEPA HAD BEEN UNVEILED BY A MAGICIAN...

I wave my wand and piff, poff, poof...

U wot?

TRANSFERS ARE HARD TO GET RIGHT. THIS MIGHT BE WHY MANCHESTER UNITED ARE SAID TO BE LOOKING AT HIRING A DIRECTOR OF FOOTBALL — A MOVE THAT WILL DO LITTLE TO LIGHTEN JOSÉ MOURINHO'S MOOD.

I know you're disappointed, but look on the bright side: Luke Shaw scored a goal, so that's like having a snazzy new player...

GOD-DUH! You are so embarrassing.

Sorry about him, Jean-Paul.

SADLY, THE OPENING ROUND OF FIXTURES WAS MARRED BY THE SIGHT OF RAHEEM STERLING **SHAMELESSLY** CELEBRATING A GOAL **JUST 32 DAYS** AFTER ENGLAND'S WORLD CUP EXIT! PERHAPS THERE IS ONLY ONE WAY HE CAN REDEEM HIMSELF:

The reporters are still out there. I'll take them some tea! That seems to excuse all manner of misdeeds!

12 MINUTES LATER:

"Machine Gun Loving World Cup Traitor Flaunts Vile Wealth with SIX MUGS and FULL CREAM MILK"

It worked, that's much better than usual!

SQUIRES

THE INTERNATIONAL BREAK PROVIDED A BRIEF CHANCE TO FORGET ABOUT THE MEDIA AGENDA AGAINST THE FOOTBALL CLUB YOU LIKE. IT ALSO MEANT THAT YOU-KNOW-WHO WOULD NEED TO DO SOMETHING PRETTY SPECTACULAR TO FIND THE LIMELIGHT.

HE WAS AT WEMBLEY TO WATCH ENGLAND PLAY SPAIN. AS AUTUMN DESCENDS, THE HOSTS PROVIDED ONE LAST MEMORY OF A GLORIOUS SUMMER BY LOSING TO A BETTER FOOTBALL TEAM AGAIN. THE DECISIVE GOAL WAS SCORED BY RODRIGO, WHO WAS GIVEN ENOUGH TIME AND FREEDOM TO EXPLORE LONDON EN ROUTE TO GOAL.

CRUEL INJUSTICE DENIED ENGLAND A LATE, UNDESERVED EQUALISER, BUT THE GOOD NEWS IS THAT THEY ARE JUST ONE MYTHICAL PLAYMAKER AWAY FROM IMMORTALITY. LEGEND HAS IT THAT WHOMEVER CAN REMOVE AN ENCHANTED SWORD FROM A SLAB OF ROCK WILL INSPIRE ENGLAND TO FINALLY BEAT A DECENT TEAM IN A COMPETITIVE FIXTURE.

THE NATIONS LEAGUE AIMS TO REDUCE THE NUMBER OF MEANINGLESS FRIENDLIES. IN UNRELATED NEWS, ENGLAND PLAY SWITZERLAND IN LEICESTER TONIGHT. THE GAME PROVIDES A CHANCE FOR THE FA TO RECREATE JAMIE VARDY'S LIVING ROOM IN THE CENTRE CIRCLE, FROM WHERE THE RETIRING FORWARD CAN REVIEW HIS INTERNATIONAL HIGHLIGHTS.

WALES STARTED WITH A 4-1 WIN AGAINST IRELAND, WHOSE CHANCES WERE NO DOUBT HELPED BY ROY KEANE'S UNIQUE MOTIVATIONAL TECHNIQUES. GIVEN THE INFLUENCE KEANE SEEMS TO EXERT OVER THE TEAM, PERHAPS MARTIN O'NEILL SHOULD FOLLOW IN THE FOOTSTEPS OF THAT PARAGUAYAN CLUB AND APPOINT A DOG AS HIS ASSISTANT.

KEANE NO DOUBT ENJOYED FRANCE'S EXTENDED WORLD CUP CELEBRATIONS AFTER THEIR NATIONS CUP WIN AGAINST HOLLAND.

THE FESTIVITIES SERVED AS A REMINDER THAT IT'S PROBABLY JUST AS WELL THAT ENGLAND DIDN'T WIN THE WORLD CUP.

EARLY SIGNS SUGGEST THAT THE NEW EUROPEAN COMPETITION IS A HIT, AND IT PROVIDES A WELCOME DISTRACTION IN THESE TURBULENT POLITICAL TIMES. JUST THIS WEEKEND, FOR EXAMPLE, ANGLO-RUSSIAN TENSIONS ESCALATED AS BRITAIN DEPLOYED ITS BIGGEST WEAPON IN MOSCOW.

IT'S BEEN ANOTHER WEEK OF FUN AND LAUGHTER AT MANCHESTER UNITED. SUCCESSIVE DEFEATS TO FRANKIE LAMPARD'S DERBY COUNTY FC (FLDCFC) AND WEST HAM HAVE LEFT JOSÉ MOURINHO WITH A SEETHING SENSE OF RESENTMENT MORE COMMONLY FELT WHEN EDWARD ASKS HIM TO PLEASE TIDY UP HIS ROOM A BIT.

CENTRAL TO JOSÉ'S PROBLEMS IS HIS RELATIONSHIP WITH THE ENIGMATIC SOCIAL MEDIA PERSONALITY, PAUL POGBA, WHO REMAINS THE MOST POPULAR BOY IN SCHOOL DESPITE HIS REFUSAL TO DO HIS HOMEWORK ON TIME, IT IS WELL UNFAIR. STILL, JOSÉ HAD A MATURE WAY OF CUTTING HIM DOWN TO SIZE IN FRONT OF ALL HIS MATES:

THE 3-1 DEFEAT AT WEST HAM REPRESENTED MANCHESTER UNITED'S WORST START TO A PREMIER LEAGUE SEASON, AS MOURINHO INCREASINGLY COMES TO RESEMBLE SOME OF HIS MORE MALIGNED PREDECESSORS.

BY CONTRAST, AS WEST HAM IMPROVE, MANUEL PELLEGRINI IS LOOKING YOUNGER BY THE WEEK!

ON SATURDAY, HIS TEAM WERE ABLE TO EXPLOIT A MANCHESTER UNITED DEFENCE THAT WAS AS QUICK AND EFFICIENT AS THE WIFI AT OLD TRAFFORD.

AS THE GAME SLIPPED AWAY FROM THE VISITORS, PERHAPS MOYESINHO SHOULD HAVE ADOPTED A TACTIC SOMETIMES USED AT THE LONDON STADIUM WHEN THINGS AREN'T GOING THE WAY YOU'D LIKE:

AT LEAST THE PLAYERS LOOKED THE PART IN THEIR NEW AWAY KIT—AN HOMAGE TO THE OLD FOOTBALL PINK NEWSPAPERS. FOR EXTRA AUTHENTICITY, PERHAPS THE SHIRTS SHOULD ALSO INCLUDE ON-THE-WHISTLE, HAND-STITCHED MATCH REPORTS.

WHILE MOURINHO'S CRITICS WHO AREN'T RELIANT UPON HIS CONTINUED ANTICS FOR A WEEKLY FOOTBALL CARTOON ARE CALLING FOR HIS HEAD, THE SPORT IS FULL OF UNLIKELY COMEBACK STORIES. FOR EXAMPLE, DANIEL STURRIDGE SCORED AN ABSOLUTE BEAUTY AGAINST CHELSEA AT THE WEEKEND, HAVING JUST RETURNED FROM 2014!

EVEN IF MOURINHO CAN'T SAVE HIS JOB, HE STILL HOLDS THE CLUB IN HIGH ENOUGH REGARD THAT HE COULD FOCUS ON RUNNING ONE OF THOSE ONLINE FAN CHANNELS THAT MIGHT BE AN ELABORATE PERFORMANCE ART PROJECT, IT'S HARD TO TELL.

SQUIRES

IT'S NOT MUCH FUN WHEN YOU'RE THE ONLY PERSON NOT DANCING...

ESPECIALLY WHEN PEOPLE OF BAD EDUCATION RUB YOUR NOSE IN YOUR OWN MISERY.

AAAAH! The last Dashboard Confessional album only got a 4.7 on Pitchfork and My Chemical Romance are never reforming!

I'M NOT OK.

AT THE END OF SATURDAY'S DRAW BETWEEN CHELSEA AND MANCHESTER UNITED, A MEMBER OF THE BLUES' BACKROOM STAFF - MARCO IANNI - DISPLAYED A LACK OF GRACE THAT INCENSED JOSÉ MOURINHO; A MAN WHO IS SUCH A **STICKLER** FOR SIDELINE ETIQUETTE THAT HE COULD OPEN HIS OWN FINISHING SCHOOL.

These nails are filthy! You could give the opposition's assistant manager a serious infection when you gouge his eyeball. TOP MARKS!

Straight backs when we sprint down the touchline, Astrid!

THE INCIDENT CAME AFTER A 96TH MINUTE EQUALISER FROM ROSS BARKLEY; A PLAYER WHOSE TRUE GENIUS HAS BEEN REVEALED UNDER THE TUTELAGE OF MAURIZIO SARRI.

It's not your fault.

I know.

Look at me, son. It's not your fault.

... I know.

No. No you don't. It's not your fault.

Don't eff with me, la. Not you.

It's not your fault.

Waaaaah..!

It was a bit his fault.

Christ, Conte, don't feel like you **have** to stick around until you find a new job.

I don't mind.

IT WAS A VERY DIFFERENT STORY IN HUDDERSFIELD, WHERE BEST FRIENDS DAVID WAGNER AND JÜRGEN KLOPP CAME HEAD TO HEAD. BUT AS WAS DEMONSTRATED BY THEIR JOINT POST-MATCH INTERVIEW, WHEN THOSE GUYS GET TOGETHER, THINGS CAN GET PRETTY WILD TOO.

Hey, good buddy; what say you we dust off the old tactics board and crack a few frosty Lucozades to get the party started?

Okily dokily, Freunderoonie. After all, it is Saturday night!

MOURINHO WON'T HAVE BEEN GRATEFUL TO THE STEWARDS, COACHES, PLAYERS AND OFFICIALS WHO PREVENTED HIM FROM GETTING TO A MAN 20 YEARS HIS JUNIOR WHO HASN'T BEEN LIVING ON A DIET OF COMPLIMENTARY PILLOW MINTS FOR THE LAST TWO YEARS (PRESUMABLY). IANNI VANISHED INTO THE BOWELS OF STAMFORD BRIDGE, WHEREUPON HIS TRUE IDENTITY WAS REVEALED.

Dr Eva! Hoo boy, I did not see that coming!

THE UNITED MANAGER RECEIVED AN APOLOGY AFTER THE GAME, BUT CHELSEA AND THE FA TOOK A DIM VIEW OF THE INCIDENT. THEY'LL BE LESS THAN IMPRESSED TO DISCOVER THAT THE MOCKERY CONTINUED LATER.

Do you like apples? Well how do you like **them** appl—

2-2

Your question is a bad question, I'm sorry. If you understand fruit, you do not ask this...

Come on, Ross. We'll workshop this...

SQUIRES

IF YOU IGNORE THE FACT THAT THE TOP FOUR ALL WON (AND FOR THE SAKE OF **NARRATIVE** THIS CARTOON BEGS THAT YOU DO), IT WAS A WEEKEND THAT BUCKED SOME LONG-STANDING TRENDS IN THE **PREMIER LEAGUE:**

CRYSTAL PALACE **WON WITHOUT WILFRIED ZAHA**, DEFEATING A LEICESTER TEAM WHO PLAYED AS IF THEY'D EATEN A PRE-MATCH MEAL IN THE PALACE CANTEEN.

Tuck in, lads! Spam and suet hash. Perfect for a wet winter's day...

Mwah!

LIVERPOOL FINALLY BEAT MANCHESTER UNITED...

...AND SOUTHAMPTON **WON A FOOTBALL MATCH!** THEIR 3-2 DEFEAT OF ARSENAL WAS THE FIRST UNDER THEIR NEW COACH, BRITISH ACTOR DAVID MORRISSEY.

I prepared for the role by working on The Walking Dead for two years.

My dear boy, have you just tried coaching?

HIS CHARACTER 'RALPH HASENHÜTTL' HAS MADE AN INSTANT IMPACT, WITH HIS DEMONSTRATIVE BEHAVIOUR AND COLOURFUL QUOTES, LIKE: "IF YOU WANT A GUARANTEE, BUY A WASHING MACHINE". COINCIDENTALLY, ARSENAL'S DEFENCE MIGHT HAVE BETTER CONTAINED THE AERIAL THREAT OF DANNY INGS HAD IT COMPRISED ENTIRELY OF WHITE GOODS.

BOSCH!

Smeg.

FLY EMI

WHAT'S MORE, 'HASENHÜTTL' EVEN GOT THE CLUB TO FORK OUT TO BUY EVERY SOUTHAMPTON SUPPORTER A DRINK. **FOR SHAME, SIR.** AS **IF** THE AFFECTIONS OF WE FOOTBALL FANS CAN BE BOUGHT SO CHEAPLY AND CYNICALLY WITH THE PROMISE OF **FREE BEER.**

RALPH! RALPH! RALPH! RALPH! RALPH! RALPH! RALPH!

THE ACCEPTABLE MORRISSEY

It's just a goddamn popularity contest with you people.

OVER AT MANCHESTER UNITED, JOSÉ MOURINHO'S DAYS WERE NUMBERED AFTER ANOTHER INSIPID DISPLAY THAT HAD NOTHING TO DO WITH HIM (HOW UNLUCKY CAN ONE MAN **BE?**). PERHAPS IT WAS HIS CHRISTMAS TRANSFER LIST THAT PROVED TO BE THE LAST STRAW FOR THE CLUB'S HIERARCHY.

Right. I want a Harry Maguire, a Toby Alderweireld, some hair straighteners – GHD ones, four hundred loom bands, and for Paul Pogba to fall down a quarry.

Listen kid, you aint even gettin' that steward Fellaini nearly killed. Now get outta my sight and tell Woodward to send in the next stooge.

Smeg!

FOR NOW, THERE IS PERHAPS ONLY ONE PLACE WHERE THE ATMOSPHERE IS AS SOUR AS MANCHESTER UNITED: THE CHRISTMAS REUNION OF ENGLAND'S 1986 WORLD CUP SQUAD.

The EU are penalising us! We should leave with no deal. We'll be fine, Gary.

Too right!

You mean **you'll** be fine, Chris.

Aye, they kept me job open at the sausage factory. People'll need good old British bangers after Brexit.

APRIL 2019

SOYLENT GREEN PRODUCTS.

Fookin' Crackajack.

Stop daydreaming, Waddle; we've got a huge order from Crystal Palace to fulfil, man!

SQUIRES

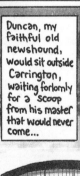

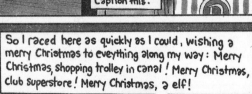

SQUIRES

ACCORDING TO *DER SPIEGEL*, EUROPE'S IMPOVERISHED BIG CLUBS HAVE FINALLY STRUCK UPON A WAY TO MAKE SOME BLOOMIN' MONEY: A EUROPEAN SUPER LEAGUE! AS EDIFYING AS THE BREAKAWAY SOUNDS, IT HAS LEFT FANS OF OTHER DOMESTIC CLUBS REELING...

Oh no. Don't go.

Truly, I am overcome with woe.

THE ALLEGED DEFECTION HAS BEEN WIDELY INTERPRETED AS A POWER PLAY BY THE BIG CLUBS TO GET A BIGGER SLICE OF THE CASH PIE. THEIR GREED SEEMS AS INSATIABLE AS MY FRIEND'S DOG WHO HAD TO HAVE AN OPERATION AFTER SCOFFING AN UNATTENDED 10KG BAG OF BISCUITS AND WAS STILL LOOKING FOR FOOD WHEN HE GOT HOME.

Well, at least Uli Hoeness has learned a valuable lesson, oh my God, he's eaten the sofa.

More.

FIVE ENGLISH CLUBS ARE SAID TO BE AMONGST THE LEAGUE'S 11 FOUNDING MEMBERS, WHO ARE GUARANTEED TO NOT BE RELEGATED FOR THE FIRST 20 YEARS OF A COMPETITION THAT PROMISES TO BE EVERY BIT AS EXCITING AS THE INTERNATIONAL CHAMPIONS CUP!

Bit awkward. Who's going to tell Sir Chips Arsenal aren't one of England's big five? Not me!

oh.

Sorry, are you the caterer?

Unbelievable. By 2021, our amazing new stadium will be nearly finished. Then you'll see some catering!

Really?

:sigh: No...

SOME OF THE CLUBS NAMED HAVE REFUTED THE STORY, WHILE OTHERS HAVE FUELLED SPECULATION BY REMAINING SILENT. EITHER WAY, IT SEEMS INEVITABLE THAT EUROPE'S BLUE CHIP CLUBS WILL EVENTUALLY CLEAR OFF, AND WHEN THEY DO, THEY'D BE WELL ADVISED TO HEAD OFF PUBLIC CRITICISM WITH A TRIED AND TESTED TECHNIQUE:

The latte-sipping *elites* like Viktoria Plzen or whoever want to stop decent, hard-working salt of the earth plutocrats from earning a few more pennies. Sad.

THE REVELATIONS CAME AT THE END OF A WEEK PACKED WITH LIFE-AFFIRMING FOOTBALL STORIES, SUCH AS THE 2022 WORLD CUP BEING EXPANDED TO FIT HALF THE PLANET'S POPULATION INTO A TINY OIL STATE; ALLEGATIONS OF FINANCIAL FOUL PLAY, AND A SELF-ENTITLED PETITION DEMANDING THAT SPANISH FOOTBALL COME HOME TO MIAMI. THE AGGREGATE EFFECT LEFT FOOTBALL FANS WONDERING IF THEY SHOULD TAKE UP A HOBBY THAT MAKES THEM FEEL LESS GROSS.

DOGGING

HOWEVER, WHAT THE MONEY MEN FAIL TO REALISE IS THAT THE SOUL OF FOOTBALL CAN NEVER BE BOUGHT (NARRATOR: 'IT CAN'). NO MATTER HOW SEEDY THE TOP LEVEL OF FOOTBALL BECOMES, NO PRICE CAN BE PUT ON THE GLOBAL LOVE OF THE GAME ITSELF; THAT INNATE FEELING THAT COMPELS YOU TO STOP AND WATCH SOME AMATEURS IN THE PARK...

Hah, I will literally watch any old sh*te. What am I like?

As pep talks go, this isn't exactly 'Any Given Sunday', gaffer...

Any old sh*te...

...OR THE SIMPLE PLEASURE OF DINKING A ROLLED-UP SOCK INTO THE LAUNDRY BASKET AND IMAGINING THE ROAR OF THE CROWD...

...OR THE SENSE OF JOY EXPERIENCED WHEN YOUR FAVOURITE, CAREFREE, BRAZILIAN FOOTBALLER ENDORSES A FAR RIGHT PRESIDENTIAL CANDIDATE.

That counts.

That bloody counts.

"The dictatorship's mistake was to torture but not kill!"

Jogo Bonito!

BUT SHOULD THE EUROPEAN SUPERLEAGUE COME INTO BEING, AND PSG END UP PLAYING AC MILAN IN, SAY, DOHA, THEY WILL STILL BE FORCED TO ANSWER FOOTBALL'S MOST IMPORTANT QUESTION:

WHY AREN'T THEY WEARING POPPIES?

SQUIRES

ALL EMPIRES EVENTUALLY CRUMBLE, AND MANCHESTER CITY'S 2-0 DEFEAT AT CHELSEA LEAVES THEM IN **CRISIS MODE** UNTIL THEIR NEXT 21-MATCH UNBEATEN RUN BEGINS AGAIN ON SATURDAY. PEP GUARDIOLA WAS HAPPY WITH HIS TEAM'S PERFORMANCE, IF NOT THE DECISION TO AWARD CHELSEA A CORNER FROM WHICH DAVID LUIZ ROSE TO SECURE THE THREE POINTS.

I was just saying to Sir Ben Kingsley: the referee's lost me another hagiographic documentary series on Amazon Prime. Thank him ever so much for that, won't you?

HOWEVER, THE GAME WAS OVERSHADOWED BY THE ABUSE SPRAYED AT RAHEEM STERLING BY AN ANGRY DELICATESSEN DISPLAY OF MIDDLE-AGED CHELSEA FANS. THIS LED TO AN INTENSE INTERNET DEBATE ABOUT THE EXACT NATURE OF THE VERBAL INSULTS.

No, he was clearly calling Sterling a 'Manc c*nt'.

At least we can agree that a young man was called a 'c*nt' in his place of work.

We have made some real progress today. Hooray for unity.

GENERIC INTERNET PERSON #1

GENERIC INTERNET PERSON #2

Silly Cu

STERLING RESPONDED WITH AN INSTAGRAM POST HIGHLIGHTING THE CONTRASTING WAY IN WHICH SECTIONS OF THE MEDIA REPORT 'STORIES' ABOUT BLACK AND WHITE FOOTBALLERS, DRAWING A DIRECT LINE TO THE ROLE IT PLAYS IN FUELLING RACISM. IT'S HARD TO EXAGGERATE THE KIND OF VILIFICATION STERLING HAS BEEN SUBJECTED TO IN RECENT YEARS AND WE HAVE REACHED THE STAGE WHERE IT WOULD NOT BE SURPRISING TO SEE HEADLINES LIKE:

19:50

Lavish football millionaire Raheem Sterling employs own digestive system to turn food into waste.

Somehow it took four people to write this story. Mad, eh?

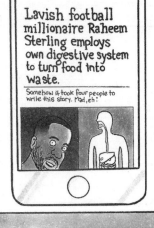

19:30

Boffins confirm Raheem Sterling the major cause of climate change

Man City star is a human being. Ipso facto

20:18

Under fire Raheem Sterling faces new allegations that he is Raheem Sterling

- Sink-buying loafer fails to issue denial.
- 'We didn't vote for this', says angry, confused man.

HIS RESPONSE IN THE FACE OF THE ABUSE HE RECEIVES FROM THE STANDS, ON THE STREETS, AND IN THE MEDIA, REVEAL THE STRENGTH OF THE MAN. ALTHOUGH ONLY SLIGHT IN STATURE, STERLING HAS PROVEN HIMSELF TO BE A COLOSSUS IN COMPARISON TO THE BIGOTS, THE HACKS, AND THE ATTENTION-SEEKING BREAKFAST TELEVISION PRESENTERS.

You have invited this.

THE ALLEGATION, ALONG WITH THE RECENT ONES INVOLVING PIERRE-EMERICK AUBAMEYANG AND MOTHERWELL'S CHRISTIAN MBULU HAVE COME AS A SHOCK TO ANYONE WHO HASN'T SEEN THE NEWS FOR THE LAST FEW YEARS, OR ISN'T A MEMBER OF AN ETHNIC MINORITY, PRESUMABLY.

Football has a racism problem? I just thought black, Asian and minority ethnic people faced discrimination in employment, education, healthcare, justice and bleak dating apps!

'Manc people? That's awful...

THERE HAVE ALSO BEEN REPORTS OF SOME FANS SINGING STEPHEN YAXLEY-LENNON'S STAGE NAME AT FOOTBALL GROUNDS, ALTHOUGH PERSONALLY I'D RATHER TAKE MORTGAGE ADVICE FROM HIM THAN SEE HIM TURN UP AT MY FAVOURITE CLUB. AT LEAST TELEVISION IS DOING ITS BIT TO COMBAT THE GLOBAL RISE OF THE FAR RIGHT, BY PROVIDING ITS KEY FIGURES WITH REGULAR COSY PLATFORMS. YOU ALMOST EXPECT TO SEE MARINE LE PEN ON STRICTLY, OR STEVE BANNON ON MOTD2.

For me, Ritchie's got to track back there, Chappers...

BREXIT WAS LIKE PRISING OPEN A DUSTY TOMB, ALLOWING A FLURRY OF TOXIC, ANCIENT OPINIONS TO ESCAPE (WORKING TITLE FOR THE FILM ADAPTATION: 'RACISTS OF THE LOST ARK'). AT LEAST WE KNOW WHICH SELF-SERVING MILLIONAIRE TO BLAME FOR THE SUBSEQUENT HATE AND CHAOS:

DAVID CAM RAHEEM STERLING

SGUIRES

SMILEY'S PEOPLE

FOOTBALL ESPIONAGE IS ALIVE AND WELL AND WAS THE FOCUS OF MUCH NATIONAL ATTENTION UNTIL SOME MANIAC ASKED NEIL WARNOCK ABOUT BREXIT.

WITH HIS LICENCE TO KILL PLAYERS BY EASTER WITH HIS PHYSICALLY AND MENTALLY DEMANDING COACHING METHODS, LEEDS UNITED'S MARCELO BIELSA HAS AN ARRAY OF GADGETS TO HELP HIM GAIN AN ADVANTAGE IN THE COLD WAR OF THE CHAMPIONSHIP.

AS WITH ALL GREAT SPY THRILLERS, AT SOME POINT THE MAIN CHARACTER GETS CAUGHT OUT. THIS WAS THE CASE LAST WEEK WHEN ONE OF LEEDS' OPERATIVES WAS CAPTURED SNOOPING AROUND DERBY'S TRAINING GROUND.

FRANK LAMPARD SEEMS TO HAVE ACCEPTED BIELSA'S NON-APOLOGY, AFTER WHAT MUST HAVE BEEN THE WORLD'S LONGEST SKYPE CALL. HOWEVER, THERE MAY STILL BE AN AWKWARD SCENE WHEN THE DERBY MANAGER LATER TAKES OVER AT LEEDS.

LAMPARD SAYS HE IS A FAN OF BIELSA AND EVEN HAS A COPY OF HIS BOOK AT HOME, BUT HE REMAINS SHOCKED AND DISAPPOINTED BY HIS TACTICS.

IF IT'S INTELLIGENCE BIELSA'S AFTER, HE SHOULD LOOK NO FURTHER THAN CARDIFF CITY, WHERE MANAGER @Colin 3612498 HAS BEEN SPEAKING OUT ON BEHALF OF RICH OLD PEOPLE WITH NOTHING TO LOSE. ON SATURDAY, HE REGALED THE MEDIA WITH HIS RAZOR-SHARP POLITICAL ANALYSIS THAT IN NO WAY EXEMPLIFIED ALL THE WORST CONVERSATIONS YOU'VE HAD WITH RELATIVES WHO'VE HALF-REMEMBERED STORIES THEY'VE SKIM-READ IN THE DAILY EXPRESS.

AS WE KNOW, FREEDOM OF SPEECH MEANS BEING ABLE TO SAY WHATEVER YOU LIKE WITHOUT BEING CALLED OUT ON IT. WARNOCK'S INSPIRING MESSAGE OF GLOBAL ISOLATION SHOULD BE SPREAD MORE WIDELY, TO HELP RAISE AWARENESS OF A CRIMINALLY UNDER-REPORTED SUBJECT: BREXIT. PERHAPS HE SHOULD DO A RECORD.

BUT OF COURSE, IF THE HEAT GETS TOO MUCH, THERE'S ALWAYS THE TRADITIONAL FAILSAFE: BLAME IT ON THE BANTZ.

AFTER THE LATEST ROUND OF RESULTS, TRYING TO WORK OUT WHO IS GOING TO WIN THE PREMIER LEAGUE REMAINS AS FUTILE AS SENDING WAYNE HENNESSEY BACK IN TIME TO BERLIN IN THE 1930s TO ASSASSINATE ADOLF HITLER.

YES, IT'S THE MADDEST STORY OF THE SEASON: CRYSTAL PALACE GOALKEEPER WAYNE HENNESSEY BEING CLEARED BY THE FA OF DOING A NAZI SALUTE IN A RESTAURANT ON ACCOUNT OF HIM HAVING 'A LAMENTABLE DEGREE OF IGNORANCE' ABOUT HITLER, FASCISM AND THE NAZI REGIME. PALACE MANAGER ROY HODGSON SAYS HENNESSEY IS 'DESPERATE' TO LEARN ABOUT THE NAZIS (OH GOD) BUT WHAT FORM THIS CRASH COURSE WOULD TAKE IS, AS YET, UNCLEAR.

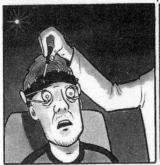

THE FA ACCEPTED HENNESSEY'S EXPLANATION, BUT SEEMS BAFFLED BY HIS APPARENT LACK OF KNOWLEDGE ON ONE OF THE MOST EVIL PERIODS OF HUMAN HISTORY, THE EFFECTS OF WHICH PERVADE TO THIS DAY.

AT THIS POINT, WE INTERRUPT THE CARTOON FOR AN IMPORTANT CLARIFICATION:

YESTERDAY EVENING, I HAD A MEAL WITH MY TEAMMATES (BINGE ATE SIX EASTER EGGS IN SOLITUDE) AND A CARTOON WAS DRAWN. I WAVED MY PEN OVER THE PAPER AND AT THE SAME TIME PUT MY HAND OVER MY MOUTH TO KEEP THE CHOCOLATE DOWN. IT HAS BEEN BROUGHT TO MY ATTENTION THAT FROZEN IN THE MOMENT IT LOOKS LIKE I HAVE MADE A COMPLETELY OBVIOUS JOKE ABOUT ANGLESEY. I CAN ASSURE EVERYONE THAT I WOULD NEVER DO THAT, AND ANY RESEMBLANCE TO THAT KIND OF BASIC HUMOUR IS ABSOLUTELY COINCIDENTAL. LOVE AND PEACE, DAVID.

ULTIMATELY, THE FA COMMISSION TOOK HENNESSEY'S WORD FOR IT. WHAT CHOICE DID IT HAVE, OTHER THAN STRAPPING HIM TO A LIE DETECTOR TEST?

SQUIRES

AS IS CUSTOMARY, EVERTON HAVE ENTERED THEIR ANNUAL

CRISIS MODE

TEMPORARY MANAGERIAL INCUMBENT **MARCO SILVA** IS LOOKING AS COMFORTABLE IN HIS POSITION AS HIS TEAM DO WHEN DEFENDING SET PIECES. HE CUT AN INCREASINGLY EXASPERATED FIGURE AS WOLVES CRUISED TO A 3-1 WIN AT GOODISON PARK ON SATURDAY.

THE CAT THAT INVADED THE PITCH AT GOODISON BECAME AN INSTANT FOOTBALL CELEBRITY (NO, IT WASN'T A QUIET WEEKEND). THIS MEANS IT WILL SOON BECOME THE SUBJECT OF A SUSTAINED ATTACK FROM CERTAIN SECTIONS OF THE MEDIA, BUT WHAT COULD IT BE ABOUT THIS SPECIFIC MOGGY THAT COULD MAKE IT A TARGET?

THE INCIDENT DOES RAISE THE AGE-OLD QUESTION; WHAT WOULD CAUSE PREMIER LEAGUE OPPONENTS MORE DISTRACTION:

EVERTON SHOULD TAKE HOPE FROM CHELSEA, WHO WERE ALSO IN **CRISIS MODE** AFTER A HEAVY DEFEAT AT BOURNEMOUTH LAST WEEK. THEIR 5-0 WIN AGAINST HUDDERSFIELD HAS POSTPONED MAURIZIO SARRI'S ONE-WAY TRIP TO ROMAN'S YACHT AND DEMONSTRATED THE BENEFIT OF NOT PLAYING A DEFENDER SUFFERING FROM A CONCUSSION.

PLUS, IT'S A LONG TIME SINCE EVERTON HAVE BEEN INVOLVED IN A TITLE RACE, BUT ON WEDNESDAY THEY PLAY A MANCHESTER CITY SIDE WHO COULD LEAPFROG LIVERPOOL WITH A WIN. NOT THAT JÜRGEN KLOPP IS CONCERNED...

WITH EVERTON FACING THE HORRIFYING PROSPECT OF NOT FINISHING 7TH, THEY MAY NOW ENACT PHASE TWO OF CRISIS MODE: SPENDING MONTHS FLUTTERING THEIR EYELASHES AND DROPPING SWEETLY-SCENTED HANDKERCHIEFS IN THE PATH OF SOME OTHER MANAGER WHO IS DOING WELL AT ANOTHER MID-RANKING PREMIER LEAGUE CLUB. INEVITABLY, HE WILL THEN DETERIORATE THE SECOND HE PULLS ON THE EVERTON BENCH APPAREL, AND THE CYCLE CONTINUES UNTIL THE END OF TIME.

ON SUNDAY, MANCHESTER CITY 'BURTON ALBIONED' CHELSEA BY A VIDIPRINTER-SPELLING MARGIN. IT WAS A PERFORMANCE AS MESMERISING AS ONE OF PEP GUARDIOLA'S HALLUCINOGENIC RETRO-SWEATERS.

THE EMIRATES MARKETING PROJECT PUNISHED CHELSEA AS IF THEY WERE A MAN WEARING A QATAR TOP. AS THEIR TALLY STEADILY INCREASED, MAURIZIO SARRI SCRIBBLED FURIOUSLY IN TO HIS SPECIAL TACTICS NOTEBOOK.

AH YES, MIKE DEAN; THE REAL HERO OF THE OCCASION. UNFORTUNATELY, THE GAME DIDN'T WITNESS DEAN'S 100TH RED CARD, BUT AS SOMEONE WHO LIVES BY THE MOTTO THAT THE BEST REFEREES ARE THE ONES YOU NOTICE FREQUENTLY AND CAN MAKE GIFS OUT OF, THE GREAT SHOWMAN WILL HAVE SOMETHING SPECIAL PLANNED FOR HIS PERSONAL CENTURY.

HAVING WATCHED HIS TEAM PUT IN A PERFORMANCE THAT RECALLED THE GLORY YEARS OF JOHN BUMSTEAD AND COLIN WEST, SARRI STROLLED PAST GUARDIOLA AND DOWN THE TUNNEL, CONFIDENT THAT NO ONE HAD NOTICED THE COLUMN OF STEAM RISING FROM THE VAST PILE OF WASTE HIS CHARGES HAD JUST DEPOSITED ON THE ETIHAD STADIUM PITCH.

CHELSEA'S SEASON HINGES ON THE NEXT FEW WEEKS. AFTER PLAYING MALMÖ ON THURSDAY, THEY THEN FACE A DIFFICULT FA CUP TIE AGAINST OLE GUNNAR SOLSKJÆR'S STEINER SCHOOL FOOTBALL TEAM. THERE, YOUNG PEOPLE ARE ABLE TO EXPRESS THEMSELVES, WITH GREAT RESULTS!

AND THEN IT'S A TRIP TO WEMBLEY, WHERE THEY HAVE A CHANCE TO CLAIM SOME SILVERWARE IN A LEAGUE CUP FINAL AGAINST... AH. IN THE MEANTIME, SARRI MUST ANSWER TO ROMAN ABRAMOVICH, WHO CONTINUES TO RUN CHELSEA WITH THE COOL-HEADED COMPETENCE OF A MAN TRYING TO WEAR A PAIR OF TROUSERS AS A JUMPER.

CONSIDERING THE RATE AT WHICH CHELSEA CHURN THROUGH MANAGERS, PERHAPS ROMAN WILL CONSIDER A MORE CREATIVE WAY TO GIVE SARRI HIS CARDS.

MEN IN SPORTS LEISUREWEAR MARCHED AROUND IN CONFUSION, LANYARDS FLAPPING BEHIND THEM. CHELSEA'S GOALKEEPER, KEPA ARRIZABALAGA, WAS REFUSING TO BE SUBSTITUTED AND **NOBODY KNEW WHAT TO DO**. IT WAS A FARCE ENRICHED BY THE FACT THAT TWO OF THE MAIN PLAYERS WERE DECKED OUT IN FLUORESCENT LIME. AN IMPOTENT MAURIZIO SARRI - HIMSELF DRESSED AS USUAL LIKE A FREELANCER TAKING HIS DOG FOR A WALK - STORMED TOWARDS THE WEMBLEY EXIT, BEFORE CHANGING HIS MIND...

THE LEAGUE CUP FINAL WAS IN THE DYING MOMENTS OF EXTRA-TIME. UP TO THAT POINT, IT HAD BEEN A CAGEY, GOALLESS AFFAIR THAT IN NO WAY MADE A MOCKERY OF ITS SPONSORSHIP BY AN ENERGY DRINK. CHELSEA'S PERFORMANCE WAS MUCH-IMPROVED FROM THEIR 6-0 DEFEAT TO MANCHESTER CITY A FORTNIGHT AGO, WHICH WAS CLEARLY ALL PART OF THE SARRI MASTERPLAN.

HOWEVER, HIS CUNNING PLOT WAS NOT IMMEDIATELY OBVIOUS TO EVERYONE, AND EVEN THE MOST LOYAL OF CHELSEA FANS HAD BEGUN TO LOSE PATIENCE.

BUT TODAY CHELSEA WERE IN WITH A CHANCE. WITH PENALTIES LOOMING, SARRI DECIDED TO BRING ON **SPOT KICK SPECIALIST** WILLY CABALLERO FOR THE TIRING KEPA. THE YOUNG GOALKEEPER HAD OTHER IDEAS, THOUGH. IN AN ACT OF BRAVERY THAT WOULD HAVE EVOKED MEMORIES OF BERT TRAUTMANN FOR THE CITY FANS BEHIND HIS GOAL, KEPA RESOLVED TO PLAY ON THROUGH THE PAIN BARRIER OF CRAMP, WHICH WE ALL KNOW CAN BE QUITE SORE. THIS LED TO AN ANIMATED EXCHANGE OF IDEAS WITH THE CHELSEA BENCH.

HAVING RIPPED OPEN HIS TOP, THROWN A BOTTLE AND A TANTRUM, SARRI HAD TO BE HELD BACK BY ANTONIO RÜDIGER AS KEPA SAUNTERED OVER AFTER THE FINAL WHISTLE.

SARRI'S MOOD WAS HARDLY LIGHTENED WHEN CHELSEA'S NEW PLAYER-MANAGER PRANCED ABOUT ON HIS GOAL-LINE LIKE AN EXTRA IN A 1980s AEROBICS VIDEO, AS A PRELUDE TO LETTING SERGIO AGÜERO'S PENALTY SQUIRM THROUGH HIS ARMS.

AFTER RAHEEM STERLING HAD CONVERTED THE PENALTY THAT WON CITY THE CUP (LIKE ANYONE CARES ABOUT **THAT**), KEPA MADE THE LONG MARCH UP THE STEPS TO COLLECT HIS MEDAL FOR BEST COMEDY NEWCOMER. HE THEN KEPT ON WALKING, OUT OF THE STADIUM AND IN TO THE WITNESS PROTECTION PROGRAMME, WHERE HE GETS TO LIVE THE REST OF HIS LIFE LIKE A SCHNOOK.

THANKFULLY, IT LATER TRANSPIRED THAT THE WHOLE INCIDENT WAS NOT A PUBLIC ACT OF DEFIANCE THAT EXPOSED THE MANAGER'S LACK OF CONTROL, BUT WAS JUST A HUGE MISUNDERSTANDING. THOSE WHO HAVE CRITICISED SARRI'S LACK OF FLEXIBILITY WILL BE INTERESTED TO SEE HOW HE NOW REDEPLOYS ARRIZABALAGA.

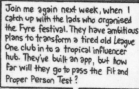

LIVERPOOL AREN'T FEELING THE PRESSURE, YOU'RE FEELING THE PRESSURE, SO SHUT UP!

A GOALLESS DRAW IN THE MERSEYSIDE DERBY HAS HANDED THE INITIATIVE BACK TO MANCHESTER CITY IN THE PREMIER LEAGUE TITLE RACE. LIVERPOOL ENDURED A DIFFICULT AFTERNOON AT GOODISON, BUT JÜRGEN KLOPP KEPT HIS COOL, EVEN WHEN MOCKED BY A SARCASTIC BALLBOY.

OF MORE PRESSING CONCERN FOR KLOPP IS THE NEWS THAT HIS LANDLORD, MR RODGERS, IS BACK IN THE COUNTRY AND WILL NO DOUBT WANT TO UNDERTAKE REGULAR PROPERTY INSPECTIONS...

NO ONE COULD HAVE PREDICTED THAT THE MERSEYSIDE DERBY WOULD BE A STUPEFYING ANTICLIMAX, BUT THE GAME WASN'T WITHOUT INCIDENT: AT ONE POINT ROBERTO FIRMINO HELD A SMALL CHILD ON THE LIVERPOOL BENCH.

THE DAY BEFORE, MANCHESTER CITY HAD RETURNED TO THE TOP OF THE TABLE AFTER A NARROW WIN AT BOURNEMOUTH; A PLACE WHERE MANY VISITORS HAVE FALLEN PREY TO AN INSIDIOUS VIRAL MEME SPREAD BY PANICKY PARENTS ON FACEBOOK: THE EDDIE HOWE CHALLENGE. FEAR IT. FEAR IT.

THE POPULAR THEORY HAS IT THAT **LIVERPOOL HAVE CHOKED**, BUT THEY APPEAR TO HAVE THE EASIER RUN-IN. CITY'S REMAINING FIXTURES INCLUDE A MANCHESTER DERBY, AND WHILE THE HEALTH OF UNITED'S PLAYERS CONTINUES TO WITHER, OLE GUNNAR SOLSKJÆR SEEMS TO GROW IN STRENGTH WITH EACH PASSING WEEK.

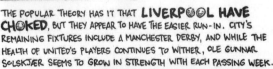

ALL LIVERPOOL NEED TO DO IS HOLD THEIR NERVE OVER THE COMING WEEKS AND GLORY COULD AWAIT THEM.

WE ARE NEARING THE CONCLUSION OF YOUR FAVOURITE FANTASY DRAMA : THE PREMIER LEAGUE (SEASON 27), AND SOME FAMILIAR THEMES ARE ALREADY PRESENT...

GIVEN THE OFFENSIVE CHANTS THAT WERE BEING SUNG ABOUT HIM LAST WEEK, MO SALAH'S BRILLIANT GOAL IN LIVERPOOL'S 2-0 WIN AGAINST CHELSEA MUST HAVE BEEN LIKE A MAGICAL DAGGER THROUGH THE HEART OF SOME ANCIENT WHITE ZOMBIES TOO.

IT WAS A REAL THUNDERBOLT, THE KIND OF WHICH LORD GREYMINT HIMSELF WOULD HAVE BEEN PROUD. HOWEVER, FOOTAGE LATER EMERGED TO SHOW THAT IT WAS INSUFFICIENT TO DISTRACT TV PUNDIT SHAY GIVEN FROM HIS FREE STUDIO LUNCH. OF ALL THE QUESTIONS THAT REMAIN ABOUT THIS SEASON, THE OVERRIDING ONE IS NOW: WHAT **WOULD** MAKE SHAY LOOK UP FROM HIS HOT BUFFET PLATE ?

SMALL DIFFERENCES COULD YET DECIDE WHO ENDS UP ON THE BEST THRONE IN THE WORLD. LAST WEEK, FOR INSTANCE, LIVERPOOL'S DENTIST RECEIVED SOME MEDIA ATTENTION. HE'S FIXED THE LUMINOUS SMILES OF JÜRGEN KLOPP AND SEVERAL PLAYERS. THIS ATTENTION TO DETAIL COULD BE OF INTEREST TO OTHER CLUBS LOOKING TO GATHER INTELLIGENCE BEFORE EMBARKING UPON THEIR OWN PREMIER LEAGUE JOURNEY.

LIVERPOOL NOW SIT TWO POINTS CLEAR, WITH BYES TO COME AGAINST HUDDERSFIELD AND CARDIFF, WHILE MANCHESTER CITY COMPLETE THEIR SPIN-OFF MINI-SERIES WITH SPURS. EPISODE ONE OF THEIR CHAMPIONS LEAGUE TIE SHOWED THAT WE NOW HAVE A CLEARER UNDERSTANDING OF BLACK HOLES THAN WHAT CONSTITUTES A HANDBALL. DANNY ROSE WAS THE LATEST PLAYER TO FALL FOUL OF THE VAR BOOTH APPARENTLY BEING CONTROLLED BY ARLENE FOSTER...

IT WON'T BE ALL PLAIN SAILING FOR LIVERPOOL, THOUGH. THEY STILL HAVE TO GO TO NEWCASTLE AND KLOPP WILL BE KEEN TO DISPEL THE NOTION THAT RAFA BENÍTEZ WILL BE ANYTHING BUT DETERMINED TO PUT UP A GOOD FIGHT AGAINST HIS OLD CLUB.

AS FOR CARDIFF, NEIL WARNOCK STILL BELIEVES THEIR SEASON CAN BE SAVED, PERHAPS THROUGH THE USE OF FLYING WATER TANKERS. UNDOUBTEDLY, HE DID A FINE JOB IN GETTING THEM PROMOTED LAST YEAR, BUT AS YOUR FAVOURITE ILLEGALLY-DOWNLOADED FANTASY DRAMA HAS SHOWN US, SOMETIMES SUCCESS CAN BE A POISONED CHALICE.

THAT'S THAT, THEN. AFTER MONTHS OF TENSION THAT COULD ONLY BE CREATED BY THE TWO BEST TEAMS WINNING ALL THEIR GAMES, **MANCHESTER CITY ARE CHAMPIONES/CAMPEONES, OLÉ OLÉ OLÉ.** THEIR PREMIER LEAGUE TITLE WAS CONFIRMED WITH A 4-1 WIN AT BRIGHTON, WHICH SPARKED SCENES OF CELEBRATION AND AN OBLIGATORY GALLAGHER APPEARANCE.

CITY'S TRIUMPH WAS EVERY BIT AS ROMANTIC AS SALFORD CITY'S PROMOTION TO THE FOOTBALL LEAGUE; A CLASSIC FAIRYTALE. BUT FOR A WHILE, PEP GUARDIOLA WAS WOUND MORE TIGHTLY THAN THE BOBBLES ON HIS CARDIE. WHEN BRIGHTON TOOK THE LEAD, IT SEEMED LIKE LIVERPOOL'S **CHUFFING MENTALITY GIANTS** MIGHT DO IT AGAIN. HOWEVER, EVEN GIVEN FOR THE RECENT TREND OF SHOCK RESULTS, WHEN BRIGHTON ARE YOUR ONLY HOPE, YOU HAVE NO HOPE, AND CITY PREVAILED. AFTER AN EPIC CAMPAIGN, CITY AND LIVERPOOL WERE SEPARATED BY A MATTER OF MILLIMETRES (AND BEATING LEICESTER AT HOME).

THE TITLE RACE GOING DOWN TO THE FINAL DAY OF THE SEASON MEANT A SUNDAY SPENT FLICKING BETWEEN THE TV CHANNELS, AT LEAST UNTIL THE OUTCOME BECAME OBVIOUS WHEN AYMERIC LAPORTE PUT CITY AHEAD AND YOU STARTED LOOKING AROUND TO SEE WHAT ELSE WAS ON...

THE OUTCOME WAS CRUEL FOR LONG-SUFFERING LIVERPOOL FANS. AS THE CLUB'S SOCIAL MEDIA CAMPAIGN CONFIRMS, **THIS MEANS MORE** TO THEM, AND IT WOULD BE HERESY TO DISPUTE THE FACT THAT THEY ARE THE ONLY FOOTBALL CLUB WITH MISTY-EYED, ELDERLY SUPPORTERS WHO CAN REMINISCE ABOUT THE GLORY DAYS OF YORE.

NATURALLY, NOT EVERYONE WANTED THEM TO WIN IT. FOR EXAMPLE, MANCHESTER UNITED FANS BREATHED A HUGE SIGH OF RELIEF AS THEIR CROSS-CITY RIVALS WON THEIR FOURTH TITLE IN EIGHT SEASONS WHILE THEY WATCHED THEIR SIDE LOSE 2-0 AT HOME TO CARDIFF. **PHEW, INDEED.** LIVERPOOL WILL CONSOLE THEMSELVES WITH ANOTHER TRIP TO THE CHAMPIONS LEAGUE FINAL. SHOULD THEY WIN, EXPECT THEM TO CELEBRATE AS WILDLY AS TRANMERE'S TOP BOY. TRY TELLING HIM IT MEANS MORE THAN THE LEAGUE TWO PLAY-OFF FINAL.

IF YOU WANT TO PICTURE THE FUTURE, IMAGINE A SKY BLUE BOOT STAMPING ON ENGLISH FOOTBALL'S FACE FOREVER (UNTIL PEP GOES TO JUVENTUS). THE GOOD NEWS IS YOU DON'T EVEN HAVE TO BOTHER IMAGINING IT, BECAUSE MANCHESTER CITY HAVE COMPLETED A DOMESTIC ~~SPORTS~~ WHITEWASH, THANKS TO A CRUSHING 6-0 WIN IN THE FA CUP FINAL AGAINST ~~THE WASHINGTON GENERALS~~ WATFORD.

Oh no, Pereyra's in. Could this be the end of our remarkable winning streak?

Ha ha, yeah. It's a genuine concern.

SOME ARGUE THE FA CUP HAS LOST ITS SHINE IN RECENT YEARS, BUT AS YOU LOOK AT THE LOGO OF AN OIL-STATE AIRLINE FLUTTERING ON THE RIBBONS TIED TO THE FAMOUS OLD TROPHY, IT IS AS OBVIOUS AS THE VACANT RED SEATS OF THE CLUB WEMBLEY MEMBERS WHO COULDN'T BE ARSED, THAT THE CUP REMAINS AS MAGICAL AS EVER. HOWEVER, SOME TRADITIONS HAVE BEEN LOST. THE KICK-OFF TIME HAS MOVED, TEAMS NO LONGER RELEASE AWFUL SONGS (ALTHOUGH CITY AT LEAST TRIED THIS YEAR), AND THE RECENT DEATH OF FREDDIE STARR ROBBED THE TV AUDIENCE OF SEEING HIM DRESSED AS HITLER IN THE BUILD-UP.

I don't understand...

Hmm, yes; it may be a little advanced. Let's go back to looking at the terrible fancy dress choices of British footballers in the 1980s...

CITY'S ACHIEVEMENTS ARE UNPRECEDENTED, BUT THEY REMAIN PLAGUED BY ACCUSATIONS OF FINANCIAL FAIR PLAY IRREGULARITIES. LAST WEEK, THEY REACTED FURIOUSLY WHEN THE CHAIR OF UEFA'S INVESTIGATORY BODY – THE FORMER BELGIAN PRIME MINISTER, YVES LETERME – CONCLUDED THEY HAVE A CASE TO ANSWER. AT LEAST ONE EX-PM IS MAKING GOOD USE OF HIS TIME.

David, are you in that bloody grot chariot? The photographer from Tatler's coming at three and I need help deboning the peasants.

How many more times, Samantha? It's an ADJUDICATORY CHAMBER.

If Thomas wins, I get a knighthood. If James wins, I get the Nobel Peace Prize. Come on muddafugger, come on...

MANCHESTER CITY'S SUCCESS HASN'T BEEN UNIVERSALLY POPULAR AND NO ONE SEEMS TO BE ENJOYING IT LESS THAN MANCHESTER CITY FANS. ONE OF THEM EVEN INVADED THE WEMBLEY PRESS BOX AFTER SEEING HIS TEAM WIN EVERY DOMESTIC TROPHY POSSIBLE TO COMPLAIN ABOUT THE COVERAGE CITY RECEIVE. FORGET THE OPPRESSED MIGRANT WORKERS OF ABU DHABI, OR THE PEOPLE OF YEMEN COWERING FROM THE SHELLS OF A SAUDI-UAE MILITARY COALITION, IT IS THE FANS OF MANCHESTER CITY WHO ARE THE REAL VICTIMS OF 2019.

I just wish Manchester City would get the credit their achievements deserve from the biased nonce media scum.

NATURALLY, THE RULING FAMILY OF ABU DHABI WOULD NEVER APPROVE OF CONTROLLING THE PRESS, BUT JUST TO PROVE THERE'S NO ANTI-CITY MEDIA CONSPIRACY, HERE'S A CUT OUT AND KEEP PORTRAIT OF DEPARTING CLUB LEGEND

VINCENT KOMPANY

AT LEAST THE CHILLED-OUT ENTERTAINER PEP GUARDIOLA IS STILL HAVING FUN, AS EVIDENCED BY HIS CHAT WITH 2.5 GOAL HERO RAHEEM STERLING BEFORE THE SHINY BLUE CONFETTI HAD EVEN SETTLED ON THE WEMBLEY TURF.

Do you know the question you are asking me? Did I receive money from another situation, right now, today? Honestly, do you think I deserve to have this type of question, the day we won the treble, did I receive money? Are you accusing me of receiving money?

Um... I only asked if you thought it was like on The Crystal Maze, where you have to collect the flying foil tokens and exchange them for cash? Bit touchy, mate.

FOR GOD'S SAKE, CAN'T WE KEEP POLITICS OUT OF FOOTBALL DISCUSSION, EVEN WHEN IT HAS A DIRECT AND OBVIOUS IMPACT? INSTEAD WE SHOULD CELEBRATE THE REAL WINNER IN A MEMORABLE SEASON: WHATABOUTERY!

Oh yeah, pick on City as usual. What about Liverpool's shirt sponsors being fined for breaching sanctions?

Who cares about shirt sponsors? What about Chelsea and how Abramovich acquired his mineral wealth?

Not that I care any more, but what about the Bin Laden family's alleged interest in Sheffield United?

That was bantz. Anyway, what about Norwich? Their owner hasn't done a decent cookery programme in years.

Oh flan off, you flanning cake. What about Notts County? Their owner tweeted a photo of his own filthy nut roast.

Wait.

I did what?

Oh sweet baby Cabriel Jesus.

PLANES, TRAINS & AUTOCRACIES

ARSENAL AND CHELSEA ARE LITERALLY IN DREAMLAND, AS THEY PREPARE FOR A EUROPA LEAGUE FINAL AT A VENUE SO INACCESSIBLE, YOU CAN ONLY GET THERE IN YOUR IMAGINATION.

WHAT **WAS** IT THAT ATTRACTED UEFA TO THE OIL-GILDED PETROSTATE OF AZERBAIJAN? WELL, IT'S SIMPLY PART OF ITS ALTRUISTIC MOVE TO SPREAD FOOTBALL TO WEALTHY, ANTI-DEMOCRATIC REGIMES WHO DON'T EVEN LET THEIR LEADERS BE CHOSEN BY 100,000 DREADFUL PENSIONERS IN THE HOME COUNTIES. HOWEVER, BY HOSTING THE FINAL IN BAKU, UEFA HAS OVERLOOKED FOOTBALL'S GUIDING PRINCIPLE: HUMAN RIGHTS-ABUSING DESPOTS ARE ONLY LEGITIMATE IF THEY SPLURGE A LOAD OF MONEY ON THE TEAM YOU LIKE.

MUCH OF THE BUILD-UP TO THE FINAL HAS FOCUSED ON HENRIKH MKHITARYAN'S DECISION TO NOT TRAVEL TO BAKU. THE ARMENIAN FEARED FOR HIS SAFETY, DESPITE AZERBAIJANI DIPLOMATS PROVIDING SEVERAL ASSURANCES, SOME OF WHICH WERE AS MUCH AS HALF-ARSED. HOWEVER, MAYBE HE'LL HAVE A LATE CHANGE OF HEART ABOUT STAYING BEHIND IN MERRY OLD ENGLAND.

CLEARLY, IT'S AN INSANE SITUATION, BUT AS YOU MAY HAVE NOTICED, NOT MUCH MAKES SENSE ANYMORE. OF MORE CONCERN TO UEFA WILL BE THAT EVEN SPONSORS ARE REPORTEDLY RETURNING THEIR TICKETS. THERE IS NO GREATER SIGN THAT YOU ARE RUNNING THE FYRE FESTIVAL OF FOOTBALL TOURNAMENTS THAN WHEN PEOPLE START TURNING DOWN CORPORATE FREEBIES. THE EVENT IS BECOMING INCREASINGLY AWKWARD FOR UEFA TO SELL.

TWO LONDON CLUBS TRAVELLING TO BAKU ALSO RAISES QUESTIONS ABOUT FOOTBALL'S CARBON FOOTPRINT. THE EFFECTS OF THE CLIMATE CRISIS ARE ALREADY CHANGING OUR WORLD BEYOND RECOGNITION: SOARING TEMPERATURES, RISING SEA LEVELS, AND SPURS REACHING THE CHAMPIONS LEAGUE FINAL. THEY HAVE ALREADY FLOWN TO MADRID FOR SATURDAY'S FINAL WITH LIVERPOOL, AND MAURICIO POCHETTINO IS DOING HIS BEST TO KEEP THE MOOD LIGHT BY SHOWCASING SOME NEW COMEDY MATERIAL.

BACK IN BAKU, AZERBAIJAN REALLY COULD PROVE TO BE THE LAND OF FIRE FOR MAURIZIO SARRI IF CHELSEA LOSE. TWO OF HIS POTENTIAL REPLACEMENTS MET HEAD-TO-HEAD IN THE CHAMPIONSHIP PLAY-OFF FINAL ON MONDAY, WHEN **FRANK LAMPARD'S DERBY COUNTY** LOST 2-1 TO AN **ASTON VILLA** TEAM LED BY **JOHN TERRY**

VILLA WERE SET ON THEIR WAY WHEN ANWAR EL GHAZI SHOULDERED ONE IN. STOOPING LOWEST WAS NO MEAN FEAT ON AN AFTERNOON WHEN THE PRESENCE OF ROYALTY BROUGHT ABOUT A COLLECTIVE OUTBREAK OF BOWING AND SCRAPING.

DEFEAT WAS CRUEL FOR DERBY, AS WAS IT FOR ALL THE TEAMS WHO LOST IN THE PLAY-OFFS AFTER A LONG, HARD SEASON. FOR EXAMPLE, WHATEVER YOU THINK OF WEST BROM'S HUMANOID BOILER MASCOT'S RECORD AS A MEANS TO AID BOILER SALES IN THE WEST MIDLANDS, IT'S IMPOSSIBLE NOT TO FEEL SORRY FOR IT ON A BOILER WITH LIMBS LEVEL. SUCH A HAUNTING IMAGE.

AS YOU MAY HAVE HEARD BY NOW, LIVERPOOL ARE CHAMPIONS OF EUROPE! AS EVERYONE ELSE SCRAMBLES TO EVACUATE THE COUNTRY, SO MANY LIVERPOOL FANS GATHERED FOR THE VICTORY PARADE THAT THE CITY CENTRE HAD TO BE DIVIDED INTO INDIVIDUAL SECTIONS.

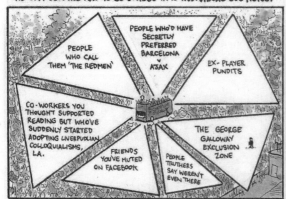

LIVERPOOL'S TRIUMPH WAS MASTERMINDED BY JÜRGEN KLOPP, WHOSE RED MACHINE IS AS WELL-OILED AS HE APPEARED TO BE ON THE OPEN-TOP BUS. NOT ONLY IS HE A UNIQUE AND INSPIRING CHARACTER, IT'S ALSO HARD TO RECALL THE LAST TIME THE MANAGER OF A CHAMPIONS LEAGUE WINNING TEAM QUOTED SALT-N-PEPA LYRICS IN A POST-MATCH INTERVIEW.

THEIR FINAL WITH SPURS WAS SHAPING UP TO BE A CLASSIC UNTIL IT WAS EFFECTIVELY SETTLED AS A CONTEST AFTER 22 SECONDS, WHEN LIVERPOOL WERE AWARDED A PENALTY FOR MOUSSA SISSOKO'S HANDBALL. IF YOU TAKE POINTING OUT OF HIS GAME, SISSOKO IS HALF THE PLAYER, BUT THERE'S A TIME AND A PLACE. WE MAY NEVER KNOW WHAT HE WAS TRYING TO WARN HIS TEAMMATES ABOUT.

VICTORY WAS PARTICULARLY SWEET FOR LIVERPOOL, WHO OVERCAME THE TWIN DISAPPOINTMENTS OF FINISHING SECOND IN THE PREMIER LEAGUE AND BEING THE LAST PEOPLE IN THE WORLD TO FIND OUT THAT LUIS SUÁREZ IS A GIT.

IT WAS A NIGHT FULL OF EMOTION, THAT MELTED THE HEARTS OF EVEN THE FIERCEST COMPETITORS.

INEVITABLY, MAURICIO POCHETTINO FACED SOME TOUGH QUESTIONS, SUCH AS WHAT ARE HIS TOP CELEBRITY TIPS FOR WEIGHT LOSS (IT TURNS OUT MR LEVY MAKES HIM SURVIVE ON A THIN GRUEL). IT WAS A TOUGH NIGHT FOR HARRY KANE TOO, WHO LOST HIS FIGHT TO PROVE HIS FITNESS AND HAD TO CONTINUE HIS RECUPERATION ON THE LAWN OF THE WANDA METROPOLITANO. STILL, THE FRESH AIR WOULD HAVE DONE HIM THE WORLD OF GOOD.

IT MIGHT HAVE BEEN A FARAGE OF A FINAL (SOMETHING AWFUL INFLICTED UPON EUROPE BY ENGLAND), BUT THE CHAMPIONS LEAGUE HAS PRODUCED PLENTY OF ENTERTAINMENT THIS SEASON: AJAX'S RUN, TOTTENHAM AND MANCHESTER CITY'S QUARTER-FINAL, MOURA'S HAT-TRICK, ROBERTSON GIVING MESSI A QUEEN'S PARK NECK MASSAGE, MORE VAR-LARITY THAN YOU COULD WAVE AN ARM IN AN UNNATURAL POSITION AT, AND OF COURSE THE AWESOME TELEPATHIC POWER OF TRENT ALEXANDER-ARNOLD AND DIVOCK ORIGI. WHO KNOWS WHAT ELSE THEY COULD ACHIEVE IF THEY PUT THEIR MINDS TO IT.

WOMEN'S WORLD CUP 2019:
TOPPED TRUMP

The most significant positive change in football during the period covered by this book has been the ~~acquisition of the entire sport by the Kingdom of Saudi Arabia~~ explosion in the popularity of the women's game.

Despite making bigger strides than Wendie Renard, it was hard to shake off the feeling that women's football hadn't quite achieved universal respect. Six months before the 2019 World Cup in France, while collecting the Ballon d'Or in a hall full of her peers, Ada Hegerberg was asked by celebrity DJ Martin Solveig whether she knew how to twerk. Kylian Mbappé looked like someone had fingered his prawn cocktail, but Solveig's years on the wheels of steel had taught him how to read a room, and he'd correctly surmised that the evening was about him and his very good jokes.

To make matters worse, the first weekend of the tournament had to battle for attention with the men's European Nations League final, the competition that would become the object of true global obsession.*

There was clearly *some* way to go, but the women's game was reaching a bigger audience. To argue that women's football is fundamentally different to the men's game was becoming an increasingly indefensible position, particularly given that England were managed by a 1990s footballer in a little blue waistcoat and finished fourth, having been eliminated by the first decent team they faced.

The United States were the dominant force in France, and it was hard to begrudge them their success, especially as each victory seemed to push Donald Trump closer to voiding himself to death. Player of the tournament Megan Rapinoe seemed particularly adept at getting under his satsuma peel. A hat-tip also to striker Alex Morgan, whose tea-sipping celebration after scoring against England boiled enough piss to fill every teacup in Albion. Her cruel mime even caused the famously unflappable Piers Morgan to take time out from pasting photos of Meghan Markle into his special scrapbook. I know what you're thinking, but no, Alex Morgan and Piers Morgan aren't related. In fact, they're barely part of the same species.

Speaking of jizz, there's a joke in the first cartoon of this set that led to the lengthiest argument I've ever had with the *Guardian*'s legal eagles. Gregg Bakowski on the sports desk was forced to act as the middleman in a battle over whether it was potentially libellous to claim that an entire generation of Italians had been spawned from a single sperm donation by Pippo Inzaghi, leaving them genetically predisposed to stray offside. In the end, a compromise was reached over the wording of the set-up and the amount of spunk that could be shown splooshing from the top of a vat containing Pippo's generous deposit. *Grazie*, Gregg!

---

* If you can remember who won the last one without looking it up, you can claim a partial personal refund for this book by finding me in the small regional Australian town where I live. Conditions apply.

WE'RE INTO THE FINAL ROUND OF GROUP MATCHES AT THE WOMEN'S WORLD CUP, AND DESPITE SOME TEXTBOOK ADMINISTRATING FROM FIFA, THERE ARE SIGNS THAT FRANCE IS BEGINNING TO EMBRACE THE TOURNAMENT.

THE LAST WEEK HAS SEEN AN AVALANCHE OF GOALS, NOT LEAST FROM THE USA, WHOSE PLAYERS FACED CRITICISM FOR CELEBRATING THEIR 13-GOAL HAUL AGAINST THAILAND WITH TOO MUCH ENTHUSIASM FOR SOME. HOWEVER, NO ONE SAID ANYTHING WHEN ARBROATH CELEBRATED THEIR 36TH GOAL AGAINST BON ACCORD.

NO ONE WAS STRONGER IN THEIR CRITICISM THAN THE TV PANEL OF IMPARTIAL FORMER CANADA INTERNATIONALS, WHO STOPPED JUST SHORT OF LIKENING THE AMERICAN PLAYERS TO THE KIND OF PEOPLE WHO MAKE YOU WATCH ALL THEIR GOAL CELEBRATIONS AS THEY THRASH YOU AT FIFA. BUT, AS THE US PLAYERS ARGUED, THERE IS NO HIGHER FORM OF RESPECT THAN COMPLETELY HUMILIATING YOUR OPPONENT IN FRONT OF A GLOBAL AUDIENCE. ALSO, CARLI LLOYD WAS QUICK TO OFFER SOME CONSOLING WORDS TO GOALKEEPER SUKANYA CHOR CHAROENYING AT THE FINAL WHISTLE.

ALSO, GIVEN THE GROWING POLITICAL HOSTILITY TOWARDS WOMEN IN SOME PARTS OF THE UNITED STATES, IT MIGHT BE A BIT ROUGH TO TELL A GROUP OF AMERICAN WOMEN WHAT THEY CAN AND CAN'T DO WITH THEIR BODIES WHILE ON A TRIP TO EUROPE. EVEN THEIR CRIMSON KIT WAS JUST A WHITE BONNET SHORT OF BEING THE FULL GILEAD AWAY.

IT LOOKED LIKE THEY WERE ON FOR ANOTHER BIG SCORE ON SUNDAY, AS THEY STORMED INTO A 3-0 LEAD BY HALF-TIME, HEAPING MORE MISERY ON THAT BAR IN AMERICA THAT OFFERS FREE SHOTS FOR EVERY USA GOAL.

HOWEVER, CHILE'S CHRISTIANE ENDLER PRODUCED A STRING OF SPECTACULAR SAVES TO KEEP THEM AT BAY. IT WAS A DISPLAY PERHAPS MATCHED ONLY BY THAT OF ARGENTINA'S VANINA CORREA, WHO SEEMED TO BE ON HER WAY TO JOINING THE RANKS OF GENEROUSLY-HAIRED GOALKEEPERS WHO HAVE TRAMPLED ON ENGLAND'S WORLD CUP DREAMS, ALONGSIDE JAN TOMASZEWSKI AND DAVID SEAMAN.

AT LEAST VAR HAS HELPED TO REDUCE THE MASSIVE ADVANTAGE GOALKEEPERS ENJOY WHEN FACING A FREE SHOT FROM 12 YARDS, BY ENFORCING A NEW RULE REQUIRING THEM TO KEEP ONE FOOT ON THE LINE. THIS CAME INTO PLAY ON MONDAY NIGHT WHEN NIGERIA'S CHIAMAKA NNADOZIE'S MICROSCOPIC INFRACTION CAUSED WENDIE RENARD TO HAVE AN EXISTENTIAL BREAKDOWN.

RENARD RECOVERED TO CONVERT THE RE-TAKE AND PERHAPS HAD SOME WORDS OF COMFORT FOR NNADOZIE AT THE END OF THE GAME.

THE **WAR OF WORDS** BETWEEN MEGAN RAPINOE AND DONALD TRUMP ESCALATED LAST WEEK WHEN AN INTERVIEW EMERGED IN WHICH THE MOST INFLUENTIAL PERSON IN AMERICA MADE THE BIZARRE ADMISSION THAT SHE WOULDN'T VISIT THE OCCASIONAL LAIR OF A DEMONSTRABLY SEXIST, RACIST AND HOMOPHOBIC GOLFER FAMED FOR HIS CASUAL BOASTS OF SEXUAL ASSAULT. AND THAT WAS **BEFORE** THE PURPLE-HAIRED FORWARD HAD EVEN MADE A CRUEL REFERENCE TO THE SIZE OF TRUMP'S TENNIS SHORTS.

DURING WHAT MUST HAVE BEEN A PARTICULARLY CHALLENGING ABLUTION FOR THE SPORADIC COMMANDER-IN-CHIEF (AS THEY PRESUMABLY ALL ARE WHEN YOU HAVE A BRITISH BREAKFAST TELEVISION PRESENTER PERMANENTLY LIVING IN YOUR RECTUM), TRUMP TWEETED ANGRILY THAT RAPINOE SHOULD FOCUS ON DOING HER JOB. AND TO THINK SOME PEOPLE SAY HE'S TOO THICK TO UNDERSTAND IRONY.

PIERS MORGAN DESCRIBED RAPINOE AS 'ARROGANT', AND WHILE THIS MAY SEEM AS HYPOCRITICAL AS FIFA MAKING THE PLAYERS POSE IN FRONT OF A 'LIVING DIVERSITY' BANNER BEFORE EACH QUARTER-FINAL, YOU HAVE TO RESPECT THE FACT THAT HE'S ABLE TO GET WIFI RECEPTION FROM IN THERE. RAPINOE'S DECISION TO NOT SING THE AMERICAN NATIONAL ANTHEM ENRAGED TRUMP FANBOYS, INCELS AND BOTS ALIKE. SOME OF THEM EVEN TOOK TIME OUT FROM MOANING ABOUT STORMZY HEADLINING GLASTONBURY TO CONDEMN HER 'ATTENTION-SEEKING' PROTEST.

IF IT WAS AN UNWELCOME DISTRACTION FOR THE AMERICAN PLAYERS, THEY DIDN'T LET IT SHOW, AS THEY WENT ON TO WIN THEIR QUARTER-FINAL AGAINST FRANCE. THIS WAS PARTLY ACHIEVED THANKS TO A STRANGELY SUBDUED PERFORMANCE FROM THE HOST'S MOST INFLUENTIAL PLAYER OF THE TOURNAMENT: VAR. HOWEVER, BY THIS POINT, TRUMP HAD ALREADY MOVED ON TO THE MORE COMFORTABLE SURROUNDINGS OF SCHMOOZING WITH THE WORST PEOPLE IN THE UNIVERSE.

IF THE PRESIDENT WERE CAPABLE OF FEELING ANY HUMAN EMOTION BEYOND BURNING VAINGLORIOUS RAGE, THE US TEAM WINNING THE WORLD CUP AND TELLING HIM TO CRAM HIS WHITE HOUSE HAPPY MEAL BANQUET MIGHT SEE HIM EXPERIENCING SOMETHING APPROACHING HUMILIATION. THEN AGAIN, IF YOU'VE SPENT THE LAST THREE YEARS DREAMING OF HIS DOWNFALL, YOU MAY HAVE DOWNGRADED YOUR FANTASIES TO HOPING THAT THE HEAD SWEATS FROM A ZINGER BURGER BINGE MAKES THE DYE RUN IN HIS RED CAP.

THE USA WILL MEET ENGLAND IN THE CHLORINATED CHICKEN DERBY. WHAT CHANCE DOES ONE TINY AMERICAN STATE STAND AGAINST THE COMBINED MIGHT OF THE OTHER 50? WELL, IF THE ENGLISH PLAYERS CAN MAINTAIN THEIR CONCENTRATION, THEY'RE IN WITH A SHOT. WE CAN ONLY SPECULATE AS TO WHERE THEIR MINDS DRIFT FOR 20 MINUTES EVERY GAME.

PLUS, THERE'S ALWAYS THE POSSIBILITY THAT THE UNITED STATES WILL WEDGE SOMEONE WOEFULLY UNQUALIFIED IN TO A POSITION OF INFLUENCE.

SOME EXTRA SPICE HAS ALSO BEEN ADDED TO THE CLASH WITH THE REVELATION THAT MEMBERS OF THE AMERICAN DELEGATION HAD BEEN CAUGHT SNOOPING AROUND ENGLAND'S HOTEL, COCKILY SCOPING OUT POTENTIAL ACCOMMODATION FOR THE FINAL. YOU WOULD NEVER SEE ANYONE ASSOCIATED WITH AN ENGLISH NATIONAL TEAM DISPLAY SUCH HUBRIS. NO WONDER PHIL NEVILLE QUESTIONED THEIR ETIQUETTE.

IN THE END, VICTORY WAS INEVITABLE, SO CONGRATULATIONS IF YOU HAD PIERS MORGAN IN THE 'WORST TAKE OF THE WORLD CUP' SWEEPSTAKE. HATS OFF ALSO TO THE US WOMEN'S NATIONAL TEAM, WHO REFUSED TO BE SPOOKED BY THE NETHERLANDS' TACTIC OF WEARING A KIT THE COLOUR OF TRUMP'S TUESDAY SPRAY TAN, AND LIFTED THEIR FOURTH TITLE, PROMPTING JOYOUS IMAGES...

EVEN THE PRESIDENT OFFERED HIS CONGRATULATIONS IN A TWEET THAT WAS TOO COHERENT TO HAVE BEEN WRITTEN BY HIM. HOWEVER, HIS HANDLERS MUST HAVE BEEN SCRAMBLING FOR THE TV REMOTE WHEN A CHANT OF "F*CK TRUMP" COULD BE HEARD CLEARLY DURING A LIVE FOX NEWS BROADCAST FROM LYON.

Oh Jesus! Turn it off and hide the nuclear codes!

UCK TRUMP! FU MP!

It's OK, he's in his mind palace.

What do you figure goes on in there?

I think we both know.

Terrifying.

Yup.

LIKE EVERYONE ELSE, THE NETHERLANDS DIDN'T QUITE HAVE ENOUGH TO STOP THE USA, BUT SARINA WIEGMAN'S TEAM PUT UP A SOLID FIRST-HALF RESISTANCE. WIEGMAN'S FACIAL EXPRESSIONS WERE ALSO A HIGHLIGHT OF THE WORLD CUP. WHEN UNHAPPY WITH HER TEAM, SHE COULDN'T HAVE LOOKED MORE DISGRUNTLED IF SHE WAS LISTENING TO YOUR UNCLE MANSPLAIN SOCCERNOMICS.

Yes, the US women's team generates more income than the men's team, but do they have anyone of the star quality of Jozy Altidore? Your social justice warriors can't answer that one.

THE AMERICANS ANSWERED EVERY QUESTION POSED OF THEM AT THIS WORLD CUP, INCLUDING WHETHER IT'S POSSIBLE TO GET S-FACED ON BUDWEISER. HOWEVER, THEY COULDN'T RESIST MOCKING THE ENGLISH WITH THEIR VILE CELEBRATIONS.

ARMS SPREAD LIKE AN AEROPLANE. A CLEAR REFERENCE TO THE REVOLUTIONARY ARMY TAKING OVER THE AIRPORTS IN 1775. DISGRACEFUL.

PLAYING AIR GUITAR WITH THE WORLD CUP TROPHY, LIKE ANY OF US ARE OVER CLIFF RICHARD'S FAILURE TO CRACK THE US CHARTS, ALSO IN 1775.

EDDIE 'THE EAGLE' EDWARDS IS A NATIONAL TREASURE AND HIS BIOPIC HAS A SCORE OF 81% ON ROTTEN TOMATOES (PRONOUNCED 'TOMATOES', FYI!). HE DOES NOT DESERVE THIS MOCKERY.

IF YOU'VE BEEN SWEPT ALONG BY THE LIONESSES' WORLD CUP ADVENTURE, THEN THE GOOD NEWS IS YOU CAN NOW EXPERIENCE GENDER NEUTRAL CRUSHING DISAPPOINTMENT EVERY SUMMER! PHIL NEVILLE HAS ALREADY SELFLESSLY BAGSIED THE JOB OF LEADING 'TEAM ENGLAND PLUS MISCELLANEOUS' AT NEXT YEAR'S OLYMPICS, SHOWING THE KIND OF HUMILITY THAT HAS UNQUESTIONABLY SEEN THE REST OF BRITAIN LEND ITS UNWAVERING SUPPORT TO ENGLAND OVER THE LAST MONTH.

Let's have one last look through my special binoculars and see how that works out, readers!

TOKYO 2020

S'only PE. Who really cares about the Olympics? I'm glad we went out in the first round. I am.

ELLEN WHITE COULD HAVE CLAIMED THE GOLDEN BOOT IF SHE HADN'T HAD A GOAL CHALKED OFF AFTER A VIDEO REVIEW AGAINST SWEDEN. THERE IS UNIVERSAL AGREEMENT THAT VAR HAS BEEN BRILLIANT AT THIS WORLD CUP, AND ITS INTRODUCTION INTO THE PREMIER LEAGUE IS AWAITED AS ENTHUSIASTICALLY AS PAUL POGBA BOARDING A LONG-HAUL FLIGHT FOR A MANCHESTER UNITED FRIENDLY TOUR.

Sigh. Oh well, I'm here now. Might as well look at the menu.

What's for tea, our Pog?

Relax. I'm looking, alright?

Oh for...

MENU
ALL COURTESY OF MANCHESTER UNITED'S OFFICIAL PULSE PARTNER
Breakfast
BEANS
Lunch
BEANS
Dinner
BEANS

OVERALL, THE TOURNAMENT WAS A HUGE SUCCESS, DRAWING LARGE TELEVISION AUDIENCES AND ATTRACTING A WHOLE NEW GROUP OF FANS TO THE WOMEN'S GAME.

And you all do this every four years? Hah, mental!

Oh, and just so you know, I'd have voted for Hillary for a third term if I could have.

Eesh.

FURTHERMORE, THE CHANT OF "EQUAL PAY" THAT RANG AROUND THE STADIUM DURING THE TROPHY PRESENTATION MUST SURELY HAVE LEFT A LASTING IMPRESSION ON GIANNI INFANTINO.

"Equal play!"
"Equal play!"

Now that's a meaningless corporate slogan FIFA can really get on board with!

SQUIRES

PERHAPS BEST OF ALL, WE WERE ABLE TO GET THROUGH THE ENTIRE TOURNAMENT WITHOUT AN APPEARANCE FROM DJ MARTIN SOLV—

The bee, it bit my bottom. And now my bottom, it is big!

Dude.

Are you...

twerking?

2019–20 (PART ONE):

NOTHING CAN GO WRONG NOW . . .

Doomsayers had long predicted a man-made force would cause mass disruption and widespread human misery, and so it came to pass in 2019, with the introduction of VAR in the Premier League. However, there were few signs of the looming hysteria as pre-season chugged along as normal: Daniel Sturridge's dog was kidnapped in LA; Huddersfield Town's players wore a shirt that was 90 per cent logo as a publicity stunt for the most banterous of online betting firms; and Arsenal's Sead Kolašinac foiled armed robbers from thieving Mezut Özil's car. That turned out to be as much action as Özil saw, until Unai Emery was replaced by an excitable humanoid Lego figure, Mikel Arteta, in December.

Then there was Swiss yellow-card-compiler Granit Xhaka's season, which was as up and down as a Toblerone. He was elected as Arsenal captain in September but stripped of 'heads or tails' duties less than six weeks later. Booed by the fans as he trudged off towards the substitutes' bench midway through a 2–2 draw with Crystal Palace, Xhaka expertly improved the situation by throwing his top to the ground, an unforgivable act of treachery that disrespected The Shirt, The Badge and The VISIT RWANDA sleeve sponsor.

All of that was a distraction from the real action: transfer gossip. As always, the summer was dominated by news of eye-shitting sums of money exchanging hands for star players. Barely a day passed without another big name announcing they'd joined *The Athletic*.

There was no such luck for those who still had the draft of their 'Some personal news . . .' announcement sitting in their Notes app, nor for the oligarch church mice Chelsea, who were placed under a transfer embargo. This was further proof that the authorities had it in for The Chels, with their 150 rule breaches involving 69 academy players over several years. Frank Lampard was forced to make do with spindly-legged academy urchins, a squad assembled for just 490 million old buttons and reliant upon the twinkle of Olivier Giroud's smile, which admittedly was quite powerful.

Manchester City also found themselves in bother, temporarily banned from the Champions League by UEFA for financial breaches, until their name was comprehensively cleared on appeal (nothing says redemption like a £9 million fine). Their title defence, however, was less successful: conceding too much ground in the first half of the season, their uncharacteristic disarray was illustrated by an autumn defeat at Norwich, which was followed by Pep Guardiola defending Bernardo Silva for likening teammate Benjamin Mendy to a racist caricature (not one of mine).

Meanwhile, like a Premier League team faced with a 30-mile away trip, Liverpool were flying. After a three-decade wait, and having come so close the previous season, this was to be their year. It would take something pretty bloody spectacular to stop them celebrating their title at a packed Anfield in May . . .

IT'S THE ONLY SPORT STORY THAT ANYONE IS TALKING ABOUT, AND ONE THAT CANNOT BE SULLIED BY A DICKENSIAN PIPECLEANER CLAIMING IT FOR HIS XENOPHOBIC CAUSE, NOR BY IMAGES OF NIGEL FARAGE AND PIERS MORGAN SMASHING THE ELITE FROM THE MEMBERS' BAR AT LORD'S: **DANIEL STURRIDGE'S STOLEN DOG HAS BEEN RETURNED SAFELY.**

DETAILS OF THE CRIME REMAIN SKETCHY, BUT WHAT WE DO KNOW IS THAT: 1) YES, THIS IS DEFINITELY A FOOTBALL STORY, 2) LUCCI THE POMERANIAN WENT MISSING AFTER A ROBBERY AT STURRIDGE'S HOME IN LA; AND 3) DANIEL STURRIDGE HAS A HOME IN LA.

Did you get the dog?

Yeah, it was sleeping in the guest suite. It doesn't look like it does on Instagram, though.

I mean, what filter are they using?!

Oh for...

IT WAS A STORY MORE DRAMATIC THAN ONE OF ANTOINE GRIEZMANN'S ANNOUNCEMENT VIDEOS...

"What is life...?"

"The wind in the trees."

"The fragile beauty of a desert flower opening towards the first rays of dawn..."

"It is the choices we make..."

"It is the sweet nectar of an €800m buyout clause..."

"It is a single tear, rolling down the fissures of an old man's cheek. His journey is nearly at its end. Soon he will be the subject of an audacious bid from West Ham. The cycle of life. Returned to dust..."

Knock it off.

INDEED, THE TALE COULD HAVE COME FROM THE PAGES OF FOOTBALL'S GREATEST CRIME NOVELIST, STEVE BRUCE. SADLY, HE'S ABANDONED THE TYPEWRITER IN THE OFFICE SHEFFIELD WEDNESDAY RECONFIGURED AT GREAT EXPENSE TO RESEMBLE THE SMOKE-FILLED QUARTERS OF AN LA NOIR PRIVATE DETECTIVE, AND SEEMS LIKELY TO MOVE ON TO A NEW PROJECT: LEARNING THE NAMES OF THE 2019-20 NEWCASTLE UNITED SQUAD.

STÉPHANE GUIVARC'H

SPENDER

DONNA AIR

A CARROT THAT LOOKS LIKE STING

THE POLICE HORSE THAT FAN TRIED TO FIGHT

OH FU**

Sigh

PJ AND DUNCAN

We've also got that lad we signed from America who no one had heard of six months ago.

Miguel Almirón.

Mig...? No, Angry Viral Bagel Dude!

You wanna piece of me, tough guy?

Ok, well, there's still the Sting Carrot. That gives us something to work with.

Mm-hm...

FOXES SWOOP FOR £60m STING CARROT

LUCKILY, *THIS* STORY HAS A HAPPY ENDING, ESPECIALLY IF YOU OVERLOOK THE FEELINGS OF VIOLATION EXPERIENCED BY THE VICTIMS OF BURGLARY. LUCCI WAS FOUND BY A GENTLEMAN CALLED KILLA FAME, WHO RETURNED THE DOG TO STURRIDGE IN ANTICIPATION OF HANDSOME REMUNERATION.

Close enough. Lucci, you're home!

When do I get my reward?

Right after Xherd- I mean, Lucci- wins the Ballon d'Or, Mr Fame.

Sweet!

Heh, and to think they said pre-season wouldn't produce enough interesting football stories, Lucci.

Yeah, there is a significant international tournament taking place at the moment, though.

Sorry, what?

Um, woof woof.

We live in troubling times. The world burns under the complicit eye of born-to-rule narcissists and venal bigots. You cringe at the japes of the unelected British prime minister and conclude that you'd genuinely have more faith in Ian Holloway as PM, because at least there's an honesty to his ignorance.

Football can serve as a form of escapism. The comedy stylings of David Luiz and the penalty antics of Manchester United provide a welcome distraction from the reality of impending human extinction. However, this is not the case for fans of certain EFL clubs, whose long-term prospects seem as healthy as those of the Wigan Athletic mascot in the event of post-no deal Brexit food shortages.

This is especially the case at Bolton and Bury - two famous old clubs who face expulsion from the Football League. In Bury's case, the current owner - Steve Dale - has treated the club with as much respect as you would for anything you bought for £1. The EFL later admitted it had allowed Dale's takeover without undertaking the necessary checks on his finances. In fairness, the EFL is a busy organisation.

Like Bury, Bolton face the very real threat of liquidation. Now reduced to sacrificing teenagers to be mauled by League One hard men, Bolton were founder members of the Football League and central to some of English football's most cherished memories: the White Horse Final, the Matthews Final, the astonishing goals of Okocha, Lofthouse and Worthington; not to mention their manager who smashed the world record for chewing the most packets of flavoured gum in a 90-minute sitting. This is BOLTON, for God's sake; we can't lose BOLTON!

If you support a team unlikely to be invited to participate in a European Super League, you'll have known the sinking feeling of reading about your club's perilous financial affairs at some point...

... as recognisable as all the nodding acquaintances you've made over the years:

It's not hard to picture your own club suffering the same fate as Bury and Bolton. It is this familiarity with terrible owners, supine administrators and frayed safety nets that has seen football fans and other clubs put their rivalries aside. For example, an unnamed Championship club provided a donation to a food bank established to help Bolton's desperate non-playing staff,

These are more than football clubs. They are the heartbeat of their communities; justifiable sources of civic pride in areas suffering from the decline of industry, the systematic vandalism of the welfare state and the ideological erosion of vital services. The market has decided: work until you die, you lost, f#ck off.

Bolton and Bury's demise may seem far removed from the gilded confines of the top flight tunnel clubs and official noodle partners, but Bolton were an established Premier League team not so long ago.

If the pyramid burns, even those at the top will eventually choke.

NORFOLK ENCHANTS!

IN THE SHOCK RESULT OF THE SEASON SO FAR, MANCHESTER CITY HAVE BEEN BEATEN BY A TEAM THAT COST LESS THAN ONE OF PEP GUARDIOLA'S SWEATERS. DESPITE THE GULF IN RESOURCES, MAN CITY SUFFERED HUMILIATION IN A PLACE CALLED 'NOR-WICH', WHICH IS BASICALLY ENDOR WITH A PEDESTRIANISED VILLAGE CENTRE AND A RESPECTED ARTS COLLEGE.

INDIVIDUAL DEFENSIVE ERRORS FROM STONES AND OTAMENDI COST MANCHESTER CITY DEAR IN THE 3-2 DEFEAT. EVEN THE USUALLY DEPENDABLE WALKER SUFFERED A DIFFICULT EVENING ON THE EAST ANGLIAN FOREST MOON.

AH YES, TODD CANTWELL, A YOUNG TALENT WITH HAIR SO LUSCIOUS IT MAKES THE ATALANTA BADGE JEALOUS. HIS GOAL SENT CARROW ROAD WILD AND WAS FOLLOWED BY A CELEBRATION THAT WAS AN ARTISTIC DIRECTOR SHY OF A FULL WEST END PRODUCTION.

NORWICH'S WIN WAS EVEN MORE IMPRESSIVE WHEN YOU CONSIDER THEY WERE HIT BY INJURIES, A SILLY SLEEVE SPONSOR AND SEVERAL DEFECTIONS TO THE LIB DEMS. WHILE THE CANARIES FRET OVER WHAT IT ALL MEANS FOR THE TITLE RACE, MAN CITY SOMEHOW TRAVEL EVEN FURTHER EAST TO TAKE ON SHAKHTAR DONETSK. IF THEY EXPERIENCE ANOTHER MELTDOWN IN UKRAINE, A SERIOUS INVESTIGATION WILL BE NEEDED.

THEY THEN FACE A WATFORD SIDE REJUVINATED BY THE RETURN OF GUIQUE SÁNCHEZ FLORES, WHO HAS SPENT THE LAST THREE YEARS WORKING AS A PROFESSIONAL OLIVER REED LOOKALIKE. PERHAPS HE WAS ABLE TO USE SOME OF THE SKILLS HE'D LEARNED TO DELIVER A ROUSING HALF-TIME TEAM TALK THAT INSPIRED A SECOND-HALF COMEBACK AGAINST ARSENAL ON SUNDAY.

OR MAYBE IT'S JUST THAT THE FAMOUSLY RESILIENT ARSENAL DEFENCE CAUGHT GLIMPSE OF A SIGHT THAT SPOOKED THEM.

ALTHOUGH GUARDIOLA'S FIRST TRIP TO THE NORTH NORFOLK HINTERLANDS WAS CHASTENING, PERHAPS HE WAS ABLE TO PICK UP SOME NEW IDEAS FROM THE HUMBLE TREE FOLK.

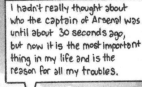

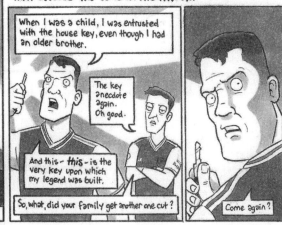

THE EARLY SIGNS OF AUTUMN ARE UPON US — THE SHADOWS LENGTHEN, THE LEAVES FALL FROM THE TREES, AND THE EVERTON MANAGER PREPARES TO MIGRATE TO WARMER CLIMES. WITH AN INTERNATIONAL BREAK LOOMING, SOME UNDER-PRESSURE COACHES MIGHT CONSIDER HIDING THEIR PHONES, ALTHOUGH THIS WILL BE EASIER FOR MARCO SILVA THAN NINETIES THROWBACK OLE GUNNAR NOSTALJÆR...

OLE SEEMS TO HAVE OVERSHOT IN HIS ATTEMPTS TO REVIVE MEMORIES OF THE FERGUSON GLORY YEARS, INSTEAD REANIMATING THE BARREN ERA OF THE LATE-EIGHTIES. PERHAPS THAT WAS WHAT HE MEANT WHEN HE REMINDED MANCHESTER UNITED FANS THAT IT'S NOT THE NINETIES ANY MORE — A STATEMENT SOME CONSIDERED TO BE AS BLOODY RICH AS THE CREATOR OF TOPLESS DARTS, PRESUMABLY.

THEIR NEWEST LOW CAME AT NEWCASTLE ON SUNDAY, WHEN THE ONLY PERSON WHO ENDURED A WORSE AFTERNOON THAN SOLSKJÆR WAS SEAN LONGSTAFF, WHOSE MUM FORCED HIM TO TAKE HIS ANNOYING SHOW-OFF LITTLE BROTHER TO THE FOOTBALL. IT WAS WELL UNFAIR.

ALSO FEELING THE HEAT IS JOHN McGREAL, MANAGER OF COLCHESTER UNITED, WHOSE INABILITY TO BEAT TOTTENHAM IN NORMAL-TIME LOOKS INCREASINGLY LIKE A POOR RESULT. SPURS' WOES CONTINUED WITH A 3-0 HAMMERING AT BRIGHTON. AFTER CONCEDING AN EARLY CALAMITOUS GOAL, PANIC SPREAD THROUGH THE SPURS RANKS FASTER THAN AN UNSUBSTANTIATED RUMOUR ON WHATSAPP.

THEIR CHIEF TORMENTOR WAS AARON CONNOLLY — A TERRIFYING BEARDED CHILD-MAN WHO WILL HAUNT MAURICIO POCHETTINO'S DREAMS; AN ODD SENSATION FOR A MAN WHO USUALLY SLEEPS AS SOUNDLY AS ANYONE WHO SPEAKS IN SUPPORT OF QATAR.

WITH THE BLIND OPTIMISM OF THAT NORWICH PLAYER WHO RACED TO COLLECT THE BALL AFTER SCORING A LATE GOAL AGAINST ASTON VILLA, MARCO SILVA WILL BELIEVE HE CAN STILL RESOLVE EVERTON'S CURRENT 30-YEAR PREDICAMENT. PERHAPS HE CAN SIGN A PLAYER DURING THE NEXT TRANSFER WINDOW WHO CAN BRING MORE COMPOSURE TO THE BACK FOUR WHEN DEFENDING SET-PIECES. AN UNTITLED DIGITAL GOOSE, FOR EXAMPLE.

SERIOUSLY, WHO'D WANT TO BE A MANAGER? IS ALL THAT SWEET MONOGRAMMED SPORTS LEISUREWEAR REALLY WORTH THE STRESS, THE ABUSE, THE RIDICULE (AHEM, SORRY)? MAYBE IT'S THOSE RARE MOMENTS OF GLORY THAT KEEP THEM GOING, OR THE FLEETING GLIMPSES OF FOOTBALL'S TRUE SOUL — THE UPLIFTING SIGHT OF TWO YOUNG BROTHERS BECOMING LOCAL HEROES BY INFLICTING A MORTAL DEFEAT UPON SOME OTHER POOR SAP.

SUNDAY'S **INTELLECTUAL PROPERTY DERBY** BETWEEN MAN RED™ AND MERSEYSIDE RED© MAY HAVE ENDED IN A DRAW BUT IT PROVIDED A TIMELY BOOST FOR THE HOME SIDE'S HEAD PATSY, OLE GUNNAR SOLSKJÆR – A MAN WHO LOVES MANCHESTER SO MUCH THAT HE HAS RECENTLY BEGUN TO RESEMBLE THE CITY'S TRAM MAP. ONE LOVE!

JÜRGEN KLOPP WAS ALSO SMILING, BUT IN THAT UNSETTLING PASSIVE-AGGRESSIVE WAY THAT SUGGESTS HE COULD JUST AS EASILY GIVE YOU A CUDDLE AS RIP YOUR SPLEEN OUT AND WEAR IT AS A SNOOD. THE HAPPY-GO-LUCKY-FUNTIMES-GUY WAS VEXED BY THE DECISION TO ALLOW MARCUS RASHFORD'S OPENING GOAL TO STAND, A POINT HE MADE AT LENGTH TO FOURTH OFFICIAL, JON MOSS.

MAN RED'S HAPHAZARD TRANSFER POLICY HAS AT LEAST CREATED OPPORTUNITIES FOR THEIR YOUNGER PLAYERS TO GAIN SOME EXPERIENCE (OF HOW IT MUST FEEL TO BE IN A SHIPWRECK). HOWEVER, TO BE TRULY SUCCESSFUL, THEY'LL NEED A CATCHY ALLITERATIVE NICKNAME LIKE 'THE BUSBY BABES' OR 'FERGIE'S FLEDGLINGS'. HOW ABOUT 'SOLSKJÆR'S SACRIFICIAL VIRGINS'?

BIG CLUBS BLOODING YOUNGSTERS HAS BECOME A THEME OF THE 2019/20 PREMIER LEAGUE SEASON. OVER AT CHELSEA, THERE IS MUCH EXCITEMENT ABOUT 'LAMPARD'S LAMBS/FRANKIE'S FOETUSES', WITH THE MANAGER RIGHTLY RECEIVING PLAUDITS FOR CHOOSING TO IMPLEMENT SUCH A YOUTH POLICY. AFTER ALL, IT WAS HE WHO:

... RESULTING IN THE CREATION OF POWERFUL OLIGARCHS LOOKING TO INVEST IN HIGH PROFILE PROJECTS TO INSURE THEMSELVES AGAINST LATER POLITICAL RECRIMINATIONS, LAMPARD'S PERFORMANCES FOR CHELSEA MAKING THEM AN ATTRACTIVE PROSPECT...

... AND LEADING TO THE ACQUISITION OF A VAST BATTERY FARM OF YOUNG FOOTBALLERS, WHICH EVENTUALLY ENDS UP WITH CHELSEA FALLING FOUL OF UEFA RULES...

CLEARLY, FOOTBALL'S FUTURE IS BRIGHT. EVEN SOLSKJÆR WAS SWEPT ALONG WITH THE WAVE OF WILD OPTIMISM AS HE STATED IT WOULDN'T TAKE MAN RED™ ANOTHER 30 YEARS TO WIN THE TITLE. WHO KNOWS WHAT WE'LL ALL BE DOING BY THEN, AS WE WATCH A HOLOGRAM TAHITH CHONG EXPLAIN WHY HIS SIDE HAS FINISHED SIXTH AGAIN.

SQUIRES

BESIDES THE REVELATION THAT CRISTIANO RONALDO'S SECRET TO ETERNAL YOUTH IS SLEEPING ALL DAY, ONE OF THE SURPRISE STORIES OF THE SEASON HAS BEEN **THE RESURRECTION OF NIGEL PEARSON.** NUMEROUS OLD STORIES ABOUT NIGEL HAVE RESURFACED IN RECENT WEEKS, WITH TRUTH AND MYTH BECOMING AS TANGLED AS WATFORD'S FIXTURE LIST. LEGENDARY TALES INCLUDE:

THAT HE ONCE FOUGHT OFF A PACK OF WOLVES WHILST ON A WALKING HOLIDAY IN THE CARPATHIANS.

THAT HE SPENT LAST SUMMER LIVING ALONE IN THE SCOTTISH HIGHLANDS.

THAT THE REAL REASON HE VISITS TRANSYLVANIA IS THAT HE'S A VAMPIRE HUNTER.

I just like naps!

THAT AFTER LEAVING OH LEUVEN HE TRAVELLED TO THE HIMALAYAS AND MASTERED THE ANCIENT SKILL OF MAKING YOURSELF INVISIBLE TO ENEMIES AND POTENTIAL EMPLOYERS.

WHAT'S UNDENIABLE IS THAT PEARSON'S WATFORD SIDE ARE UNBEATEN IN SIX PREMIER LEAGUE GAMES AND HAVE RISEN OUT OF THE RELEGATION ZONE. VICARAGE ROAD HAS BECOME AN INHOSPITABLE PLACE FOR WEARY VISITORS...

Their players' lounge is a bit grotty. There isn't even a two-way mirror for punters to pay a grand to watch them eat fusilli.

Look at that. Ask them what it means.

I prefer not to speak.

Excuse me, but why's there a red moose scratched on the wall when your nickname's The Hornets and you're about as close to Canada as Spurs are to a Champions League place?

You made me miss. I never miss.

Well you say that, but—

Heh, we'll just be on our way then.

Uh-oh, we seem to have strayed off the path, on the way back to the bus. Ben Foster explicitly warned us to steer clear of the allotments.

You see, this is why I never leave the travel tavern.

Alright, lads? You lost?

Argh! It's the Wolf man of the Metropolitan Line! Legend has it he can tear a regional journalist in half with a single confusing metaphor!

Take the boy! TAKE THE BOY!

Guys. Chillax. This is the bespectacled, new age, Nigel. The most unsettling thing I'll do is speak. In. A. Slow. And. Deliberate. Manner. And. End. My. Sentence. With. A. Laugh. Hahahahaha. Ha.

Now, let's go back to my shed, spark up a joss stick and talk about the spiritual healing power of our friend the marrow.

IT'S ALL KICKING OFF AT SANDRINGHAM FC, WHERE TWO BIG NAME PLAYERS ARE TRYING TO ENGINEER A TRANSFER WINDOW MOVE TO THE CANADIAN PREMIER LEAGUE. WANTING TO LEAVE WHILST MAINTAINING THE PERKS OF MEMBERSHIP IS **NOT THE BRITISH WAY**, AND WITH A CRUNCH DERBY LOOMING AGAINST AFC COLLECTIVE NATIONAL SHRUG, THE BOSS IS NOT AMUSED. THE TEAM ARE SUMMONED FOR A RIGHT ROYAL ROLLICKING ...

Oh that is typical House of Windsor, that is. You get one hereditary peerage and you think you're Bertie Big Bollocks? I'll f—ing stick the youth team in!

'Kin yes, lads.

When I tell you to do something, you f—ing do it, and if you come back at me, we'll have a right sort out in here. And you can pair up if you like, and you can bring someone else with you, and you can bring your f—ing dinner.

Ooh, there's a place I've definitely been to where you can get a cracking Sloppy Giuseppe.

You see what you're leaving me with? Who's gonna be your replacement, the f—ing mascot?

My name's Edward, mother.

Half these wallies can't even remember their kit.

Hey, we missed the WhatsApp message...

Bloody Gibbo.

No wonder the deep thinkers on Sandringham Fans TV are losing their well-adjusted minds.

Well I can't think of a bigger scandal to hit Sandringham FC in recent times.

I hear Meghan eats centipedes and keeps Kate's soul in a haunted ballerina jewellery box.

Treacherous snowflakes! Imagine wanting to move to a country where you're not subjected to my ridiculous breakfast bile!

You see, that's exactly the kind of bizarre vitriol we're talking about.

Well your grandfather looked through those examples you sent and he says they were fine...

Raheem Sterling himself couldn't have expected fairer coverage!

Listen, I understand, I do. We need to create a modern team environment, a Southgatian safe space founded on respect that will see us thrive in 21st Century Britain. After all, we aren't in medieval times anymore.

Come on, pass me your special talking box...

My name's Meghan, Your Majest—

Gertcha.

So...

Yeah, we're sending them out on loan, but we've got a top, top Lord coming in from the fringes. Generations of selective breeding have left him well-equipped to restore some respect to the outfit.

Make way for Bertie, lads. 118th in line for the top job and here to put the **buck** into Buckingham Palace.

Sakes

SQUIRES

1. GEORGE GRAHAM 2. LUKAS PODOLSKI 3. SERGE GNABRY 4. NAYIM 5. IGORS STEPANOVS 6. DAVID SEAMAN
7. TONY ADAMS 8. HERBERT CHAPMAN 9. PER MERTESACKER 10. LUCAS TORREIRA 11. MESUT AND UNAI'S RELATIONSHIP COUNSELLOR
12. IAN WRIGHT 13. JOHN BERCOW 14. THAT VITÓRIA FAN WHO WENT TO EUROPA LEAGUE GAME DRESSED LIKE A HIGH-RANKING
CHURCH OFFICIAL 15. STEVE BOULD 16. PIERS MORGAN 17. JEREMY CORBYN 18. HÉCTOR BELLERÍN 19. YOUNG HARRY KANE
20. BARRON TRUMP 21. AARON RAMSEY 22. DONALD TRUMP 23. WILFRIED ZAHA 24. MATTEO GUENDOUZI
25. JEAN-PAUL, THE FRENCH EXCHANGE STUDENT 26. STAN KROENKE 27. DANIËLLE VAN DE DONK 28. SEAD KOLAŠINAC
29. THE ARSENAL FAN FROM OLD TRAFFORD, 1998 30. RAY PARLOUR HAVING A REST 31. JASON FROM TOP BOY, WHOSE ONE WISH IS TO WATCH
ARSENAL 32. SIR CHIPS KESWICK 33. OSAMA BIN LADEN 34. THE MODERN FAN FROM THE FAST SHOW 35. LAURENT KOSCIELNY
36. DAVID LUIZ 37. FREDDIE LJUNGBERG 38 UNAI EMERY 39. WAYNE SHAW, SUTTON UNITED 40. GRANIT XHAKA 41. RECLINING FAN
42. ATOM SÁNCHEZ 43. HUMBER SÁNCHEZ 44. ALEXIS SÁNCHEZ 45. THIERRY HENRY 46. STEVE MORROW 47. ARSÈNE WENGER
48. GUNNERSAURUS REX 49. PAT RICE 50. PETR CECH 51. TV 52 & 53. PHYSIO AND KIERAN TIERNEY 54. SHKODRAN MUSTAFI
55. LORD HARRIS OF PECKHAM 56. MESUT ÖZIL

SIGH, IT'S TIME FOR FOOTBALL TO TAKE DOWN ITS TASTEFUL REMEMBRANCE DECORATIONS FOR ANOTHER YEAR. BUT BEFORE THE POPPY MASCOT SHUFFLES AWAY IN ITS CLOWN SHOES OF RESPECT — AND IN THE SPIRIT OF DIGNIFIED, PRIVATE REFLECTION THAT SWEPT THROUGH THE COUNTRY LAST WEEKEND — LET'S SEE OUT POPPY SEASON WITH A GOOD OLD SING SONG. JOIN IN IF YOU'RE NOT A TRAITOR!

IT'S THE MOST WONDERFUL TIME OF THE YEAR,

THE CHILDREN ARE BRAYING,

'CAUSE JAMES McCLEAN'S PLAYING,

THEY BOO AND THEY JEEEEER,

IT'S THE MOST WONDERFUL TIME OF THE YEAR.

IT'S THE HAP-HAPPIEST SEASON OF ALL,

YOUR IMPRESSION OF CHURCHILL,

WAS QUITE CONTROVERSIAL,

THAT'S F*CKIN' HANDBALL!

IT'S THE HAP-HAPPIEST SEASON OF ALL.

YOU'RE NOT GETTING SERVED IN THE BAR, UNLESS YOU GO FULL MARK FRANCOIS...

WHERE THE EFF IS YOUR POPPY? YOU SOME SORT OF COMMIE?

BARK, BARK, BARK BARK, BAAAAAARK.

YOU'RE NOT GETTING SERVED IN THE BAR.

IF ONLY THERE WERE A WAY,

TO INJECT POPPIES INTO YOUR VEINS,

YOU'D UPSTAGE YOUR RIVALS, THEIR CRAP POPPY TRIFLES,

BRITAIN'S GONE INSAAAAAAANE,

INJECT POPPIES INTO YOUR VEINS.

Are you sure this is a good idea, Mr Chairman?

Think of the self-sacrifice of those who suffered before you! Sir Kevin had to go behind that scary multistorey in town to buy these.

I did, yeah.

IMAGINE KNOCKING FOR YOUR MATE,

SEEING WHAT HE'S SCRAWLED ON HIS FACE...

THE HELL OF THE SOMME, DRAWN IN WAX CRAYON...

OH BLOODY HELL, JAAAAAASE.

THAT'S ABSOLUTE QUALITY, MATE

THE FACE OF ARCHDUKE FERDINAND,

A TIFO ACROSS THE MAIN STAND,

HE GOT SHOT THROUGH THE BRAIN,

GIFTING US THIS GREAT DAY,

OH ISN'T IT GRAAAAAAAND,

ARE YOU SURE THAT'S ARCHDUKE FERDINAND?

MILITARY FETISHISM - PUTTING 'THE PHWOAR' INTO WAR

IT'S THE MOST WONDERFUL TIME OF THE YEAR,

DON'T GET IN A TIZZY, YOUR GROUNDSMAN'S BEEN BUSY,

YOU'D BETTER ADHEEEEERE,

IT'S THE MOST WONDERFUL TIME...

YES, THE MOST WONDERFUL TIME,

OH THE MOST WONDERFUL TIME,

OF THE YEEEEEEAR!

GOD SAVE THE QUEEN AND (CHECKS NOTES) CHELSEA,

GREAT BRITAIN HAS LEFT THE EUROPEAN UNION, IN A WAY!

THE EUROPEAN EXPERIMENT IS DEAD – A STUNNING VICTORY FOR **PASSION** OVER NERDY ECONOMIC ANALYSIS. NOW IT'S TIME TO FIND OUT JUST HOW SUCCESSFUL A NATION CAN BE IF IT WERE TO BE MANAGED BY TIM SHERWOOD. WHO NEEDS EMPLOYMENT PROTECTION AND ENVIRONMENTAL LAWS WHEN YOU HAVE FLAGS – **GREAT BRITISH FLAGS**? SOON EVERY DAY WILL FEEL LIKE AN ENGLAND AWAY GAME IN A EUROPEAN PORT CITY.

HARK, THE BELLS – LOADS OF THEM, LETTING OFF FIREWORKS! BRITAIN IS FINALLY FREE OF THE OPPRESSOR IT NEVER REALLY THOUGHT ABOUT UNTIL FOUR YEARS AGO. NO WONDER BREXIT SUPPORTERS ARE (CHECKS NOTES AGAIN) STILL DISPLAYING MOURINHO LEVELS OF OUTRAGE.

WHAT CAN FOOTBALL EXPECT FROM THIS BRAVE NEW ERA? BASICALLY, THE IMMEDIATE RESTORATION OF AN IMAGINED, MARMALADE-TINGED PAST; A MONOCULTURAL UTOPIA WHERE SCUFF-KNEED URCHINS KICK A MITRE MULTIPLEX ABOUT ON A COBBLED STREET, UMBRELLAS AND BOWLER HATS FOR GOALPOSTS, RIDING THEIR BIKES HOME TO WATCH 'LOVE THY NEIGHBOUR', AND POSTING WHITE DOG TURDS THROUGH THE LETTERBOX OF THE SIKH FAMILY AT NUMBER 26. **RULE NOSTALGIA!**

FORCING ALL THE FOREIGNERS OUT WILL HELP THE ENGLAND TEAM TOO (SORRY, SCOTLAND, WALES AND OTHER, THIS WAS NEVER ABOUT YOU). WITH NO MORE SERGIO AGÜERO TO BLOCK THE CAREER PATH OF PATRICK BAMFORD, EXPECT EUROPE TO QUIVER AT THE FEET OF NEIL WARNOCK'S ENGLAND AT THE EUROS THIS SUMMER.

HOWEVER, THERE IS WORK TO BE DONE, AND THE PRIME MINISTER CAN'T BE EXPECTED TO BE ARSED TO READ BRIEFINGS WHEN THERE IS BANTZ TO ATTEND TO; EPIC BANTZ. THOSE DOGS IN BRUSSELS ARE TRYING TO SECURE THE BEST DEAL FOR THEIR MEMBER STATES WHO HAVEN'T LOST THEIR MINDS. FOOTBALL CAN HELP OUT BY PROVIDING SOME OF ITS TOP, TOP NEGOTIATORS.

BRITAIN CAN ALSO TAKE BACK CONTROL OF ITS FOOD PRODUCTION AND IMPORTS, FREED FROM THE SHACKLES OF BUREACRATIC HEALTH STANDARDS. AFTER ALL, WHAT CAN BE CLEANER THAN A CHLORINATED CHICKEN? FOOTBALL FANS WILL BE AT A NATURAL ADVANTAGE HERE TOO, AS THEIR PALATES HAVE GROWN ACCUSTOMED TO ALMOST EVERY CULINARY OUTRAGE.

OF COURSE, IT WON'T ALL BE MECHANICALLY-PRODUCED CARROT SUBSTITUTE, THERE WILL HAVE TO BE SOME STICK TOO. ONCE THOSE HUMAN RIGHTS LAWS HAVE BEEN TORN UP AND THE TRAITORS AT THE BBC INTERNED INDEFINITELY, SOME OF ITS PROGRAMMES WILL NEED NEW PRESENTERS.

SO SIT BACK AND ENJOY THE RIDE. AFTER ALL, IT'S ONLY A MATTER OF TIME UNTIL THAT ANGRY JAR OF WASPS THAT HAVE BEEN SHAKEN UP REALISE THEIR LIVES HAVEN'T MIRACULOUSLY IMPROVED AS A RESULT OF THE ABOLITION OF MYTHICAL BANANA CURVATURE LAWS. AND PERHAPS, ONCE EVERY POSSIBLE SCAPEGOAT HAS BEEN EXHAUSTED, IT WILL BE THE MONORAIL SALESMEN WHO ORCHESTRATED THE WHOLE CIRCUS WHO ARE SCRUTINISED AS IF THEY WERE A CENTRE-FORWARD WHOSE ARMPIT HAS STRAYED OFFSIDE.

COVID AND 2019–20 (PART TWO):
CORONABALL

I'd always suspected I'd see out the end of the world watching football of questionable quality, and so it came to pass that on a grey Saturday afternoon, two weeks before the first Covid lockdown, I attended a goalless Hyundai A-League clash between Sydney FC and Perth Glory. That may sound reckless, but we're not talking Liverpool vs Atlético Madrid here. With more people on the pitch than in the stands, it was probably the best place in Sydney to enjoy some classic social distancing.

With 156 confirmed Covid cases in Australia, everyone was suddenly very hygiene-conscious, but I did wonder whether we'd all get through this unscathed after seeing a man in the stadium toilets hawk up a greenie and flob it on the floor, rather than into the urinal two feet from his face. He did push the door open with his elbow, though, so swings and roundabouts.

As the coronavirus infection rate rose, speculation grew as to how football could continue, with rumours spreading faster than You Know What. In England, one such story suggested the over-seventies would be banned from stadiums. Not only would this have created mass confusion about who would offer round the half-time mints, but Roy Hodgson would have had to pass himself off as a hip young cat to continue his vital work at Crystal Palace. With more players and managers testing positive, it wasn't long before football was suspended completely. It felt like a watershed moment when Arsenal's game with Brighton was postponed because Mikel Arteta had caught the virus: if a man moulded from Danish plastic could get sick, anyone could.

Like most other people who make a living hacking away at the football-content coalface, I suddenly wondered what I'd write about. What if this thing lasted a whole *month*? It was an anxious time. The situation appeared gloomier back home in the UK, and, watching from afar, I became increasingly worried for my friends, family and – because I'm a really great guy – people who weren't even blood relatives.

Thankfully, I had absolute faith in the British government, led by roly-poly TV funnyman Boris Johnson, and was confident they would be working hard to minimise the impact of the pandemic rather than using it as a smokescreen for one long, venal, last-days-of-Rome fuck-party, wetting their beaks while your loved ones died alone. In fairness to Matt Hancock – health minister, shit – he did try his absolute best to make scapegoats of Premier League footballers, asking them (rather than his party's billionaire patrons) to donate their salaries to help NHS workers and people in need. Annoyingly, many of them were already busy fundraising. Selfish bastards! When football did eventually resume in the Premier League and Championship three months later, it was to a backdrop of branded tarpaulin, artificial crowd noises and cardboard cut-outs of fans, creating the sensation the season was being played out via a Zoom call. Some of those matches could definitely have been emails.

49

Liverpool players took to a temporary stage erected at great expense in front of the vacant Kop to lift the club's first league title since 1990, watched on by millions around the world, including owner John W. Henry (net worth $5.1 billion) and the club staff he'd furloughed.

The season ended with Champions League and Europa League mini-tournaments, which was quite good fun but probably gave the football authorities and club owners some fresh ideas about how to further exploit the game for their own financial gain. Having thrashed Barcelona 8–2 to give us all a much-needed laugh, Bayern Munich went on to beat Qatari Sports Investments, Paris, in the final. When you find yourself rooting for Bayern, it really hits home that you're living through one of the strangest periods in modern history.

AS THE CORONAVIRUS CRISIS DEEPENS, BRITISH FOOTBALL HAS VOWED TO **KEEP CALM AND CARRY ON** (WITH A FEW MINOR CONCESSIONS), THUS DEMONSTRATING A STOICISM IN THE FACE OF ADVERSITY FOR WHICH THE NATION IS SELF-FAMED. AH, THE DUNKIRK SPIRIT – SIPPING TEA ATOP THE GLOWING BLITZ RUBBLE; REMAINING EMOTIONALLY-DISTANT WHEN CALLING THE POLICE TO REPORT KFC FOR RUNNING OUT OF CHICKEN; PANIC BUYING ALL THE LOO ROLL WHILST CHEERILY SINGING THE DAME VERA LYNN CLASSICS...

IT WAS RUMOURED THAT THE PREMIER LEAGUE WAS CONSIDERING BANNING THE OVER-70s FROM ATTENDING MATCHES. HOWEVER, NO SUCH MEASURE HAS BEEN IMPOSED, SO ROY HODGSON DOESN'T HAVE TO CON HIS WAY IN TO STADIUMS JUST YET.

SOME FOOTBALL FIGURES HAVE BEEN PROACTIVE IN THEIR ATTEMPTS TO COMBAT THE SPREAD OF THE VIRUS. FOR EXAMPLE, JOSÉ MOURINHO HAS BEEN WASHING HIS HANDS OF RESPONSIBILITY FOR WEEKS, WHILST SINGING A FAMILIAR OLD TUNE.

HOWEVER, SHOULD THE NEED UNFORTUNATELY ARISE, THERE IS NO ONE BETTER SUITED TO SELF-ISOLATION THAN FOOTBALL'S OLDEST TEENAGER.

GIVEN THE ALARMING RATE AT WHICH THE VIRUS SPREAD ELSEWHERE, AND THE CAPACITY OF THE BRITISH GOVERNMENT TO DEAL WITH ANYTHING MORE CHALLENGING THAN NAMING A PUPPY, IT IS UNDERSTANDABLE THAT SOME PEOPLE ARE JUMPY ABOUT CATCHING THE INFECTION.

CYNICS ARGUE THAT A GREATER THREAT TO PUBLIC HEALTH IS **ACTUALLY** POSED BY EDERSON'S SMILEY FACE TATTOO THAT WHISPERS EVIL THOUGHTS TO HIM, AND WHICH SEEMS TO HAVE RETURNED.

IF YOU'RE WORRIED THAT THE BRITISH PM'S STANDARD RESPONSE TO A CRISIS IS TO ENJOY A NICE HOLIDAY, THERE'S NO NEED TO LOOT THE ANDREX FACTORY FOR YOUR BOG ROLL BUM SHELTER JUST YET. GOOD NEWS REACHES US FROM THE CHIEF MEDICAL OFFICER, **DR. MATTHEW LE TISSIER**, WHO LAST WEEK TWEETED AN OPINION THAT COULD BE PRINTED OFF AND USED IN THE EVENT OF A NATIONAL LOO ROLL SHORTAGE.

THANKS, DR. MATT!

Um...

LIKE EVERY SPORT OTHER THAN COMPETITIVE PASTA SHOPPING, FOOTBALL HAS BEEN MOSTLY SUSPENDED. IT IS A SITUATION UNLIKELY TO CHANGE UNTIL SCIENCE FINDS A WAY TO INJECT TINY JAMES MILNERS INTO EVERYONE'S IMMUNE SYSTEMS.

UNTIL IT RETURNS, WE'RE ALL GOING TO HAVE TO FILL THE VOID CREATED BY THE ABSENCE OF JEFF STELLING. IF YOU'VE ALREADY COMPLETED NETFLIX, AND POLISHED OFF THAT ESCAPE TO THE COUNTRY BOX SET, YOU COULD ALWAYS TRY LIVE STREAMING RONALDINHO PLAYING PARAGUAYAN PRISON FOOTBALL.

MAYBE YOU'RE REALLY EMBRACING THE WHOLE APOCALYPTIC VIBE (PUSHING THAT OLD MAN INTO A FREEZER TO GRASP THE LAST FOUR BOXES OF SURFACE WIPES FELT GOOD, ADMIT IT). IN WHICH CASE, YOU COULD TRY THE LATEST ZOMBIE DRAMA NONSENSE, SET IN PARIS. IN LAST WEEK'S EPISODE, FRINGE CHARACTER LAYVIN KURZAWA MADE A MORONIC DECISION THAT JEOPARDISED THE SAFETY OF THE WHOLE ADMITTEDLY ANNOYING GROUP...

THE BBC DIDN'T EXACTLY HELP TO LIFT THE MOOD. THERE WAS ONLY ONE WAY THEIR CHOICE OF REPLACEMENT FOR MATCH OF THE DAY COULD HAVE BEEN MORE SPIRIT-CRUSHING.

DEBATE CONTINUES ABOUT THE BEST WAY TO RESOLVE THE SEASON, WITH THE ONLY POINT OF AGREEMENT BEING THAT SWINDON SHOULD BE PROMOTED TO LEAGUE ONE, PREFERABLY TAKING OXFORD'S PLACE (SORRY, YELLOWS FANS; I DON'T MAKE THE RULES). IT'S PARTICULARLY TOUGH ON LIVERPOOL, SO CLOSE TO WINNING THEIR ELUSIVE LEAGUE TITLE. GIVEN THEIR TRACK RECORD, IT'S IMPROBABLE THAT ANYTHING WOULD HAVE DENIED THEM.

(LOOK, THERE WAS HARDLY ANY FOOTBALL ON, RIGHT?)

HOWEVER, FOOTBALL SEEMS LESS IMPORTANT WITH EACH PASSING DAY; INCREASINGLY TRIVIALISED WITH EVERY SCROLL OF THE PHONE SCREEN. PERHAPS AFTER THE VIRUS PASSES, AND SOCIETY RETURNS TO SOMETHING APPROACHING NORMALITY, WE'LL EMERGE BLINKING INTO THE SUNLIGHT WITH A NEW SENSE OF PERSPECTIVE ABOUT THE GAME WE LOVE, AND EACH OTHER.

NEXT WEEK: WE SCRAPE THE ARCHIVES AND RE-LIVE THE MAGIC OF THE 1999 INTERTOTO CUP !! 60 TEAMS, 114 MATCHES, 3 WINNERS, ONE SCOTT MINTO.

TAKE CARE, EVERYONE X

PROJECT RESTART

RATHER THAN FOLLOW THE EXAMPLES OF THE FRENCH AND SCOTTISH LEAGUES AND REPLACE FOOTBALL WITH A MASSIVE BARNEY, THE PREMIER LEAGUE HAS DISCUSSED TENTATIVE PLANS TO RESUME THE 2019-20 SEASON. CUE MASSIVE BARNEY, WITH EVEN SOME OF THE CLUBS AT THE BOTTOM END OF THE TABLE WHO ARE NOBLY CALLING FOR RELEGATION TO BE SCRAPPED FOR THE INTEGRITY OF THE COMPETITION BEING ACCUSED OF SELF-INTEREST!

SQUIRES

MOST CLUBS HAVE A HEALTHY DEPENDENCE ON TV REVENUE, SO THE NEED TO PLAN FOR A RETURN IS UNDERSTANDABLE. HOWEVER, SOME PLAYERS HAVE RAISED CONCERNS ABOUT THEIR SAFETY.

We've only just recovered from being pushed under a bus by Matt Hancock.

THE GOVERNMENT BELIEVES THAT THE RESUMPTION OF THE PREMIER LEAGUE WOULD CHEER UP THE RELATIVELY SMALL PERCENTAGE OF THE POPULATION WHO CARE ABOUT IT. ANY PLAN WOULD NEED GOVERNMENT APPROVAL, REQUIRING THEM TO PAUSE FROM THEIR PUBLIC DISPLAYS OF SELF-CONGRATULATION FOR HOW BRILLIANTLY THEY'VE HANDLED THE COVID-19 CRISIS.

A death toll that could fill Carrow Road, one of the Premier League's smaller stadiums!

CLAP CLAP CLAP CLAP

OH HERE WE GO. WHY ARE YOU CRITICISING THEM? THE DEAR LEADER ROSE FROM THE GRAVE TO SIRE A SON, THE ONLY AMBIGUITY BEING THE BASIC QUESTION OF WHETHER HE'S NOW FATHERED ENOUGH KIDS TO FILL MOSS ROSE OR THE MARACANÃ. WHY DO YOU HATE BABIES, LEFTY HERODIST SCUM?! NEXT YOU'LL BE SAYING THAT GASLIT APPLAUSE FOR NHS STAFF DOESN'T MAKE UP FOR A DECADE OF SCHUMACHERING THE CRAP OUT OF THEM!

You're the real heroes. Would you like a little badge?

SOME HAVE INTERPRETED PROJECT RESTART AS BEING SYMPTOMATIC OF FOOTBALL'S GREED. MAYBE THE GAME'S REPUTATION COULD BE IMPROVED IF IT GOT A 100-YEAR OLD CAPTAIN TO DO LAPS OF HIS GARDEN TO HELP FILL THE FUNDING VOID FOR THE NEGLECTED HEALTH SYSTEM.

THE NHS

POP!

CRACK!

RUPTURE!

YES, IT'S A RETRO-CLASSIC NOSTALGIA JOKE ABOUT BRYAN ROBSON'S INJURY RECORD!

THREE STEPS FROM BACK DOOR!

DISLOCATE!

CENTRAL TO THE PROJECT RESTART PLAN IS THE NEED FOR GAMES TO BE PLAYED AT NEUTRAL BIOSPHERES — STERILE ENVIRONMENTS WHERE TV SUBSCRIBERS CAN HEAR THE ECHO OF THE PLAYERS' SHOUTS — ALLOWING THEM A SEAMLESS PREMIER LEAGUE EXPERIENCE. SEVERAL POTENTIAL VENUES HAVE BEEN IDENTIFIED, BUT TO EMPHASISE THE POINT THAT GOBSH*TES WHO WRITE OPINION PIECES FOR NEWSPAPERS SHOULDN'T BE PUT IN POSITIONS OF GENUINE POWER, HERE ARE SOME ALTERNATIVE SUGGESTIONS:

COMPLETE THE SEASON ON A DECOMMISSIONED OIL RIG.

This is why I said we should have brought more than one ball.

oh this should be good...

PROJECT RESTART

CART EVERYONE OFF TO SOMEWHERE UNAFFECTED BY THE VIRUS; A PLACE WHERE NOTHING BAD CAN HAPPEN, LIKE AN ANTARCTIC RESEARCH BASE.

PROJECT RESTART

PERHAPS THE SAFEST OPTION COULD BE TO COMPLETE THE SEASON WITHOUT ANY PLAYERS AT ALL, WITH FINAL LEAGUE POSITIONS INSTEAD DECIDED BY WHO CAN BUILD THE BEST ROBOT.

As the old saying goes: you're guaranteed wins with clockwork and springs!

BOOM

CRUNCH

OF COURSE, IT WOULD ONLY TAKE ONE PERSON TO TEST POSITIVE FOR COVID-19 FOR PROJECT RESTART TO COLLAPSE. A CAUTIOUS APPROACH IS THEREFORE ESSENTIAL TO ENSURE THERE'S ONLY ONE WAY THE VIRUS CAN TAKE HOLD IN THE PREMIER LEAGUE...

Congratulations, you've passed the owners and directors test and are free to take over a generic traditional sleeping giant.

Now to enjoy some positive publicity!

HAVING PLAYED THE LONG GAME AND WAITED UNTIL NOBODY COULD LEAVE THE COUNTRY TO AVOID IT

LIVERPOOL ARE CHAMPIONS!

HOWEVER, IN ORDER TO APPRECIATE THE GOOD TIMES YOU HAVE TO EXPERIENCE THE BAD, AND THEIR 19TH LEAGUE TITLE NEEDS TO BE SEEN IN THE CONTEXT OF THE BARREN 30-YEAR PERIOD OF UNPARALLELED MISERY (17 TROPHIES) THAT PRECEDED IT...

1990-91 2ND

KENNY WALKS OUT.

1991-92 6TH

SOUNESS WALKS IN. THE REBUILDING PROJECT BEGINS.

Why would we sign Eric Cantona when we've got Istvan Kozma?

1992-93 6TH

NO SILVERWARE, BUT AT LEAST RONNIE ROSENTHAL'S STILL BANGING IN THE G.... OH.

1993-94 8TH

SOUNESS IS REPLACED BY ROY EVANS, DESPITE BEING YEARS AHEAD OF HIS TIME.

LIVERPOOL D BRISTOL CITY 1 90:01

Well that's the FA Cup out of the way. Now to focus on the Oh for f... sake.

1994-95 4TH

FINALLY, THE PREMIER LEAGUE TROPHY IS LIFTED AT ANFIELD!

1995-96 3RD

WHO NEEDS LEAGUE TITLES WHEN YOU'RE THE COOLEST DUDES AT THE PROM?

1996-97 4TH

DAVID JAMES SUFFERS NO SIDE EFFECTS FROM STAYING UP LATE TO COMPLETE TOMB RAIDER.

Morning, David.

Gaffer.

1997-98 3RD

A SEASON AS THRILLING AS MICHAEL OWEN'S SWEATER COLLECTION.

This one has a stripe!

1998-99 7TH

THE DREAM TEAM!

Nope.

1999-2000 4TH

A FINAL DAY 1-0 DEFEAT AT PAUL JEWELL'S BRADFORD MEANS THEY MISS OUT ON A CHAMPIONS LEAGUE PLACE.

2000-01 3RD GREAT. MORE CLUTTER.

2001-02 2ND

LIKE SOUNESS TEN YEARS EARLIER, GÉRARD HOULLIER REQUIRES HEART SURGERY. IT'S AS IF MANAGING LIVERPOOL IS AS BAD FOR YOUR HEALTH AS A BACON DOUBLE PIE-BURGER.

2002-03 5TH THE CHAMPIONS OF FRIENDSHIP.

I'LL F... YOUR MUM!

DIOUF

2003-04 4TH VA VA VOOM!

SINAMA 24 LE TALLE 20

2004-05 5TH

YE GODS, WHEN WILL THIS FOUL JINX END?!

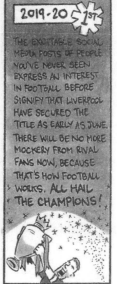

THE PREMIER LEAGUE IS BACK, JUST IN TIME TO LIFT EVERYONE'S MORALE! WHO NEEDS A CORONAVIRUS CURE WHEN YOU HAVE NORWICH v SOUTHAMPTON? NATURALLY, SOME BITTER NULL-AND-VOIDERS HAVE QUESTIONED THE WISDOM OF RESUMING THE SEASON WHILE PEOPLE ARE STILL DYING AND THE INFECTION RATE REMAINS SO HIGH, BUT MAYBE THEY CAN BE WON OVER WITH A SLICK ADVERTISING CAMPAIGN. FIRE UP THE 'BEST OF SIMPLE MINDS' CD, LADS...

It's a whole new ball game
(because football isn't football without fans).

After an absence of 16 years, **LEEDS LEEDS LEEDS** are back where they **BELONG** – their promotion meaning they'll have been a Premier League side for almost as many seasons as Bolton! Fans across the world have been celebrating the achievements of the club commonly known as 'The neutrals' favourite'. It turns out that even Jaime Lannister supports Leeds.

Defeats for promotion rivals West Brom and Brentford handed Leeds the title, evoking memories of their league triumph in 1992, when David Batty, Eric Cantona and Gary McAllister squeezed on to Lee Chapman's sofa for some low-key televised celebrations. Perhaps some of the current squad should have recreated the moment by cramming into Marcelo Bielsa's modest, one-bedroom, stats dungeon.

It's been a long road back for Leeds. Financial implosion, relegation, administration and points deductions meant the only honour they'd received in years was becoming a verb.

Their fans endured years of trauma under a succession of owners apparently determined to build a banter dynasty. It seems like an eternity since they slipped out of the Premier League. Want to feel old? This is what that boy who was filmed crying in the stands when Leeds were relegated in 2004 looks like now:

Fourteen Spinal Tap drummers tried unsuccessfully to guide Leeds back to the big time, each of them meeting with a cruel fate.

But then came Bielsa, one of the most respected coaches in the game (although, in fairness, nobody has probably thought to ask Pep and Poch about the influence Steve Evans had on their football philosophies). Leeds were transformed into a buzzing, high-energy attacking force and opposition managers were blown away by his almost obsessive levels of research and knowledge.

This of course led to last season's highly entertaining 'Spygate' episode, when a member of Bielsa's coaching entourage was caught watching a Derby County training session. Although Derby went on to beat them in the play-off semi-finals, it was Leeds who enjoyed the last laugh on Sunday, when they walked out at Pride Park to a teeth-clenched guard of honour from the Derby players.

We can all look forward to Leeds renewing some old hostilities in the Premier League next season, where Bielsa will come up against not only Lampard, but some of his famed admirers.

Finally, their fans can sleep well, knowing that a bright future awaits, with their beloved manager almost certain to renew his contract. After all, this is Leeds, what can go wrong?

DANCE AROUND THE DRESSING ROOM IN YOUR PANTS BECAUSE ABOUT EIGHT YEARS AFTER THIS SEASON STARTED THE USUAL BIG CLUBS HAVE FINISHED IN THE TOP FOUR! OH MUNDANE NORMALITY, HOW WE HAVE MISSED YOU. MANCHESTER UNITED CLAIMED A PLACE IN NEXT SEASON'S CHAMPIONS LEAGUE WITH A 2-0 WIN AGAINST THE POOR CHURCH MICE OF LEICESTER (ESTIMATED OWNER'S VALUE : £4.6BN). VICTORY WAS SEALED WITH AN OPPORTUNISTIC GOAL FROM 2018'S JESSE LINGARD, AFTER A PIECE OF GOALKEEPING FROM KASPER SCHMEICHEL THAT WAS AS IMPRESSIVE AS LINGARD'S YEAR 11 BEARD.

My goal drought is over! Finally, I can shave off this bloody beard. Honestly, Bruno; I don't know how you cope! They're so itchy, aren't they?

LEICESTER WERE UNABLE TO MATCH THE HEIGHTS OF THEIR GOAL-WASTING 9-0 DEMOLITION OF SOUTHAMPTON IN THE BEFORE TIMES. THEIR POST-COVID FORM WAS SO UNDERWHELMING THAT YOU HAVE TO WONDER IF BRENDAN RODGERS FOLLOWED THE MEDICAL ADVICE OF THE WORLD'S MOST STABLE EPIDEMIOLOGIST.

Right, boys; get these down you. They'll boost your immune system and give you a brilliant white Brendan smile. Hey, Vardy: Chat Cillit, get Banged!

I haven't said that in four years, but fine...

HOWEVER, THEY STILL QUALIFY FOR THE EUROPA LEAGUE, WHERE THEY'LL BE JOINED BY SPURS, GIVING JOSÉ A REASON TO CELEBRATE.

GOOD NEWS FOR CHELSEA TOO. THEIR WIN AGAINST WOLVES SECURED A TOP-FOUR FINISH AND, MORE IMPORTANTLY, NO ONE BROKE THE CODE OF HONOUR, TO THE RELIEF OF MADE (IN CHELSEA) GUY, FRANK 'FRANKIE' LAMPARD.

Something to moan about in October!

One day, some kids from the academy carried Jody Morris's groceries home. You know why? It was outta respect.

Well, that and the transfer embargo giving them a whiff of the first team.

AT THE OTHER END OF THE TABLE, RELEGATION WAS CONFIRMED FOR BOURNEMOUTH AND WATFORD. HEAT MAP ANALYSIS SHOWS THAT THE HORNETS' HR DEPARTMENT WAS THE HARDEST WORKING TEAM IN THE LEAGUE THIS SEASON. WHAT WOULD THE THREE MANAGERS THEY FIRED DURING THE CAMPAIGN HAVE BEEN THINKING ON SUNDAY? MAYBE THEY EVEN GOT TOGETHER.

Here we are, lads. Breathe it in.

Watford's a lot hillier than I remember.

What do we do now, Nigel?

We sit. We reflect. We drink my homemade kombucha. Come on, tops off.

Christ, that's yeasty.

THERE WERE ECSTATIC SCENES OF SINGING AND DANCING IN THE ASTON VILLA DRESSING ROOM AFTER THEIR 1-1 DRAW AT WEST HAM, A FINE RESULT WITH THE ADDED BONUS THAT IT SAVED THEM FROM RELEGATION. NOT EVEN THE MOST PROFESSIONAL OF CURMUDGEONS COULD BEGRUDGE THEM THEIR MOMENT OF JOY.

Morning, Trevor. How are Lucy and the kids? Splendid. Don't you love the sweet smell of fresh jasmine on a summer's day?

I certainly do, Mr Keane.

...So I said to Quinton, I said: "Quinton, if that's a lemon drizzle cake then I'm a Bakewell tart!"

Oh, Mr Keane, you are a caution!

Yeah.

Micah, I simply insist you join me in the green room for a tipple afterwards. Nigel Pearson's given me some of his delicious kombucha and I hear it's as yeasty as...

Um... yeah, ok...

OK, and we're live in five... four... three... two... one...

IT'S BEEN A WEIRD SEASON; ONE BESET BY ANXIETY AND HUMAN TRAGEDY. HOWEVER, IF YOU THOUGHT A PANDEMIC WOULD PROVIDE PEOPLE WITH A SENSE OF PERSPECTIVE AND DIMINISH THEIR OUTRAGE THEN YOU ARE MERCIFULLY WRONG, MY FURIOUS FRIEND. LAST WEEK, THE RIGHTEOUS ANGER OF SOME FANS WAS ENFLAMED BY THE OPINION OF A GROUP OF PEOPLE THEY REGARD WITH CONTEMPT ANYWAY.

The Association of Professional Orphanage Arsonists has voted for Jordan Henderson as their footballer of the year?! To the Court of Arbitration for Sport!

(IN FAIRNESS, EOIN DOYLE WAS ROBBED)

IT'S ONLY FITTING THAT THE FINAL WORD GOES TO THE TEAM OF THE YEAR, ~~SHEFFIELD UNITED~~, LIVERPOOL, WHO YOU MAY HAVE HEARD WON THE LEAGUE. THEIR TITLE CELEBRATIONS REPORTEDLY COST A BOMB (WHO NEEDS A WOMEN'S TEAM WHEN YOU'VE GOT A TEMPORARY PLINTH?), REPRESENTING AS MUCH VALUE FOR MONEY AS ANY FIREWORKS DISPLAY. THE SKIES LIT UP FOR MILES AROUND, FOR WHAT FELT LIKE DAYS.

I don't suppose you brought any food did you, Nigel?

Even better; a book of Jim Beglin's poetry about Jürgen Klopp.

"There was a young man from Stuttgart..."

AS FOOTBALL'S OLDEST COMPETITION, THE FA CUP IS BLESSED WITH STORIES THAT ECHO THROUGH THE AGES. THE WHITE HORSE, STANLEY MATTHEWS, STEVEN GERRARD, THAT NEWCASTLE FAN WHO WAVED HIS WANG LIKE A HELICOPTER AT OXFORD IN THE FOURTH ROUND: ALL SEARED INTO OUR MEMORIES. THE 139TH FINAL BETWEEN ARSENAL AND CHELSEA ADDED TO THIS COLLECTIVE NARRATIVE BY PRODUCING A CLASH THAT WILL BE REMEMBERED AS **THE AUBAMEYANG CONTRACT RENEGOTIATION FINAL!**

CLEARLY, THIS WAS A FINAL LIKE NO OTHER WITH VAST BANKS OF EMPTY SEATS AT WEMBLEY, A SIGHT USUALLY RESERVED FOR THE TEN MINUTES AFTER HALF-TIME. THIS WAS ALSO THE FIRST CUP FINAL WHERE EMELI SANDÉ HAS BEEN POSITIONED ON THE ROOF TO RETRIEVE LOST FOOTBALLS.

NO PANDEMIC CAN STOP THE GOD-SAVE-THE-QUEENING, THOUGH. THE NATIONAL ANTHEM WAS BELTED OUT BY A SOCIALLY-DISTANT CHOIR, WHO SADLY DIDN'T STICK AROUND TO PROVIDE OPERATIC VERSIONS OF BELOVED TERRACE CLASSICS.

ARSENAL MADE THE BOLD DECISION TO PICK AN OLDE ENGLISH TYPEFACE FOR THEIR FANCY NEW HESSIAN SMOCKS. IN THE OPENING EXCHANGES, THEY REALLY BOUGHT INTO THE AESTHETIC BY GIVING THE IMPRESSION THEY'D OVERDONE IT AT THE TUDOR BANQUET WHEN FAILING TO STOP THE IMPISH CHRISTIAN PULISIC FROM GIVING CHELSEA THE LEAD.

BUT THE FINAL WASN'T ABOUT TRIVIALITIES LIKE FONTS AND TRANSFER RUMOURS, IT WAS REALLY ABOUT CHELSEA'S ONGOING GOALKEEPER ISSUES. DROPPED FOR THE FINAL, IT SEEMS THAT KEPA ARRIZABALAGA'S ON HIS WAY OUT, EVEN THOUGH IT'S *TRES 2020* TO PLACE A MILLIONAIRE WITH POOR HANDLING SKILLS IN A POSITION OF RESPONSIBILITY. STILL, FRANK LAMPARD'S A MAN WITH CONNECTIONS, SO HE MAY ALREADY HAVE A REPLACEMENT LINED UP.

THERE WAS A TWIST IN THE TALE, AS CHELSEA'S DEFENCE – WHICH THIS SEASON HAS BEEN AS IMPENETRABLE AS *BRIGHTON'S* – WERE EXPOSED BY A BARRAGE OF LONG BALLS OVER THEIR BACK LINE, LIKE LIVESTOCK LAUNCHED FROM A TREBUCHET.

THE PENALTY FROM WHICH AUBAMEYANG EQUALISED WAS THE RESULT OF SUCH AN ATTACK. CHELSEA'S BEST CHANCE OF SUCCESS DISAPPEARED WHEN PULISIC TWANGED HIS HAMSTRING, DESPITE BRAVELY TRYING TO PLAY ON WITH A TERMINATOR-LIKE DETERMINATION TO SEE THE STORY THROUGH TO ITS CONCLUSION.

AUBAMEYANG STRUCK THE WINNER MIDWAY THROUGH THE SECOND HALF WITH A QUICK SHIMMY THAT SWITCHED THE NARRATIVE TO WILLIAN'S CONTRACT NEGOTIATIONS. CHELSEA'S HOPES OF SAVING THE MATCH WERE FURTHER DASHED WHEN REFEREE ANTHONY TAYLOR GAVE MATEO KOVACIC A SECOND YELLOW CARD, DESPITE PROTESTS THAT GRANIT XHAKA HAD MADE A SONG AND DANCE ABOUTH. BOTH FOULS.

THE FINAL WHISTLE LED TO WILD CELEBRATIONS WITHIN THE ARSENAL RANKS.

ALL THAT REMAINED WAS FOR AUBAMEYANG TO RUIN THE DAY FOR THE WHITE-GLOVED FA EMPLOYEE WHOSE JOB IT IS TO LOOK AFTER THE FAMOUS OLD TROPHY.

IF SOMEONE HAD TOLD YOU LAST YEAR THAT **LINFIELD** WOULD STILL BE IN THE CHAMPIONS LEAGUE AS THE COMPETITION REACHES THE QUARTER-FINAL STAGE, YOU'D PROBABLY HAVE GUESSED THERE HAD BEEN A CATASTROPHIC GLOBAL EVENT THAT HAD THROWN FOOTBALL INTO A BIZARRE TIME VORTEX. BECAUSE YOU ARE VERY PERCEPTIVE. EVEN THE MOST CYNICAL OF LOWER-LEAGUE FANS CAN'T HELP BUT BE SWEPT UP BY THE DRAMA OF IT ALL; DROOLING AT THE PROSPECT OF BAYERN v BARCELONA, GIDDY WITH ANTICIPATION AT HOW PSG ARE GOING TO COCK IT UP THIS TIME.

WE NOW KNOW WHICH TEAMS WILL BE PLAYING OUT THE TOURNAMENT IN LISBON. REAL MADRID'S 2-1 DEFEAT TO MAN CITY MEANS THEY WON'T BE GOING TO PORTUGAL. WELL, NOT ALL OF THEM...

TWO MISTAKES FROM RAPHAËL VARANE SEALED THEIR FATE, AND EVEN SERGIO -THEIR PERSONAL SHOREDITCH BARBER- STRUGGLED TO RAISE THEIR MORALE.

Short back and sides? No? How about a whisky sour and a ride on my Raleigh Chopper? Would that cheer you up?

Obviously, yes.

WOULD IT HAVE MADE A DIFFERENCE IF RAMOS HAD PLAYED? IT WILL FOREVER REMAIN AS MUCH OF A MYSTERY AS THE IDENTITY OF THE PERSON WHO SNIPPED OFF THE END OF ZIDANE'S TIE.

WHAT WE DO KNOW IS THAT JUVENTUS ARE OUT, DEFEATED ON AWAY GOALS BY LYON. EUROPE WEEPS. JUVE COULDN'T EVEN BE SAVED BY A PENALTY AWARDED AGAINST MEMPHIS DEPAY FOR NOT MOVING HIS HAND OUT OF THE WAY OF A FREE-KICK CANNONED AT HIS GROIN; AN INCIDENT THAT DEMANDED REPEATED VIEWINGS.

FAILURE WAS UNACCEPTABLE FOR JUVENTUS, WHO SACKED MAURIZIO SARRI JUST A FORTNIGHT AFTER CLAIMING THEIR NINTH CONSECUTIVE SCUDETTO. JADED BY DOMESTIC SUCCESS, WINNING THE LEAGUE IS NOW A ROUTINELY JOYLESS EXPERIENCE.

LUCKILY, THERE WAS AN OBVIOUS, WELL-QUALIFIED SUCCESSOR WHO COULD QUELL THE LISTLESS SELF-LOATHING THAT ACCOMPANIES ALMOST A DECADE OF PERFUNCTORY DOMINANCE...

Heh... Rhubarb gin and a black cap shine? I'll even Tipp-Ex the soles...

That was amazing.

We need to talk.

12 GCSEs, yeah?

HAH, NO, NOT FRANK. JUVENTUS WOULDN'T TAKE A PUNT ON SUCH A ROOKIE, NOT EVEN ONE WHO SPENT A YEAR VOLUNTEERING AT DERBY FOR THE DUKE OF EDINBURGH AWARD SCHEME. BESIDES, LAMPARD WAS LOCKED IN HIS OWN WENGERESQUE BAVARIAN NIGHTMARE, FORCED TO ENDURE REPEATED BLASTS OF 'THE CAN CAN SONG' AS BAYERN TOOK ADVANTAGE OF CHELSEA'S DISORGANISED DEFENSIVE LINE.

JUVENTUS INSTEAD OPTED FOR ANDREA PIRLO - THE DREAMBOAT COACH WHO NEVER TASTED DEFEAT IN TEN DAYS OF MANAGING THE UNDER-23 TEAM AND WHO HAS CLEARY IMPRESSED THE CLUB'S HIERARCHY.

(CAN CAN INTENSIFIES)

For the love of...

You don't need an A* in Latin to know that you should wait until after they've scored before doing the dance...

Christ, you smell good. What is that?

Oh please.

Linseed oil, Norwegian pottery glaze, Head and Shoulders, rare vinyl, leather-bound books about architecture, Californian shiraz barrels, 20 B&H, bespoke Japanese foot stools, Matey, Joop, a spritz of Joe Hart's tears, chinos, rain on a hot pavement, artisan alpaca cheese, Tuscan Bovril, confidence...

BARCELONA CLAIMED THEIR PLACE IN THE LAST EIGHT WITH A COMFORTABLE WIN AGAINST NAPOLI. NOT EVEN THE TIMELORDS OF LINFIELD COULD HAVE STOPPED YOU-KNOW-WHO IN THIS FORM. HOWEVER, IF THERE'S ONE THING THAT CAN STOP THE GAZPROM FLOWING

IT'S YOU-KNOW-WHAT. TWO MEMBERS OF THE ATLÉTICO MADRID PARTY TESTED POSITIVE FOR COVID-19 THIS WEEKEND, THE VIRUS NIPPING IN MESSI-LIKE AT THE LAST MOMENT, WHEN ATLÉTI HAD ALREADY COMMITTED TO A SPECIFIC COURSE OF ACTION.

YOUR HOPES AND PLANS FOR 2020

COVID-19

(LABELS INTERCHANGEABLE DEPENDING ON WHETHER YOU'VE SIGNED A BLOOD OATH TO DEFEND EITHER MESSI OR KOULIBALY).

EVEN IF THE WHOLE FESTIVAL OF ARTIFICIAL CROWD NOISE IS SCUPPERED, THERE ARE STILL PLENTY OF WAYS TO KEEP YOURSELF ENTERTAINED THIS SUMMER.

... hand-carved sandlewood magazine racks, New York subway vapor, nicotine chewing liquorice, every variety of bread, a single pearl of Gattuso's testosterone deposited via a vintage pipette, Alpen, eyebrow serum, Valencian orange vape juice, reclaimed grease from Ramos's unicycle, beard mezze, Frazzles, success...

...ck me...!

THERE MUST BE A WORD IN GERMAN TO DESCRIBE THE SELF-LOATHING YOU EXPERIENCE WHEN THE GEOPOLITICS OF MODERN FOOTBALL MAKES YOU GLAD THAT BAYERN MUNICH HAVE WON ANOTHER TROPHY

Oh, the shame...

THANKFULLY, **SOME** OF US ARE ABLE TO RETAIN A PROFESSIONAL IMPARTIALITY, REMAINING AS ZEN ABOUT PSG'S DEFEAT IN THE CHAMPIONS LEAGUE FINAL AS A NORWEGIAN SPIRITUAL GURU.

Ømmm...

THE DUTY FREE DERBY WAS BILLED BY QATAR AIRWAYS AT 'THE GLASSICO', WHICH WAS A GREAT JOQE AND DIDN'T MAKE YOU FEEL LIKE PUQING. GIVEN THE CIRCUMSTANCES SURROUNDING THIS YEAR'S FINAL, WE SHOULD JUST BE GRATEFUL UEFA DIDN'T MOVE IT TO THE DEPARTURE LOUNGE OF DOHA AIRPORT, NOT THAT IT WOULD HAVE MADE MUCH DIFFERENCE TO THE OUTCOME.

Sorry, my friend, but today you have as much chance of scoring as you do of getting a coffee for under a tenner!

OF COURSE, MANY PSG FANS HAVE AS MUCH INTEREST IN HEARING ABOUT THE PERNICIOUS INFLUENCE OF SOFT POWER AS YOUR SISTER'S KIDS.

They're a reputation-laundering project for an oil regime!

Neymar's got 98 vanity on Fifa.

They denied us the chance of seeing what Nagelsmann would have worn for the final!

JUST WHEN YOU THOUGHT 2020 COULDN'T GET ANY CRUELLER, WE WERE CONFRONTED WITH HEARTBREAKING IMAGES OF NEYMAR FLOODING THE PITCH WITH HOT SALTY TEARS FOR THE PARTY HE'D NOW HAVE TO CANCEL.

I've already paid the deposit for the dry ice machine!

WHAT *IS* IT THAT PEOPLE FIND SO OBJECTIONABLE ABOUT THE BOLSONARO-HUGGING POSTER BOY FOR THE QATARI SPORTS INVESTMENT PROJECT? IT REMAINS A MYSTERY, BUT HE CERTAINLY SEEMS TO RUB A LOT OF PEOPLE UP THE WRONG WAY.

HOWEVER, HE CAN ALWAYS RELY UPON THE FANATICAL SUPPORT OF A MODERN SUBSET OF FOOTBALL FANS. RATHER THAN FOLLOWING CLUBS, THESE PEOPLE SUPPORT INDIVIDUAL PLAYERS WHO WOULD DEFINITELY WANT TO MEET THEM IN REAL LIFE.

So, um, where's this dry ice machine...?

I haven't got one!

Then I think you should leave my house, Jed.

THANKFULLY, SOME TRADITIONS REMAIN. AS IS CUSTOMARY, THE FINAL WAS AS ENTERTAINING AS A THOMAS MÜLLER STAND-UP SET.

Guys, that air-shot by the PSG substitute at the end. Maybe they should call him Eric Maxim *Chop-At-Nothing*...

HAHAHAHAHA

YES, THOMAS!

THE MATCH WAS DECIDED BY A HEADER FROM KINGSLEY **GOALMAN** (TAPS MICROPHONE), A PLAYER WITH A FASCINATING BACK STORY THAT SADLY DOESN'T INVOLVE TONY PULIS. THE FORMER PSG YOUTH PLAYER FOUND FIRST TEAM OPPORTUNITIES BLOCKED BY **THE QALACTICOS** (SERIOUSLY, IS THIS THING ON?), SO HE DEPARTED AND ROSE TO CLAIM FOOTBALL'S ULTIMATE PRIZE...

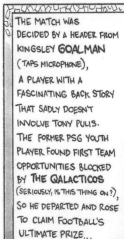

The subject of newspaper rumours about a possible transfer to Manchester United!

AND SO, BAYERN MUNICH WERE CROWNED AS CHAMPIONS AFTER A FANTASTIC NIGHT COMPLETELY FREE OF REGRET.

Morning. Glass of freshly-squeezed Gazprom!

Ugh. Bayern? Really? Why do you keep *doing* this?!

SEASON 120 ep. 10

PLOT SYNOPSIS: A FURIOUS LIONEL SUBMITS A 'TRANSFER REQUEST WHEN RONALD KOEMAN IS GIVEN ACCESS TO HIS EXECUTIVE BATHROOM AT THE NOU CAMP... (CUE BASS GUITAR SOUNDTRACK)

That's it. That is it. I'm done. Through. It's over. I'm gone. Finished. Over. I will never play for you again!

HOWEVER, LIONEL BEGINS TO REGRET HIS DECISION AS HE CONSIDERS HIS CAREER OPTIONS...

Come and join me at City, Leo. Sales of our new fourth kit will soar! It pays subtle homage to Manchester's proud maritime history.

NOT WANTING TO SPEND THE NEXT FOUR YEARS CREATING EXCUSES TO NOT ATTEND NEYMAR'S SOCIAL EVENTS AT PSG, AND FACED WITH THE PROSPECT OF A LENGTHY LEGAL BATTLE, ONLY ONE COURSE OF ACTION REMAINS FOR LIONEL: PRETEND IT NEVER HAPPENED.

Ah, this is Més que un Morning, right?

How ya doin'?

What are you doing here?

What? I work here.

I thought you quit?

What, quit? Who quit? Burofax? What? Ha ha ha...

Arturo, how was your weekend?

Oh excellent weekend. What about your weekend, Gerard?

Yep. Gooood weekend.

Morning everyone. Just a reminder, it's Ronald's welcoming party at the Hard Rochemback Cafe on La Rambla this Wednesday and I want you all there...

Is that Messi?!

What?

Am I crazy, or didn't you quit?

What? Are you kidding? When?

Last Tuesday. It made international news. There are angry protesters outside. You must have driven past them. I can hear them right now.

What, that? I was teasing. Dressing room banter. You just don't get my sense of humour. Arturo, don't I joke around all the time?

I wouldn't say all the time...

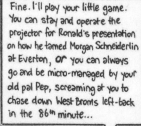

Fine. I'll play your little game. You can stay and operate the projector for Ronald's presentation on how he tamed Morgan Schneiderlin at Everton, or you can always go and be micro-managed by your old pal Pep, screaming at you to chase down West Brom's left-back in the 86th minute...

Schneiderlin was like a wild stallion when he first arrived, but I broke him over a series of delicious brunches like this one. Move on to slide 74, Lionel. Chop, chop; you aren't playing against Bayern now...

BASS SLAPS

Next Season: BARÇA SURRENDER A COMFORTABLE FIRST LEG LEAD TO SUFFER A HUMILIATING DEFEAT IN THE CHAMPIONS LEAGUE QUARTER-FINAL, BUT LIONEL MISSES IT ALL!

2020-21:
FOOTBALL IS NOTHING WITHOUT BREAKAWAY PLANS

The pandemic gave us all time to think about what was important in life. For some, this meant making sure the elderly couple at number six had ample access to dried pasta, bog rolls, and Robert Lewandowski's TikToks. The eternal maverick Matt Le Tissier apparently used the time to repeatedly smash his head with a spanner. Others considered the economic inequality in our society and concluded, 'Yes, let's have some more of that,' and so the season included not one but *two* plans to restructure football to benefit the most in need: oligarchs, multi-club nation state projects and American venture-capitalist locusts (*makes heart shape with hands*). First came 'Project Big Picture', which hilariously tried to convince us that the Glazers and John W. Henry cared passionately about the English football pyramid. OK, Joel, name one Fleetwood Town album. Then came the Super League, which at least had a snazzy website. Perhaps the most pernicious aspect of the Super League plot was its timing, which denied us the space to truly enjoy Spurs sacking José Mourinho on the eve of their Carabao Cup final and the club's new official paint partner, Dulux, trolling them online. However, in this weirdly disjointed phantom season, Tottenham briefly mounted a title challenge. Could these be the tumultuous conditions in which José could thrive? Nope, though the team was boosted by the return of Gareth Bale, on loan from Madrid's swankiest golf club.

Football was on the box nearly every day, with broadcasters introducing a new pay-per-view service for some games. This surprised a lot of subscribers, who thought that's what they were already doing via a sizeable monthly Direct Debit. Most of the season was played behind closed doors, until a limited number of fans were gradually allowed back in to boo the pre-match anti-racism gesture. Football was healing.

Liverpool's title defence was derailed by the loss to injury of Virgil van Dijk after a wild hack from Jordan Pickford in an autumn Merseyside derby, but luckily they didn't go on about it (*looks to camera*), perhaps because VVD RIP was in the team that lost 7–2 at Aston Villa the previous game. Like I say, it was a strange season. Despite those setbacks, Liverpool were going well, until the new year, when their collapse in form coincided with Manchester City embarking upon their annual relentless winning streak (which still shows no sign of becoming predictably boring for the rest of us). A late run of form did enable Jürgen Klopp's team to grab a Champions League place, helped by Alisson Becker's injury-time header at West Brom, which apparently made him the first goalkeeper ever to score in a football match!

The Reds' late surge denied Leicester City a Champions League spot. Brendan Rodgers's team had to settle for the twin consolation of winning the FA Cup and seeing Chelsea fans video themselves when they thought Ben Chilwell had scored a late equaliser in the final. Quite why they chose to share the video remains a mystery, but as we moved out of the pandemic, it became clear that large swathes of the population had been using the Matt Le Tiss Spanner Method.

Chelsea had hired Tommy Tactics Tuchel to replace Frank Lampard mid-season, with scant regard for the fact that Frank is considered one of the nation's top football coaches related to a Redknapp. Despite this betrayal, Chelsea ended the season lifting the Champions League, in another all-Prem classic final against Manchester City – two of the clubs who'd conspired to destroy the competition just a few weeks earlier. Legacy fans everywhere rejoiced, as did Roman Abramovich, who paraded the trophy around the pitch in scenes that would never look old (*stares at camera with an intensity that breaks it into a million pieces*).

GIVEN THE UNCERTAINTY ABOUT WHETHER THIS FOOTBALL SEASON WILL ACTUALLY END, IT MADE SENSE TO PLAY THE MOST EXCITING GAME ON THE FIRST DAY: A TOP KNOT(CH) 4-3 THRILLER BETWEEN LIVERPOOL AND L♥♥DS. BIELSA'S TEAM WERE MINUTES AWAY FROM EARNING A MEMORABLE DRAW UNTIL RODRIGO STUCK OUT A LEG AND CONCEDED A PENALTY. THE NEW RECRUIT WORE THE RESIGNED LOOK OF A MAN WHO KNEW HIS FUTURE NOW HELD A FOUR-HOUR POWERPOINT PRESENTATION IN A FLAT ABOVE A SWEET SHOP.

Right, any questions?

Do they ever let you eat the sweets?

Oh for... Yes, for the last time: Chomps when they've passed their sell-by date.

SADLY, THE SEASON HAD ALREADY BEEN WRITTEN OFF WHEN ARSENAL WORE THEIR THIRD KIT AT FULHAM. IT'S A SHAME FOR THE GUNNERS, WHO LOOKED ASSURED AND COMPETENT IN A 3-0 WIN, PLAYING WITHOUT A CARE FOR THE LIVELIHOODS THEIR NEWFOUND CONFIDENCE IS JEOPARDISING.

I'm sorry, but the footy bantz factory is closed until at least October.

NEWCASTLE EMERGED VICTORIOUS FROM THE DERBY D'ANDY CARROLL WITH A 2-0 WIN AGAINST WEST HAM AT THE LONDON STADIUM, WHICH STILL GLISTENS LIKE THE WHITEST OF ELEPHANTS. 'EL CRISISO' WAS WON WITH A PAIR OF GOALS FROM SUMMER SIGNINGS CALLUM WILSON AND JEFF HENDRICK. A DELIGHTED STEVE BRUCE SAID LAST WEEK THAT MIKE ASHLEY HAD "FLEXED HIS MUSCLES", PAINTING A PICTURE WITH WORDS IN A MANNER TYPICAL OF THE GREAT NOVELISTS.

GREASE ME UP, BRUCIE. IT'S TIME TO WRITE A CLUB STATEMENT!

Mega! I'll fetch the sandwich spread!

Dimplex

BRUCE ALSO SAID ASHLEY HAD "BEATEN OFF" ASTON VILLA TO SIGN WILSON, BUT GOD KNOWS, WE'VE ALL BEEN THROUGH ENOUGH ALREADY. ANYWAY, WE DON'T WATCH FOOTBALL BECAUSE OF CLUB OWNERS, WE WATCH IT BECAUSE OF VAR. THE POPULAR VIDEO REVIEW SYSTEM MADE AN IMPACT DURING THE CRYSTAL PALACE V SOUTHAMPTON GAME, HELPING JON MOSS TO REALISE HE'D BEEN A BIT HARSH WITH ONE OF HIS DECISIONS...

Do you prefer Walker or Peters?

Walker-Peters.

Nup, I'm never gonna remember all that, man.

UM, ARE EVERTON GOOD? THEIR NEW SIGNINGS CLICKED AND A DOMINIC CALVERT-LEWIN HEADER SECURED A DESERVED 1-0 WIN AT TOTTENHAM. SERIOUSLY, IS NOTHING SACRED? THEIR WIN MIGHT HAVE BEEN MORE COMPREHENSIVE HAD RICHARLISON FOUND A BETTER FINISH TO HIS FERRIS BUELLER-STYLE RACE THROUGH THE SPURS DEFENCE IN THE FIRST HALF.

IN THESE UNSETTLING TIMES, AT LEAST ONE MAN CAN BE RELIED UPON TO PROVIDE A SENSE OF NORMALITY. JAMIE VARDY CONTINUED HIS RECORD OF SCORING IN EVERY GAME HE'S PLAYED AT THE HAWTHORNS AND NOT EVEN AN EMPTY STADIUM COULD DIMINISH HIS TIRELESS DEDICATION TO S***HOUSERY.

JAMIE
LAUGHS AT YOU

It seemed to be fine, but then just exploded on Sunday afternoon.

DON'T WORRY IF YOUR TEAM PUT IN THE KIND OF PERFORMANCE THAT MAKES YOU LONG FOR THE SEASON-CANCELLING VAMPIRE ROBOT UPRISING THAT INEVITABLY AWAITS US IN 2021. AFTER ALL, THE MAJOR QUESTIONS ARE NEVER ANSWERED IN THE FIRST WEEK OF THE SEASON.

If squatting down provides the perfect vantage point to watch a game, how come Dennis Wise isn't revered by the world's top coaches?

Dennis...?

And how come you haven't even completed the Duolingo app yet? Do you just watch football all the time or something?

That owl's really pushy...

And tell me: do they ever let you eat the sweets?

Oh my God.

HE'S NO BAS DOST

BUT GARETH BALE IS BACK AT TOTTENHAM HOTSPUR!

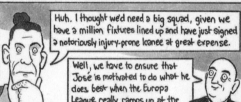
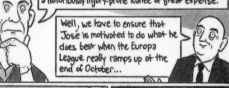

TO DARE IS TO DO**st**

NOTHING MATTERS ANYMORE. EVERYTHING WE THOUGHT WE KNEW WAS WRONG, APART FROM THOSE SUSPICIONS ABOUT UNITED'S BACK FOUR. ANARCHY REIGNS, GOALS FLY IN, THE MOST EXPENSIVE DEFENDER IN THE WORLD WRESTLES HIS OWN TEAMMATE, AS IF TO HOWL "EFF CONVENTION!" THE SOARING GOAL-RATE AGAIN PROVES THAT SWINDON TOWN'S PREMIER LEAGUE TEAM WERE DECADES AHEAD OF THEIR TIME.

CLEARLY, NO ONE KNOWS WHAT THE HELL IS GOING ON. IS IT THAT PLAYERS ARE MORE KNACKERED THAN THE PERSON EMPLOYED TO HIT THE FAKE CROWD NOISE BUTTON? OR IS IT JUST THAT WITH GAMES PLAYED IN THE SOULLESS ATMOSPHERE OF A RESERVE MATCH, WE NOW SEE HOW PLAYERS RELIED UPON THE TACTICAL ADVICE OF THAT SEASON TICKET HOLDER WHO ALWAYS SHOUTS THE SAME THING.

EITHER WAY, IT WAS A GRIM SUNDAY FOR JÜRGEN KLOPP, WHO EXPERIENCED ALL SEVEN STAGES OF BEING THRASHED BY ASTON VILLA.

AFTER THE **DRAMA** OF SLOPPYGATE, IMAGINE IF ROY KEANE HAD BEEN A STUDIO GUEST!

AT LEAST IT CHEERED UP PATRICE EVRA, WHO HAD A FACE LIKE A SLAPPED RAW CHICKEN AFTER MANCHESTER UNITED'S BASTING AT THE HANDS OF SPURS.

TOTTENHAM FELL BEHIND TO A SECOND-MINUTE PENALTY, BUT LADS IT'S MANCHESTER UNITED, AND SPURS HAD SOON BUILT SUCH A COMMANDING LEAD THAT EVEN JOSÉ COULD CHILL OUT.

LUCKILY FOR SOLSKJÆR, RESULTS ARE OF SECONDARY IMPORTANCE TO TRANSFER BUSINESS, AND THE SIGNING OF EDINSON CAVANI WILL SOLVE ALL OF UNITED'S ISSUES. FOR ALL THE CONCERN ABOUT ENGLISH FOOTBALL, THE AMOUNT OF MONEY SPENT BY PREMIER LEAGUE CLUBS OVER THE SUMMER SHOWS IT COULDN'T BE HEALTHIER IF IT WAVED GASPING FROM A GILDED BALCONY. TAKE ARSENAL, WHO SPENT £45M ON ONE PLAYER, TO THE UNDOUBTED DELIGHT OF ALL THE STAFF THEY RECENTLY LET GO.

LIVERPOOL HAVE MOVED INTO THEIR SWANKY NEW £50M TRAINING BASE, COMPLETE WITH A VOLLEYBALL COURT, SOFT FURNISHINGS AS CRIMSON AS XHERDAN SHAQIRI'S CHEEKS ON A WINTER'S MORN, AND THREE ANFIELD-SIZED PITCHES THAT CAN BE CONVERTED TO FIELD HOSPITALS TO TREAT ALL THOSE SOFT TISSUE INJURIES.

BUT THE MOST IMPRESSIVE FEATURE CAN BE FOUND ON THE SEVENTH AND A HALF FLOOR: THE JAMES MILNER DOOR - A PORTAL INTO THE MIND OF THE UNDERRATED UTILITY MAN.

THE PORTAL EVEN ALLOWS JAMES MILNER TO EXPERIENCE FOR HIMSELF HOW DISORIENTATING IT MUST BE TO PLAY AGAINST JAMES MILNER, WITH THE SENSATION THAT HE'S LITERALLY EVERYWHERE.

THE ONLY DESIGN FLAW IS THAT AFTER A WHILE, VISITORS ARE EJECTED FROM MILNER'S CONSCIOUSNESS AND DUMPED 13 MILES AWAY FROM THE STEEL AND GLASS TRAINING GROUND AND ITS MULTIPLE GRANOLA OPTIONS.

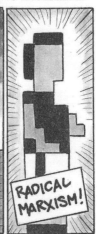

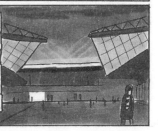

ALL HAIL THE SAVIOURS OF THE ENGLISH FOOTBALL PYRAMID!

DISPLAYING THE GENUINE ALTRUISM OF A BANKING ADVERT SOUNDTRACKED BY A BREATHY COVER VERSION, KINDLY VENTURE-SCORPIONS JOEL GLAZER AND JOHN W HENRY HAVE DEVISED A PLAN TO HELP THE EFL NAVIGATE THE FINANCIAL QUAGMIRE AND LITTLE RICK PARRY COULDN'T BE HAPPIER. EVERYONE'S A WINNER!*

PROJECT BIG PICTURE IS HERE! AS WELL AS SAVING THE EFL, IT WILL SELFLESSLY RELIEVE THE PREMIER LEAGUE'S LANDFILL CLUBS OF MAKING DECISIONS ABOUT THEIR FUTURE. WHO WANTS TO STRESS ABOUT BORING OLD RULES AND REGULATIONS, OR MAKING CHOICES ABOUT WHO OWNS YOUR CLUB? LET THE SELF-APPOINTED "LONG-TERM SHAREHOLDERS" WORRY ABOUT THAT WHILE YOU JUST FOCUS ON PLAYING RUDDY FOOTBALL. YOU CAN GUARANTEE THEY HAVE YOUR BEST INTERESTS AT HEART, JUST AS YOU CAN BE SURE THEY'LL STICK TO THEIR PROMISE TO SHARE 25% OF THEIR TV CHEDDAR WITH THE EFL. GOAL!

* TWO OF YOU WILL NEED TO DROP OUT OF THE FOOTBALL LEAGUE SOZ.

SOME EFL CLUBS HAVE EXPRESSED APPROVAL ABOUT THE PLAN. AT THE MOMENT, THEY'D ACCEPT MONEY FROM JUST ABOUT ANYONE, REGARDLESS OF THE CONSEQUENCES.

THE COVID CRISIS HAS EXPOSED THE IMBALANCE IN ENGLISH FOOTBALL AND IT'S TIME WE ALL STARTED THINKING OF CREATIVE SOLUTIONS TO HELP BIG CLUBS OVERCOME THE TYRANNY OF HAVING TOO MUCH SH*T TO CRAM INTO THEIR MANSIONS. MANCHESTER CITY'S CEO, FERRAN SORIANO, LAST WEEK SAID WHAT WE WERE ALL THINKING...

GUYS, IT'S BEST IF YOU THINK OF FOOTBALL CLUBS LIKE SUPERMARKETS. IMAGINE THE MOST GLAMOROUS SUPERMARKET IN THE LAND, WITH ALL THE BEST GEAR AND HIP SHOP ASSISTANTS WITH EARPIECES. WHY THE HELL SHOULD THEY HELP OUT THE DINGY CONVENIENCE STORE DOWN THE ROAD, EVEN IF IT HAS BEEN AT THE HEART OF THE COMMUNITY FOR 146 YEARS AND SUPPLIES AND PRODUCES MOST OF THE GOODS THAT SUSTAIN THE SUPERMARKET?

IN ANOTHER PR MASTERSTROKE, THE PREMIER LEAGUE MANAGED TO STAY IN THE HEADLINES DURING THE INTERNATIONAL BREAK BY VOTING TO MAKE SOME GAMES PAY-PER-VIEW. NO MORE FREELOADING FOR YOU £80-A-MONTH PARASITES! TIMING IS EVERYTHING, WITH THE NEWS COMING WHEN EVERYONE IS SUPER FLUSH AND THE PRODUCT IS AT ITS MOST ATTRACTIVE. WHO WOULDN'T WANT TO PAY EXTRA FOR THIS?

DESPITE TELLING THE PREMIER LEAGUE TO HELP THE EFL, THE GOVERNMENT HAS CONDEMNED PROJECT BIG SMALL-PRINT, BECAUSE WE ALL KNOW HOW THEY FEEL ABOUT NAKED SELF-INTEREST AND THE RINGFENCING OF POWER BY A WEALTHY ELITE. HOWEVER, THEY HAVE BACKED A COOL WEBSITE TO GENERATE RANDOM CAREER ALTERNATIVES FOR CONCERNED EMPLOYEES OF EFL CLUBS.

IT'S A COMPLEX SITUATION WITH NO QUICK FIXES (OTHER THAN THE PREMIER LEAGUE COMFORTABLY AFFORDING TO JUST PAY THE £250M EFL BAILOUT AND AGREEING TO A FAIRER DISTRIBUTION OF TV REVENUE IN THE LONG RUN LOL). IN THE MEANTIME, WE CAN AT LEAST ENJOY THINKING ABOUT THE REACTION OF SUPERMARKET SUPREMO STEVE PARISH WHEN HE HEARD ABOUT PROJECT NOT YOU, MATE.

THE PREMIER LEAGUE ENJOYED ANOTHER NORMAL ONE THIS WEEK, AND AFTER THE ATTEMPTED COUP OF PROJECT BIG BOLLOCKS IT WAS NICE TO AGAIN FOCUS ON MATTERS ON THE PITCH (IE A MUSTY VIDEO BUNKER IN STOCKLEY PARK). AS ORWELL ONCE SAID, FOOTBALL IS NOW BASICALLY DRONE WARFARE MINUS THE MASS CIVILIAN CASUALTIES. THE VAR EYE-IN-THE-SKY ADMINISTERED CRUEL JUSTICE TO DENY LIVERPOOL A LATE WINNER IN SATURDAY'S MERSEYSIDE DERBY, ZOOMING IN TO REVEAL THE EXACT MOMENT JORDAN HENDERSON LOST HIS FAITH IN HUMANITY.

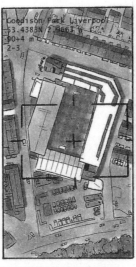

CHECKING GOAL *POSSIBLE OFFSIDE*

DECISION   NO GOAL

Ladies and gentlemen, we got him.

A SEETHING LIVERPOOL HAD ALREADY BEEN ON THE VERGE OF FORMING THEIR OWN BREAKAWAY LEAGUE AFTER JORDAN PICKFORD ESCAPED PUNISHMENT FOR A WILD LUNGE THAT LEFT VIRGIL VAN DIJK WITH AN ACL INJURY. HOWEVER, ACCUSATIONS OF PREMEDITATED MALICE ON PICKFORD'S PART OVERLOOK THE FACT THAT HE GENERALLY PLAYS LIKE HE'S EXPERIENCING THE MANIC EFFECTS OF A LONG-TERM EXPOSURE TO MERCURY. IT MAKES YOU WONDER HOW HE FUNCTIONS ON A DAILY BASIS.

COME ON! Crack some more of those glow sticks!

They're old thermometers.

Double frothaccino with extra froth for J... No, sir!

JORDAN'S!

RAVE ON!

Me coffee...

IT HAS BEEN AGREED THAT ON THE FOURTH MINUTE PAST EACH HOUR, THE PEOPLE OF BRITAIN WILL STAND ON THEIR DOORSTEPS AND APPLAUD THE FALLEN VIRGIL.

He may be dead, but we know he's up there somewhere, smiling down at us.

Hello, police? Yeah, they're back.

BUT HOW SHOULD PICKFORD BE PUNISHED FOR THIS BRUTAL MURDER? SUSPENSION? LIFE BAN? BOOTED INTO THE SUN LIKE ONE OF HIS CLEARANCES? OR SOMETHING MORE MEDIEVAL...?

No, please, I'm sorry! I'll lay off the thermometers, I promise. I beg of you, anything but this!

COMING UP
WEST BROMWICH ALBION v BURNLEY
INSERT GROATS NOW

MEANWHILE, SERGIO AGÜERO ESCAPED PUNISHMENT FOR AN INCIDENT INVOLVING SIAN MASSEY-ELLIS. TYPICALLY, SOME **WOKE SNOWFLAKES** POINTED OUT THAT YOU SHOULDN'T GRAB WOMEN BY THE NECK, EVEN WHEN THEY GIVE A THROW-IN AGAINST YOU! LUCKILY, THERE WAS NO SHORTAGE OF MEN TO GRABSPLAIN WHY AGÜERO WAS INNOCENT. HERE ARE A SELECTION OF RESPONSES, AS READ BY EMMELINE PANKHURST:

"I've got a neck and I didn't see a problem with it."

"In an identical power dynamic, Paul Pogba once patted Anthony Taylor on the head. Is *that* sexism???"

"Why should the government feed hungry children? Stick to football. Sorry, wrong thread."

Jesus

"Hey, come on guys. Come on. Guys. Sergio is the nicest person I ever met in my life."

BUT HEY, FOOTBALL ISN'T *JUST* ABOUT ONLINE ABUSE AND UNWANTED WORKPLACE INTERACTIONS, THERE ARE SOME NICE STORIES OUT THERE, SUCH AS THE IMMEDIATE IMPACT GARETH BALE ENJOYED ON HIS RETURN HOME.

LANZIN

Ah, the green, green grass of Spurs.

...AND WHAT OTHER THAN FOOTBALL (OR THE PROMISE OF A TRIP TO A MAGICAL CHOCOLATE FACTORY) HAS THE POWER TO MAKE A 57-YEAR-OLD MAN RISE FROM HIS SICK BED AND DANCE LIKE THE STADIUM IS EMPTY?

I've got a golden thicket!

Christ, have some dignity, man.

I've never felt so alive! Even my laughter crevasses are eroding! I haven't looked this peng since my Dunfermline Athletic Panini sticker. Maybe I'll take up salsa. I can do anything. I'm the king of the world! **NOTHING CAN STOP ME N—**

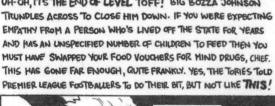

SH**☃**TE CHRISTMAS

IN A SHOCK DEVELOPMENT, IT TURNS OUT THAT THE PROPOSED CHRISTMAS COVID TRUCE WAS A NOTION AS FANCIFUL AS TOTTENHAM'S TITLE BID, ROBBING US OF THE PROSPECT OF A VIRULENT FESTIVE KICKABOUT IN NO MAN'S LAND.

SOME BOUNDERS HAVE CONDEMNED BORIS JOHNSON'S HANDLING OF THE CRISIS, BUT THE BORN-TO-RULE NEWSPAPER COLUMNIST IS DOING THE BEST HE CAN, DAMNINGLY. NOT EVEN THE MOST INCISIVE OF SOOTHSAYERS COULD HAVE FORESEEN THIS TURN OF EVENTS . . .

Not too worried about the PM making big promises about everyone being able to enjoy a big old Christmas knees up. The Tories have got the dominancy, so I'm sure the virus will respect the 'BORIS SAVES CHRISTMAS' headlines...

HONESTLY, YOU CRASH **ONE** LITTLE COUNTRY INTO THE SEA AND EVERYONE GETS ON YOUR CASE. IT SEEMS NO ONE IS ABOVE CRITICISM THESE DAYS...

HOW THE 🦌 IS HE GONNA GET TO EVERY CHIMNEY WITH 🦌ING RUDOLPH UP TOP? 🦌ING SACK HIM AND BRING IN THE TOOTH FAIRY!

SANTA FANS TV

Last Christmas we delivered all the presents with only 25% of the houses having chimneys and only a 67% chance of traversing the whole world in one night. If we tweak our moral definition of who's been naughty or nice, we only need to deliver to 3% of houses. Now, get the 🦌 out of my living room, you little 🦌s.

Rude.

IF YOU ARE STUCK AT HOME THIS YEAR, THERE ARE A FEW WAYS YOU CAN PASS THE TIME THAT DON'T INVOLVE EATING TWIGLETS UNTIL YOUR CLOTHES ARE AS TIGHT AS JACK GREALISH'S SHORTS.

FOR EXAMPLE, HAVE YOU OPENED YOUR ADVENT CALENDAR TO REVEAL THE IDENTITY OF TODAY'S WATFORD MANAGER?

IF YOU CAN'T HANDLE ONE 🦌ING DAY WITHOUT LIVE TELEVISED FOOTBALL AND ARE WORRIED ABOUT RUPTURING YOUR SPLEEN LAUGHING AT THE MRS BROWN'S BOYS CHRISTMAS SPECIAL, YOU COULD ALWAYS ENJOY SOME SEASONAL MOVIE FAVOURITES...

Well, hello there.

Yay! It's Tamás Priskin!

TRADING PLACES

THE MAUPAY CHRISTMAS CAROL

PIE HARD

Yippee ki yay.

efl

Not too worried about people noticing he's just sticking the heads of football personalities on Christmas film posters and that he's clearly already checked out and marinating his brain in mulled Thunderbird...

JANUARY!

EVERYONE'S FAVOURITE MONTH; A TIME WHEN THE THERMOMETER SEEMS AS LIKELY TO REACH DOUBLE FIGURES AS SHEFFIELD UNITED. AT LEAST THE HORIZONTAL SLEET MIGHT PROVIDE A CIRCUIT BREAKER FOR FOOTBALLERS HOLDING PARTIES, SUCH AS THE ONE THAT LEFT JOSÉ MOURINHO SO DISAPPOINTED WITH SOME OF HIS PLAYERS.

What we looking at here, doc? Six weeks of physio before it's fully grown back?

What child of Iberia wouldn't want to spend Christmas in the sole company of a dismembered limb of what we can all agree was definitely a pig? What could go wrong?

What the hell, Sergio? I thought you were going to be alone. That's why I spent £500 on that delicious ham for you.

Yeah, Sergio.

Ham ham ham ham ham ham ham? Ham. Ham ham ham ham ham ham ham ham ham. Ham, ham ham ham ham ham ham!

SUCH COVID RULE BREACHES ARE NOT LIMITED TO THE PREMIER LEAGUE. IN SCOTLAND, QUEEN OF THE SOUTH WERE FORCED TO ISSUE AN APOLOGY WHEN GEORGE GALLOWAY ATTENDED ONE OF THEIR MATCHES.

WHO'D BE A SOCIAL MEDIA MANAGER, EH? PITY THE DELICATE, RICE-PAPER-SKINNED, 12-YEAR OLD WHO APPARENTLY RUNS LEEDS' TWITTER ACCOUNT. SO WOUNDED WAS HE (AND THE OWNER) BY KAREN CARNEY'S OPINION OF ST. MARCELO'S BRAVE BOYS THAT HE INADVERTENTLY DETONATED AN EXPLOSION OF SEXIST ARSEHOLES DIRECTLY INTO HER TIMELINE. NO ONE COULD HAVE PREDICTED THIS OUTCOME, AND THE BLAME CLEARLY LAY WITH THE REPLY GUYS, NOT THE PERSON WHOSE TWEET UNLEASHED THEM.

Oh, this is not a good look.

Because of the new Covid restrictions?

The what?

Meow!

Dear God.

INNOCENT

GUILTY

Oopsie. Would you like a tour of our training ground?

FOOTBALL'S FESTIVE PERIOD CAME TO A CLOSE WITH SOUTHAMPTON'S 1-0 WIN AGAINST LIVERPOOL ON MONDAY NIGHT, A RESULT THAT PRODUCED AN EMOTIONAL RESPONSE FROM RALPH HASENHÜTTL.

YES, LAMPARD IS UNDER PRESSURE AT CHELSEA, HAVING BEEN LET DOWN YET AGAIN BY HIS PLAYERS WHO MUST HAVE DECIDED INDEPENDENTLY TO THROW EVERYONE FORWARD FOR A 30TH MINUTE FREE-KICK AGAINST MANCHESTER CITY. IT'S ANOTHER BLOW TO ENGLISH MANAGERS, FOLLOWING THE NEWS THAT THE LEAVE FAN SAM ALLARDYCE IS BEING PREVENTED FROM IMPORTING THE FINAL PIECES OF HIS PLAN TO RESCUE WEST BROM BY **BLOODY BREXIT!**

SOBS UNCONTROLLABLY

Lieber Gott

EARLIER

Ralph? Roman. Get a result tonight and I might have a little job for you here.

Heh, I'm stood right here.

Nah, to be fair, this is crushing.

HONK!

Calais

ALPHA-TECH BLUETOOTH HEADSETS to the Max!

Mr Piggle's TRADITIONAL PORK PIE CHEWING GUM PRODUCT OF ROMANIA

IN TERMS OF IRONY, THERE'S PERHAPS ONLY ONE SCENARIO THAT COULD TRUMP IT ON THE ALANIS SCALE: IF A BIG EUROPEAN CLUB FINALLY GAVE HIM THE CHANCE HE SO RICHLY DESERVES.

IMPRESSIVELY, JANUARY HAS MANAGED TO BECOME EVEN MORE DEPRESSING THAN USUAL THIS YEAR, WITH ANOTHER LOCKDOWN FORCING EVERYONE TO STAY AT HOME WITH THEIR PETS AND THE LAST REMNANTS OF CHRISTMAS FOOD.

We would be delighted to offer you the job of Head Coach at Real Madrid, Mr Allardychi. Just one tiny thing to check: does your passport allow you to live and work in Europe?

Un momento, Señor Pérez.

HONK!

Ham.

Meow...

ARE YOU FEELING A LITTLE JADED BY THE CONSTANT DELUGE OF FOOTBALL? IS IT ALL CONGEALING INTO ONE HOMOGENEOUS MASS OF BRANDED TARPAULIN AND DISPUTES ABOUT VAR? PERHAPS YOU'RE EXPERIENCING 'ROY WOOD SYNDROME' WHEREBY THE SPLENDOUR OF SOMETHING SPECIAL IS DIMINISHED THROUGH REPETITION...

THE PREMIER LEAGUE IS ACCUTELY AWARE OF THIS, AND ITS DESIRE TO KEEP THE PRODUCT FRESH WAS THIS WEEKEND ILLUSTRATED BY A NEW RANGE OF OUTFITS FOR ITS POPULAR ACTION FIGURES.

Oh I wish there could be football every day...

When the fake crowds singing, Oh christ, not Wolves again...

NEW! BIG SAM PEAK-HOODED, DUCK DOWN COCOON.

CHANGE TOO AT LIVERPOOL. IT'S ONLY A WEEK SINCE SOME RIDICULOUS HANDSOME FOOLS WERE WRITING THEIR SEASON OFF, BUT TWO SUCCESSIVE WINS HAVE PUT THEM RIGHT BACK IN THE HUNT TO FINISH SECOND TO MANCHESTER CITY. WHAT'S MORE, A BUSY TRANSFER DEADLINE DAY SAW THE ARRIVAL OF TWO NEW CENTRE BACKS, MEANING JÜRGEN KLOPP CAN FINALLY RELY ON A SETTLED DEFENSIVE PAIRING.

No, it was not ideal that the new boys were kicked by a centaur while filming the announcement video, but Phil Babb and Nicky Tanner know the plan, and we'll be fine so long as they avoid any injuries.

CONVERSELY, MANCHESTER UNITED'S RUNNERS-UP BID HAS FALTERED OVER THE LAST WEEK. MOST DAMAGINGLY, THEY SUFFERED A SHOCK HOME DEFEAT TO SHEFFIELD UNITED, WHICH WAS APPARENTLY THE FAULT OF THE OFFICIALS, RATHER THAN DEFENDING WITH SPEED AND URGENCY OF CONTINENTAL DRIFT.

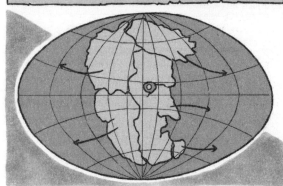

STILL, IT'S NOT ALL BAD NEWS FOR THEM. EDINSON CAVANI'S AMAZING MOVEMENT CONTINUES TO BE ANALYSED AS IF GILLIAN MCKEITH WAS STILL ON THE TELLY...

It's...spectacular.

Inside and outside the box.

Oh dear.

AND THEY MAY WELL HAVE BEATEN ARSENAL ON SATURDAY IF THEY HADN'T ENCOUNTERED SUCH DETERMINED DEFENDING, AS DEMONSTRATED BY DAVID LUIZ CELEBRATING A CLEARANCE AND HÉCTOR BELLERÍN LAYING HIS BODY DOWN FOR THE CAUSE OF FASHION. WORK IT, H.

IF YOU THOUGHT NEWCASTLE WINNING THEIR FIRST GAME IN 11 WAS PROOF THAT THE PREMIER LEAGUE HAD TRULY JUMPED THE SHARK, REMEMBER THEY WERE PLAYING EVERTON. THE VICTORY WAS TIMELY FOR STEVE BRUCE, WHO HAS RECENTLY SEEMED ON THE VERGE OF GOING THE FULL FRANK GRIMES.

Look at me, I'm the mighty Rafa Benítez!

I play ultra-defensive football but no one criticises me because I'm Rafa Benítez and I've got rosy cheeks and a little beard.

I can yank hold of Jonjo Shelvey's ears and I'll be fine, because I'm Rafa Benítez!

TOMMY 'TUCHEL'S OFF AND RUNNING AT CHELSEA TOO. HIS FONDNESS FOR DRY STATISTICAL ANALYSIS IS SURE TO EARN HIM A PLACE IN THE HEARTS OF THE CHELSEA FAITHFUL, BUT IF HIS STATEMENTS DON'T EXACTLY SCREAM SEXY FOOTBALL, IMAGINE THEM BEING PERFORMED IN THE STYLE OF PRINCE AND THE NEW POWER GENERATION.

Gett off

Sixteen key recoveries in the final third...

Gett off

When you've got XG stats, you don't need heartrending words...

Gett off

Let a Tuchel be a Tuchel and a Frank be a Frank...

Gett off

If you want a baby, here I am (here I am).

JM

TUCHEL'S FIRST MAJOR TEST COMES AGAINST TOTTENHAM ON THURSDAY. JOSÉ'S ENTERTAINERS BRING JOY WHEREVER THEY GO, MOST RECENTLY AT BRIGHTON, WHERE THEY GIFTED THE SEAGULLS THE DELIGHTS OF EXPERIENCING A RARE HOME WIN. HOWEVER, SPREADING SUNSHINE THROUGHOUT THE LAND CAN TAKE AN EMOTIONAL TOLL, AND MOURINHO NOTED A STRANGE SENSE OF SADNESS AMONG HIS TROOPS.

Scrolled

If only we could identify the common denominator at the root of this widespread malaise. Alas, it will remain one of life's great mysteries...

NEW! CHUNKY KNIT JOSÉ!

OF COURSE, IT'S NOT JUST THOSE LADS WHO ARE FINDING LIFE TOUGH, BUT THERE ARE SOME REASONS TO BE CHEERFUL. OK, THERE'S ONE REASON TO BE CHEERFUL...

THE RETURN OF ROY HODGSON'S LOCKDOWN BARNET

SO IF YOU'RE FEELING A BIT SPURSY, IMAGINE CURLING UP AND SLEEPING IN THAT GENTLY BOUNCING COIFFURE, LIKE A LUSTROUS, SLIGHTLY COARSE CLOUD WOVEN FROM THE HAIR OF A 73-YEAR-OLD MAN.

FEELING BETTER? YOU'RE WELCOME X

#Yööt DEM

I BELIEVE THE CHILDREN ARE THE FUTURE AND IT SEEMS THAT FOOTBALL IS *FINALLY* COMING ROUND TO MY WAY OF THINKING. NOT ONLY ARE KYLIAN MBAPPÉ AND ERLING BRAUT HAALAND TEARING IT UP IN THE CHAMPIONS LEAGUE, BUT MANCHESTER UNITED'S SHOLA SHORETIRE MADE HIS DEBUT AT ABOUT THE AGE YOU'D EXPECT SOMEONE TO DO SO AND LIVERPOOL ARE MOSTLY RELIANT ON REGENS.

IT'S AN UNFORTUNATE FACT OF LIFE THAT YOUR YOUTH DISAPPEARS FASTER THAN A NEWS STORY ABOUT THE HEALTH MINISTER ACTING UNLAWFULLY. CONSIDER POOR OLD GERARD PIQUÉ EXPERIENCING A MID-LIFE CRISIS IN HIS ATTEMPTS TO STOP MBAPPÉ. IN TRYING TO CLING ON TO HIS YOUTH, HE COULDN'T HAVE LOOKED MORE TRAGIC IF HE'D USED A TERM LIKE 'YOOT DEM' AND BEEN A WEEK LATE TO A MEME.

JUST LIKE MBAPPÉ, HAALAND SEEMS TO BE ON AN UNASSAILABLE RISE. FOR SOME OF US WHOSE BEST DAYS COINCIDED WITH THE CHART SUCCESS OF BABYLON ZOO, THE ASCENT OF THE NORWEGIAN YORKSHIREMAN PROVOKES GLASSY-EYED MEMORIES OF MICHAEL OWEN'S EARLY CAREER, AND MAY SIMILARLY LEAD TO HIM EARNING THE HIGHEST OF ACCOLADES: HIS OWN RANGE OF PERSONALISED DOUBLE-DENIM!

IT'S NOT JUST ON THE PITCH WHERE THE YOUNG 'UNS ARE TAKING CHARGE, IT'S HAPPENING IN THE BOARDROOM TOO. SUNDERLAND HAVE BEEN TAKEN OVER BY THE 23-YEAR-OLD KYRIL LOUIS-DREYFUS. HOW COULD A SWISS BOY WITH CHEEKS AS SMOOTH AS A MILKA COWPAT AFFORD TO BUY HIS OWN FOOTBALL CLUB AT SUCH A TENDER AGE? WELL, IT'S A FAMILIAR STORY...

SUCH AN ANTI-AVOCADO STANCE WOULD BE MUSIC TO THE EARS OF CHRIS WILDER, WHO REFUSES TO BOW DOWN TO THE BLOODY "DO-GOODERS AND LEFTIES" WHEN COMMUNICATING WITH THE FECKLESS YOUTH OF TODAY. PERHAPS THE PROOF OF HIS METHODS IS IN THE SHEFFIELD UNITED PUDDING, WHICH IS BULGING WITH 11 JUICY POINTS.

NOT EVERYONE FINDS IT SO EASY TO RELATE TO THE YOUNG FOLK, BUT LUCKILY THERE ARE SOME PEOPLE WHO ARE DOWN WITH THE KIDS AND ABLE TO DECODE THEIR NONSENSE.

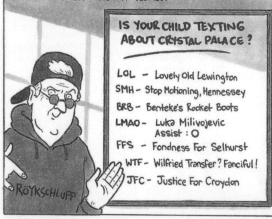

FOOTBALL'S A YOUNG PERSON'S GAME, AND THE STRESSES OF MANAGEMENT TAKE THEIR TOLL (FOR EXAMPLE, DAVID MOYES IS 32!). JUST LOOK AT THE DEVASTATING EFFECT ARSENAL'S ERRATIC SEASON HAS HAD ON MIKEL ARTETA:

HOWEVER, THE AGEING EFFECTS OF FOOTBALL MANAGEMENT PALE IN COMPARISON TO THOSE SUFFERED BY THE UNFORTUNATE SOULS WHO WATCHED BURNLEY v WEST BROM ON SATURDAY, WHICH HAD A MORE DETERIORATING EFFECT THAN DRINKING FROM THE WRONG CUP OF CHRIST.

'Knives Oot

BEING A FOOTBALL MANAGER IS TOUGH AT THE BEST OF TIMES, BUT WHEN THERE'S A MOLE LEAKING INFORMATION ABOUT A PUBLIC BUST-UP, AS HAPPENED AT NEWCASTLE LAST WEEK, IT CAN EVEN UNDERMINE THE SUCCESS OF A COMPREHENSIVE GOALLESS DRAW AGAINST WEST BROM. LUCKILY, IN STEVE BRUCE, THE MAGPIES HAVE A SOFTLY-SPOKEN SLEUTH THIRSTY TO UNCOVER THE TRUTH...

Right, lads; I've gathered you to this dusty trophy room to reveal the findings of my investigation into the source of the leak.

Oh here we go, The No. 1 Dinner Ladies' Detective Agency...

Steve Bruce Investigates!

It was my toughest case yet, and I don't mind telling you, at times I felt I had as much chance of succeeding as the 2030 World Cup bid.

ENGLAND
+ MISCELLANEOUS
2030
DIVERSION!

THE ONLY PEOPLE WE HATE MORE THAN THE REST OF THE WORLD ARE EACH OTHER.

SGVIBES

It was an inquiry that demanded all of my skills as a noted crime writer. The question was, who was devious enough to cover up such a heinous act?

THE AGGRIEVED WINGER MATT RITCHIE?

I know what you're capable of Ritchie. We all saw you kick a corner flag into a gentleman's Professor Plums that time. Admit you're the mole!

So, no training again today then...

THE PRECOCIOUS LONGSTAFF BROTHERS?

Can ah have a Calippo, Gaffah?

Fiendish mind games!

THE OWNER OF THIS WHOLE CIRCUS, OLD MR ASHLEY, WHO SEEMED STRANGELY NERVOUS WHEN I INTERVIEWED HIM?

BOAK!

By 'eck.

FOOTBALLER FATALE, JONJO SHELVEY?

LEE CHARNLEY SEEMED KEEN TO HELP OUT, BUT WAS HIS OWN SLEUTH OUTFIT DESIGNED TO DISTRACT ME? IF SO, IT WORKED.

I COULDN'T DISCOUNT AN OUTSIDE INFLUENCE. AN OLD NEMESIS, PERHAPS?

Trouble in paradise?

Oh bog off, Poirot!

AND WHAT ABOUT ALL THE PLAYERS WHO DIDN'T EVEN TURN UP FOR QUESTIONING, DESPITE ME GIVING CLEAR INSTRUCTIONS TO MATT RITCHIE TO PASS ON THE DATE, TIME AND VENUE?

Oops.

No, it was none of those people, but the culprit is here with us in this room right now...

That Sports Direct mug, which has been echoing our every conversation as far and wide as a Joelinton finish!

Joelinton finish
Joelinton finish
Joelinton finish

SPO

As far and
Joelinton finish
As far and wide as
a Joelinton finish
As far and wide as
a Joelinton finish
As far and wide as
a Joelinton fini
a Joelinton fin
As far and wide
a Joelinton fi
As far and
a Joelinton

Oh the cheek of it!

What an absolute joke we are, eh? Still, it could be worse, we could be Liverpool!

HA//AHAHAHAHAHA!

They're eighth.

eighth
eighth
eighth
eighth
eighth

SP

11

FINALLY, EUROPE'S SELF-PROCLAIMED LEADING CLUBS HAVE THROWN OFF THE SHACKLES OF FISCAL OPPRESSION BY ANNOUNCING THE FORMATION OF A NEW COMPETITION THAT COULD HAVE ALMOST AS MUCH SPORTING CREDIBILITY AS THE INTERNATIONAL CHAMPIONS CUP!

NATURALLY, THE PLAN HAS LED TO ANXIETY AMONG THE FANS OF CLUBS LEFT BEHIND...

THE PANDEMIC ACCELERATED THE NEED FOR THE FOUNDING CLUBS TO RINSE THE GAME FOR THEIR OWN FINANCIAL ADVANCEMENT. ALTHOUGH THIS MAY SEEM LIKE AN EXTREME REACTION TO THE THREAT OF HAVING TO PLAY WEST HAM, THIS SELFLESS GROUP OF 12 VULTURE CAPITALISTS, BANKERS, OLIGARCHS AND PETRO-PRINCES ARE ACTING TO SAVE (THEIR NARROW DEFINITION OF) FOOTBALL!

AS ANDREA AGNELLI SAYS, THE SUPER LEAGUE WILL GIFT THE REST OF US PLEBS WITH HEADLINE FIXTURES AND ENGAGING ROLE MODELS, AND WE COULDN'T BE MORE GRATEFUL!

CLEARLY, YOU COULDN'T HAVE A DEFECTION OF HIGH-ACHIEVERS WITHOUT THE 2008 CARLING CUP WINNERS. THE INCLUSION OF TOTTENHAM DOES AT LEAST PROVIDE SOME DRY HUMOUR TO A WHOLLY DEPRESSING SPECTACLE.

KILLING FOOTBALL'S ECOSYSTEM IS A SMALL PRICE TO PAY FOR ENHANCING ARSENAL'S GLOBAL BRAND, YET THE MOVE HAS LED TO SOME CRITICISM. THE NOTION THAT A PUFFED-UP GROUP OF CLUBS COULD FORM A BREAKAWAY MOTIVATED BY GREED WAS ABHORRENT TO THE PREMIER LEAGUE, AND EVEN BORIS JOHNSON WAS ABLE TO SCORE A RARE GOAL FOR MORALITY, HILARIOUSLY.

OH GOOD, HERE COMES FLORENTINO PÉREZ. HE'LL PLACATE ALL YOU OVERLY-EMOTIONAL LEGACY FANS (⅜ RETCH!).

FIFA AND UEFA ARE UNDERSTANDABLY FURIOUS. IF ANYONE'S GOING TO IMPLEMENT A TERRIBLE PLAN, IT SHOULD BE THEM, GOD DAMN IT. IN A BID TO OUTDO THE SUPER LEAGUE, UEFA SWIFTLY RATIFIED ITS OWN HORRIBLE REVAMP OF THE CHAMPIONS LEAGUE AFTER LOBBYING FROM THE EUROPEAN CLUB ASSOCIATION. JUST WAIT UNTIL EDWIN VAN DER SAR TELLS AGNELLI THE GOOD NEWS!

FURTHER DOWN THE LINE, WHEN THE OWNERS REALISE THE INHERENT, UNACCEPTABLE RISK THAT PLAYING FOOTBALL MATCHES CAN HAVE ON YOUR SHARE PRICE, THEIR INSATIABLE HUNGER FOR MORE WILL AGAIN STIR THEM INTO ACTION. THIS WILL RESULT IN A BREAKAWAY FROM THE BREAKAWAY, WITH THE DETRITUS OF THE SUPER LEAGUE CAST ASIDE.

MAYBE THEN, THOSE CUT ADRIFT WILL SHARE THE SENSE OF REVULSION MANY OF US ARE FEELING AS WE TRY TO PROCESS THE DISCONNECT BETWEEN THE RELENTLESS AVARICE OF THE FOUNDING CLUBS AND THE GAME WE FELL IN LOVE WITH AS CHILDREN — SOMETHING PURE THAT COULD NEVER BE REDUCED TO A COLLECTION OF BLAND CORPORATE BUZZWORDS.

VIVA LA REVOLUTION ★

IT'S BEEN A WEEK SINCE 'THE DIRTY DOZEN' TOOK THE NUCLEAR OPTION OF MUTUALLY-ASSURED REPUTATIONAL DESTRUCTION BY ANNOUNCING A BREAKAWAY SUPER LEAGUE, THUS UNLEASHING A FIRESTORM OF CRITICISM AND CREATING THE UNLIKELIEST OF RESISTANCE HEROES.

The revolution will not be on free-to-air.

THE PROJECT COLLAPSED AMIDST FAN PROTESTS AT SOME OF THE PREMIER LEAGUE'S 'BIG SIX' CLUBS. AT ARSENAL, SUPPORTER ANIMOSITY TOWARDS THE OWNERS COINCIDED WITH EXCITEMENT WHEN SPOTIFY FOUNDER DANIEL EK TWEETED THAT HE WANTED TO BUY THE CLUB.

That's what this situation calls for: more billionaires!

AT THE VERY LEAST, IT MAY BE ONE WAY OF SECURING STREAMING ROYALTIES FOR THE RECORDING ARTIST, IAN WRIGHT.

Do the right thing.

You may actually be the only artist whose talents have been appropriately compensated.

FAN CRITICISMS WERE ECHOED BY PLAYERS AND MANAGERS, LEADING TO AN EMBARRASSING BACKDOWN AND A SERIES OF HIGHLY ENTERTAINING PERFORMATIVE APOLOGIES BY NUMEROUS CLUB OWNERS WHO WERE CLEARLY COMFORTABLE HUMILIATING THEMSELVES IN PUBLIC. JOHN W HENRY LOOKED LIKE HE'D BEEN EMBALMED.

Christ. I said we should have got the Bob Paisley hologram to do this.

It's fine. Give him another formaldehyde nutri-bullet and hope people focus on the flowers.

AND ARSENAL'S CEO, VINAI VENKATESHAM HAD TO RING ROUND ALL THE OTHER PREMIER LEAGUE CLUBS TO APOLOGISE.

Heh. Grovel some more...

EVEN A FACELESS SPOKESPERSON FOR THE SUPER LEAGUE'S FINANCIAL BACKERS, JP MORGAN, RELEASED A STATEMENT THAT IN NO WAY READ LIKE THE VEILED THREAT OF AN AI DEATHBOT.

We'll learn from this.

THAT'S WHAT WE'RE WORRIED ABOUT, MATE.

IT WAS ALSO A SPIFFING RESULT FOR BORIS JOHNSON AND HIS 'LEGISLATIVE BOMB' THREAT. HOWEVER, QUESTIONS ARE NOW BEING ASKED ABOUT A MEETING BETWEEN DEAR BREEDER AND ED WOODWARD BEFORE THE SUPER LEAGUE ANNOUNCEMENT. HOW COULD WOODWARD HAVE REPORTEDLY LEFT THE EXCHANGE WITH THE FALSE IMPRESSION THAT THE FAMOUSLY INDUSTRIOUS PM WAS IN FAVOUR OF THE PROPOSAL?

We're doing a Super Lea—

BRAVO!

Jam roly-poly in the Commons canteen...

MAYBE THE GOVERNMENT SHOULD BE DOCKED SOME POINTS

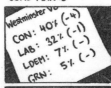

Westminster V...
CON: 40% (-4)
LAB: 32% (-1)
LDEM: 7% (-)
GRN: 5% (-)

BUT THAT WOULD ONLY PUNISH THEIR SUPPORTERS.

Now I know why you cry.

HOWEVER, LIKE HOMER SIMPSON CHASING AN AIRBORNE ROAST PIG, FLORENTINO PÉREZ IS CLINGING ON TO THE HOPE THAT THE SUPER LEAGUE PLAN IS STILL GOOD. HAVE ANY OF US SLEPT SINCE HIS REVELATION THAT REAL MADRID MIGHT NOT BE ABLE TO AFFORD HAALAND OR MBAPPÉ WITHOUT RIPPING UP THE FABRIC OF EUROPEAN FOOTBALL? MAYBE SOMETHING DOES NEED TO CHANGE IF A BIG-BRAINED BUSINESS GENIUS LIKE PÉREZ CAN'T MAKE MADRID PROFITABLE.

We spent €115m on Hazard... €63m on Jovic! And what's this...? €47m on ironing boards?!

Smart ironing boards. They tell you when you need to do your ironing. Besides, think of the money we're saving by getting you to do our accounts.

PING! Sorry, that's my ironing board...

THE SUPER LEAGUE PROJECT MAY BE ON HOLD FOR NOW, BUT YOU CAN GUARANTEE IT WILL RETURN IN A MORE POLISHED FORM WHEN THE TIME IS RIGHT.

¡TA-DA!

Shiny!

PING!

ESL 2.0

IT WON'T BE THE LAST TERRIBLE IDEA WE HEAR, BUT AT LEAST FOOTBALL'S TOP BRASS CAN BE RELIED UPON TO PROTECT THE INTERESTS OF CLUBS OUTSIDE THE ELITE, AS SEEN BY EFL CHAIRMAN RICK PARRY'S CONTINUED SUPPORT FOR PROJECT BIG PICTURE (RIP).

Now is the time to hand over our wallets to the wallet inspectors!

THE PEOPLE WHO DROVE THE SUPER LEAGUE PLOT WILL BE RELYING ON FANS TO FORGET AND MOVE ON, BUT THE WHOLE SORRY EPISODE HAS SHOWN SUPPORTERS THAT THEY HAVE POWER, AND NOW IS THE TIME TO PUSH FOR CHANGE. SOME OWNERS WILL BE TERRIFIED THAT THIS AWAKENING HAS COINCIDED WITH SPECTATORS SLOWLY BEING ALLOWED BACK INTO STADIUMS, AS SEEN AT WEMBLEY ON SUNDAY.

Oh that is some elite level bantz.

We always win the cup when the year ends in 61!

ANKLE JUICE

CARABAO

MANCHESTER CITY

TOTTENHAM HOTSPUR

CARABAO CUP FINAL 2021

SOMEWHERE IN IRELAND, THE RETIRED RACEHORSE **ROCK OF GIBRALTAR** GRAZES IN A LUSH FIELD OF GENTLY SWAYING GRASS. THE CHAMPION STUD IS OBLIVIOUS TO THE FACT HE'S CAUSED MORE TROUBLE THAN THE **MONOLITHIC LIMESTONE PROMONTORY** AFTER WHICH HE'S NAMED, BECAUSE AS WE'VE ESTABLISHED, HE'S A HORSE.

Vulture capitalism, eh? Bloody hell.

IT WAS A DISPUTE OVER THE OWNERSHIP OF RoG BETWEEN SURALEX AND MANCHESTER UNITED DIRECTORS JOHN MAGNIER AND JP McMANUS THAT CONTRIBUTED TO THEM SELLING THEIR SHARES TO THE GLAZER FAMILY. THEY EVENTUALLY TOOK FULL CONTROL OF THE CLUB IN 2005, UTILISING THE KIND OF EYE-WATERING FINANCIAL ARRANGEMENT THAT'S FREELY AVAILABLE TO EVERYONE. HOORAY!

I'd like to buy one of your helicopters with loans that I'll pass on to others to pay off while I fly about flicking the vees.

Of course. I'll fetch you the keys!

I want a green one.

Oof. Excellent choice.

ALARM.

YEARS OF SUPPORTER DISCONTENT BOILED OVER ON SUNDAY, RESULTING IN THE PROTEST AT OLD TRAFFORD THAT CAUSED THE POSTPONEMENT OF UNITED'S GAME WITH LIVERPOOL. THE SCENES WOULD UNDOUBTEDLY HAVE ALARMED THE OWNERS.

It's Joel Glazer! He's escaping!

Hang on, isn't that Ade Edmondson?

Can somebody call the fire brigade, please?

Ok, that's an obscure reference, but I'm sure the real Joel Glazer is still shaken to the core.

FLORIDA

This is awful!

We forgot the dodo eggs! Just head back to shore, Avram; brunch is ruined.

AN INVESTIGATION WILL NOW TAKE PLACE INTO HOW FANS GAINED ACCESS TO A STADIUM THEY SAY THE OWNERSHIP HAS NEGLECTED FOR YEARS.

How on earth did they penetrate The Fortress of Drea—

Huh.

SKY SPORTS PUNDIT GRAEME SOUNESS WAS PARTICULARLY VEXED BY THE PROTESTS. IT'S WELL ESTABLISHED THAT HE ABHORS VIOLENCE AND THERE'S ONLY ONE EXPLANATION HE'D HAVE ACCEPTED FROM THE FAN HE CLAIMS THREW A BEER CAN AT HIM.

My sock. Look what they did to my sock!

THE FAMED PACIFIST ALSO CLAIMED THE PROTESTS WERE THE RESULT OF UNITED'S RECENT LACK OF SILVERWARE; AN OPINION THAT LEFT SOME WONDERING WHETHER ANOTHER STUDIO GUEST MAY HAVE BEEN BETTER QUALIFIED TO PROVIDE EXPERT ANALYSIS.

AND THERE WAS A FURTHER INDIGNITY THAT LEFT UNITED FANS SCREAMING INTO THEIR GLOBAL PILLOW PARTNERS:

We have to like Jamie Carragher now?!

OF COURSE, MANCHESTER UNITED AREN'T THE ONLY CLUB WHERE THE OWNERS ENJOY A CONTEMPTUOUS RELATIONSHIP WITH THE FANS, SO THE PROTESTERS COULD SURELY RELY ON RIVAL SUPPORTERS TO CAST TRIBALISM ASIDE IN A SHOW OF SOLIDARITY.

If the prawn sandwich brigade are so unhappy, why don't they just form their own phoenix club and a........ prawn sandwiches!

GLAZERS OUT

BUT WITH THE GLAZER FAMILY APPARENTLY UNWILLING TO SELL THEIR CASH COW, IT'S FEARED THIS STORY MAY HAVE A LESS SATISFYING ENDING THAN YOUR FAVOURITE SUNDAY NIGHT POLICE PROCEDURAL DRAMA.

They've ruined Foyle's War!

FOYLE'S WAR

MEANWHILE, ROCK OF GIBRALTAR STUBS OUT A CIGARETTE, SLIPS OUT OF A SILK KIMONO AND STRIDES INTO A PADDOCK TO PERFORM A STUNNING METAPHOR OF WHAT THE GLAZERS HAVE DONE TO MANCHESTER UNITED FOR THE LAST 16 YEARS...

Oo-er.

FOXES NEVER QUIT

The tension. Oh God, the tension...!

LEICESTER CITY LIFTED THE FA CUP FOR THE FIRST TIME IN THEIR HISTORY ON SATURDAY, THANKS TO AN EMOTIONAL 1-0 WIN AGAINST CHELSEA IN A FINAL THAT SOME PEOPLE ARE EVEN CLAIMING WAS A FITTING HORS D'OEUVRE FOR BRIGHTON v WEST HAM (CALM DOWN, EH?).

IT WAS THE PRESENCE OF FANS THAT MADE THE OCCASION TRULY MEMORABLE. WHEN YOURI TIELEMANS SPANNERED ONE IN FROM MILES OUT, THERE WAS A JOYOUS EXPLOSION OF HUMAN ENERGY THAT COULD NEVER BE REPLICATED BY A SOUND DESK. EVERYONE COULD TELL THAT THIS MEANT MORE.

A crucial psychological blow in THE RACE FOR FOURTH™!

20,000 PEOPLE WERE PRESENT, ALL OF THEM ISSUED WITH PROTECTIVE CHIN STRAPS TO PREVENT COVID SPORES PENETRATING THEIR HAIR FOLLICLES, AND TESTED WITH NASAL SWABS THAT MAY HAVE UNLOCKED THE GENIUS LOBE IN A FEW OF THEIR BRAINS...

Booing the pre-match anti-racism gesture! That'll inspire our black players!

TOO RIGHT, MATE. KEEP POLITICS OUT OF FOOTBALL, YEAH. JUST SING THE SONG IMPLORING LONGEVITY FOR THE UNELECTED HEAD OF STATE AND APPLAUD THE PLAYERS AS THEY AIR-FIST-BUMP HER HEIR-BUT-ONE. PROBS BEST YOU DON'T LOOK AT WHAT CHOUDHURY AND FOFANA ARE UP TO, THOUGH.

NOTHING COULD SOUR THE DAY FOR LEICESTER, THOUGH. IT WAS FITTING THAT SO MANY OF THEIR CLUB LEGENDS PLAYED SUCH AN INSTRUMENTAL ROLE IN THEIR SUCCESS.

THE TIRELESS GURNING OF VARDY!

THE ACROBATICS OF SCHMEICHEL!

THE ALBRIGHTONING OF ALBRIGHON!

THERE WAS EVEN A CAMEO FROM WES MORGAN, WHICH MAKES YOU WONDER WHICH OTHER HERO OF LEICESTER YORE WOULD HAVE COME ON IF THE GAME HAD GONE TO EXTRA-TIME.

Do you understand your role, Mark Morrison?

Yes I do. Yes I do, do, do.

VICTORY WAS VINDICATION FOR THE METHODS OF BRENDAN RODGERS, SO OFTEN AN EASY TARGET FOR MOCKERY (SHAME ON YOU). FORCED TO RETIRE FROM PLAYING AT THE AGE OF 20, RODGERS SPENT THE BEST PART OF THREE DECADES HONING HIS CRAFT AS A TOP, TOP COACH.

HE STUDIED, HE LEARNED, HE BRIEFLY PROVIDED PRIVATE COACHING SESSIONS FOR ROMAN ABRAMOVICH'S KID...

OK, son; dribble round those cones and shoot at goal.

We've got people to do that.

HE MASTERED THE PSYCHOLOGICAL SIDE OF THE GAME...

... INSPIRING THE BACKROOM STAFF TO BUY IN TO HIS MISSION STATEMENT AND CORE VALUES...

You better lose yourself in the cleaning, the moment. You own it, you better never let it go. You only get one shot, do not miss your chance to blow, this opportunity comes once in a lifetime...

... UNTIL IT ALL CAME GOOD ON SATURDAY AND HE WAS ABLE TO CELEBRATE WITH HIS NEAREST AND DEAREST WHO'D BEEN WITH HIM ON EVERY STEP OF THE WAY.

Danny McGrain! It's Brendan! No, Brendan. Rodgers...! What? No, the Leicester manager. I'm calling you from Wemb... Brendan Rodgers!

Danny?

AND YET CHELSEA SEEMED TO HAVE COMPLETELY RUINED THE NARRATIVE WITH A LATE, CALAMITOUS EQUALISER, UNTIL VAR INTERVENED TO MAKE A CALL TIGHTER THAN TOMMY TUCHEL'S ELECTRIC BLUE LEGGINGS.

CHECKING GOAL – POSSIBLE BANTZ

BEN CHILWELL INSTRUMENTAL IN A HEART BREAKING LEVELLER AFTER THE LEICESTER FANS HAVE BOOED HIS EVERY TOUCH: FUNNY

WAITING FOR THE CHELSEA FANS TO UPLOAD VIDEOS OF THEMSELVES LOSING THEIR MINDS BEFORE DISALLOWING THE GOAL BECAUSE HIS JAZZY NEW T-SHIRT IS A MAN-MADE FIBRE OFFSIDE: FUNNIER

VERDICT: OFFSIDE
RULES IS RULES

THE TEARS OF SYMPATHY FOR CHELSEA FLOWED LIKE RIVERS THROUGH THE STREETS OF ENGLAND, BUT THE DAY BELONGED TO LEICESTER AND THE EMOTIONAL BOND BETWEEN THE PLAYERS, FANS, MANAGER AND OWNER; THE KIND OF RELATIONSHIP MOST OTHER CLUBS CAN ONLY ENVY.

Do you think they love me like that, Avram?

It's OK, I don't expect you to answer.

After all, I did have you stuffed...

CRACK OPEN THE GAZPROM, BECAUSE FOUR OF THE CLUBS WHO PLOTTED TO DESTROY FOOTBALL LAST MONTH HAVE QUALIFIED FOR THE CHAMPIONS LEAGUE!

No one is happy for you! x

IT'S BEEN A RIDICULOUS PREMIER LEAGUE SEASON, BUT AT LEAST IT HAD A FITTINGLY DAFT END, WITH ARSENAL'S GABRIEL HUNTING FOR A LOST TOOTH IN THE RAIN.

A trophy!

ARGUABLY, THAT WASN'T THE BIGGEST STORY OF THE DAY IN WHICH CHELSEA AND LEICESTER WERE LOCKED IN A BATTLE TO SEE WHO COULD BLOW IT IN THE MOST SPECTACULAR MANNER. CHELSEA WENT DOWN 2-1 TO ASTON VILLA AS THE HAUNTED AZURE FIGURE OF TOMMY T BLINKED ON LIKE A LANCED BLUEBERRY.

The greatest travesty is that no one will remember our recoveries in the final third against Wolves.

HOWEVER, HE'LL HAVE APPRECIATED THE RESPECT FROM VILLA GOALSCORER BERTRAND TRAORÉ, WHO SET A NEW BENCHMARK FOR NOT CELEBRATING AGAINST YOUR OLD CLUB.

I played for Chelsea in career mode on Mario Smash Football.

That's class.

CHELSEA LOOKED DOOMED, IN WHAT WAS DEVELOPING INTO AN ENTERTAINING AFTERNOON FOR NEUTRALS.

Oh no, what a pity.

Nah, to be fair, that is f***ing delicious.

BUT WITH 15 MINUTES LEFT, LEICESTER 'DID A LEICESTER' BY LETTING FOURTH PLACE SLIP BY SURRENDERING TO A DEFEAT BY SPURS. EVEN LAST WEEK'S FA CUP HERO, KASPER SCHMEICHEL, SUFFERED A CATASTROPHIC LAPSE OF CONCENTRATION.

Is... is Brendan wearing a monogrammed face mask...?

SPURS CELEBRATED WILDLY. AFTER ALL, IT'S NOT EVERY DAY YOU RESCUE ONE OF YOUR MOST-HATED RIVALS AND QUALIFY FOR THE EUROPA CONFERENCE THING. VICTORY WASN'T ENOUGH TO OVERHAUL WEST HAM, THOUGH. TO THINK SOME OF YOU DOUBTED DAVID MOYES - A GENIUS WHOSE THROBBING BRAIN SHOULD NOW BE STUDIED TO HELP SOLVE HUMANITY'S GREATEST CHALLENGES. IF YOU CAN FIX WEST HAM...

"Get Mark Noble to shepherd all the carbon into one corner and run the Doomsday Clock down."

Brilliant!

IF YOU NEEDED FURTHER PROOF THAT FOOTBALL SOMETIMES DELIVERS A FAIRYTALE ENDING, JUST IMAGINE JOHN W HENRY'S LITTLE FACE WHEN LIVERPOOL SEALED THEIR PLACE IN THE COMPETITION HE CONSPIRED TO KILL.

IT WAS A TOUGH SEASON FOR THE REDS. THEY WERE THE FIRST SIDE IN HISTORY TO SUFFER SOME INJURIES, BUT THEY NEVER COMPLAINED ABOUT IT AND QUALIFIED WITH A SUPERB RUN OF RESULTS THAT INCLUDED ALISSON BECKER'S DRAMATIC WINNER AT WEST BROM, WHICH HAD SUCH A PROFOUND IMPACT ON SAM ALLARDYCE.

This is a young man's game, Sammy.

LIVERPOOL'S 2-0 DEFEAT OF CRYSTAL PALACE ALSO SAW ROY HODGSON BOW OUT OF FOOTBALL MANAGEMENT. LET'S NOT PISS ABOUT HERE, HODGSON'S ENJOYED A LONG AND DISTINGUISHED CAREER, BUT THE MUCH-TRAVELLED COACH WANTS TO EMBARK ON A NEW ADVENTURE. AS THE OLD SAYING GOES: LIFE BEGINS AT 73...

Age ain't nuttin' but a number, Raymondo. Crank up the Ride mixtape, we're going to the government's review panel on football governance!

Wait. I haven't retired—

♫ Take me for a ride away from places I have known. If I stay around I'll just remember I'm alo-hone ♫ Join in, Ray...

IT WAS A DAY FOR EMOTIONAL FAREWELLS. NUNO ESPÍRITO SANTO AT WOLVES, SERGIO AGÜERO AT MANCHESTER CITY...

We love him with every fibre of our beings. He's so special. So nice. To replace him would be like trying to replace the moon and the stars.

You could offer him a new contrac—

And his skin. So firm. Have you smelled him? Phenomenal. Almondy.

...AND THERE WERE MORE THAN A FEW TEARS SHED OVER DAVID LUIZ'S DEPARTURE FROM ARSENAL, LET ME TELL YOU.

I'm ruined...

AND SO ENDS A COMPLETELY WILD SEASON - FOR GOD'S SAKE, AT ONE POINT IT LOOKED LIKE EVERTON MIGHT WIN THE LEAGUE, UNTIL SENSE INTERVENED, TERRIFYINGLY.

Your teacher, old Carlo, has told me you've been f***ing slacking off a bit with your finishing 10th. We cannae be having that...

BUT IF YOU THOUGHT THIS SEASON WAS CHAOTIC, WAIT UNTIL YOU SEE THE IMPACT OF GABRIEL WHISTLING EVERY TIME HE EXHALES.

PHEEP!

What now?!

PLUTOCRATS.... 1
BUCKET HATS.... 0

CHELSEA ARE CHAMPIONS OF EUROPE, AFTER A MAGICAL NIGHT FOR PEOPLE WHO SUPPORT ALL ENGLISH CLUBS (WHO PLOTTED TO DESTROY THE FOUNDATIONS OF COMPETITIVE FOOTBALL) IN EUROPE!

UEFA PRESIDENT ALEKSANDER ČEFERIN CAN'T HAVE BEEN THE ONLY ONLOOKER PRESENTED WITH A LARRY DAVIDESQUE MORAL QUANDARY.

City lost... but Chelsea won.

But City lost... but Chelsea won...

CONSIDERING IT WAS LESS THAN A WEEK SINCE CHELSEA WERE BLOCKED BY THESE LADS...

... MAYBE IT WOULD HAVE BEEN WISE FOR CITY TO HAVE PICKED AN EXPERT HOLDING PLAYER, BUT AS IS TRADITIONAL ON THESE OCCASIONS, PEP HAD A LAST-MINUTE BRAINWAVE. WE CAN ONLY SPECULATE AS TO THE THOUGHT PROCESS THAT LED HIM TO STARTING TOP SCORER ILKAY GÜNDOGAN AS A DEFENSIVE MIDFIELDER.

Guys, DM me your pizza order for after. We don't want a repeat of 'Pineapplegate'.

DM him... DM him... MAKE HIM A DM !!

IN CONTRAST, CHELSEA HAD N'GOLO KANTÉ. OMNIPOTENT, BRILLIANT, NICE. IF HE COULD MAKE YOU FEEL OK ABOUT CHELSEA WINNING THE CHAMPIONS LEAGUE, HE COULD MAKE YOU FEEL OK ABOUT ANYTHING.

Bonjour madam, I'm very sorry but I hit your cat with my typically humble motor vehicle.

Think of the money I'll save on cat food!

Even I'm ok with this.

CHELSEA'S GERMAN CONTINGENT PLAYED A CRUCIAL ROLE IN THE VICTORY. KAI EFFING HAVERTZ SCAMPERED INTO A FERNANDINHO-SHAPED SPACE TO SCORE THE DECISIVE GOAL, ANTONIO RÜDIGER COMMITTED A BODY CHECK THAT LEFT BOTH KEVIN DE BRUYNE AND HIS INTERNATIONAL BOSS SHATTERED LIKE THE PATTERN ON CITY'S SHIRTS, LOONEY TUNES STYLE...

That's Belgium stuffed, Folks!

AND FOR THE MUCH-MALIGNED STRIKER TIMO WERNER, IT WAS REAL ROY OF THE ROVERS STUFF. SPECIFICALLY, ONE OF THE SIDE CARTOONS WITH AN ELABORATE PREMISE.

TOASTER TOES TIMO!

CHELSEA'S SUPERSTAR STRIKER TIMO WERNER WAS THE BEST IN THE LAND, OUTSIDE THE BOX. BUT DUE TO A GENIE'S CURSE, HIS FEET WOULD TURN INTO TOASTERS WHENEVER PRESENTED WITH A GOALSCORING OPPORTUNITY.

I'll be the toast of the King's Road when I stick this one aw—

Oh crumbs, I've sliced it etc. !!

THE WIN WAS CHELSEA'S THIRD AGAINST THEIR FELLOW SUPER LEAGUE BACKTRACKERS IN RECENT WEEKS. THOMAS TUCHEL IS OFTEN WRONGLY CRITICISED FOR HIS LACK OF PASHUN (HE'S NOT EVEN THE BLOOD RELATIVE OF A REDKNAPP, FOR FRANK'S SAKE!), BUT HE SEEMS TO HAVE THE BEATING OF GUARDIOLA. AS THE CLOCK TICKED DOWN, TUCHEL COULD BE SEEN WAVING HIS ARMS WILDLY, AS IF WAFTING HIS VEGETARIAN GUFFS TOWARDS THE CITY BENCH. FIGURATIVELY AND LITERALLY, HE WAS IN PEP'S HEAD.

COME ON !!

Oh God!

It smells like nothing's died!

INDEED, TUCHEL TAKES THE PSYCHOLOGICAL SIDE OF THE GAME SERIOUSLY, WHICH IS WHY THE CHELSEA DRESSING ROOM IS PLASTERED WITH MOTIVATIONAL SLOGANS.

FORWARD MOMENTUM!

FINAL THIRD TRANSITIONS!

SCHNELL!

NOT YOU, TAMMY!

... AND HIS SUCCESS IS SET TO BE REWARDED WITH THE GIFT OF THE MOST DURABLE SUBSTANCE KNOWN TO MAN: A NEW CHELSEA CONTRACT!

Oh, it's made of ash.

Saves time dunnit.

IT WAS A REDEMPTIVE WIN FOR TUCHEL, WHO WAS ON THE LOSING SIDE WITH PSG LAST YEAR. A LOT HAS CHANGED SINCE ROBERT LEWANDOWSKI WAS PHOTOGRAPHED IN BED WITH THE TROPHY LAST SUMMER.

MEANWHILE, CITY CAN CONSOLE THEMSELVES WITH THE FACT THEY WON THE PREMIER LEAGUE AND COMPLETED AN HISTORIC QUADRUPLE: FOUR CONSECUTIVE LEAGUE CUPS! YOU CAN GUARANTEE THEY'LL BE BACK, AND THAT PEP WON'T MAKE THE SAME MISTAKE NEXT TIME.

Get your boots on, kiddo.

It's time to blow some minds.

MEN'S EUROS 2021:
BUM FLARE OF THE VANITIES

'What happened?' asked Sarah, as I sat blinking at a TV screen filled with Italian #limbs.

'England lost on penalties,' I croaked.

'Oh well,' she replied breezily. 'At least you got to watch more football. Are you making the coffee?'

It's good to have someone around to keep you grounded, even when you're literally already slumped on the ground. A person to haul you back into reality, like Giorgio Chiellini garrotting Bukayo Saka with the hook of an umbrella. However, if I needed a reminder that there are worse things that can happen in life, I just had to think back to a few weeks earlier, when Christian Eriksen suffered a cardiac arrest on the field during Denmark's opener against Finland. As Eriksen recovered in hospital, the Danes became many neutrals' favourites, but sympathy for their cause ran dry in the semi-final against England after Joakim Mæhle's *brutal* foul on Raheem Sterling to concede an extra-time penalty.

Worse was to follow with Kasper Schmeichel's despicable attempt to distract Harry Kane by firing green lasers out of his eyes. Mercifully, Kane was not to be deterred: he closed his eyes and smashed the ball – a technique that would serve him well at the next World Cup – expertly playing a one–two off the dastardly Schmeichel and planting the ball in the net.

The Covid-delayed Euro 2020(1) was as good as a home tournament for England, with all but one of their games en route to the final being played at Wembley. A limited number of fans were allowed to attend fixtures dotted around the Continent, apart from at the Puskás Aréna in Budapest, where the doors were flung open: air-borne contagions being no match for the coordinated clapping of black-shirted nationalists.

England's pre-tournament friendlies and early group-stage matches were soundtracked by the familiar summer song of fans booing their own team, this time for taking the knee. Phil Foden had even dyed his hair the colour of Karl Marx's beard! BOOOOOO! Several high-ranking Tories who'd spent the last year clapping on their doorsteps in lieu of funding a functional health service also made it clear they weren't fans of gesture politics.

But as the team progressed, the cheers drowned out the grunts [check typo], and the nation was soon united in celebrating the images of a tearful German child on the big screen during a tense second-round victory. Come the final, thousands would jib their way into Wembley – politicians desperate to attach themselves to something popular, creating a dangerous and toxic atmosphere more commonly seen in the halls of Westminster.

Despite reaching the final, though, victory wasn't to be. Gareth Southgate invoking the war beforehand did not prove to be as effective as making some fucking substitutions when it was obvious – even to someone conditioned to watching football purely for the mega-LOLs – that Italy were dominating the midfield. Luke Shaw's knighthood would have to wait, but the young group of players had done themselves proud and they could take consolation in the fact that they had at least been able to play more football.

FOOTIE FACTS

Besides England, there were twenty-three other teams competing at the tournament!

While football connoisseurs were left drooling by the Three Lions' goalless draw with Scotland, fans of wacky Continental game shows enjoyed the mainstream laughs of 'Mad Monday', when Spain beat Croatia 5–3 and France fell to Switzerland on calamities.

THE EUROS ARE HERE! AFTER 15 MONTHS OF TRAGEDY, LOSS, CONFINEMENT AND LONELINESS, FOOTBALL FANS ARE FINALLY ABLE TO GET OUT AND SHARE IN THE JOYOUS COMMUNAL EXPERIENCE OF A MAJOR TOURNAMENT ON HOME SOIL (MOSTLY). WITH A TALENTED YOUNG SQUAD AND THE ENDLESS POSSIBILITIES OF SUMMER STRETCHING OUT AHEAD, IT PROMISES TO BE A JOYOUS FESTIVAL OF POSITIVI—

AH, YES. WITH DEPRESSING PREDICTABILITY, FOR THE SECOND TIME IN A WEEK, ENGLAND'S PLAYERS HAVE BEEN BOOED FOR A PEACEFUL ANTI-RACISM GESTURE. IT CONCLUDES A TROUBLED BUILDUP TO THE TOURNAMENT. FIRST MAGUIRE DID HIS ANKLE, THEN TRENT DID HIS THIGH, NOW CONSERVATIVE MP LEE ANDERSON SAYS HE'LL BOYCOTT ENGLAND GAMES ON HIS TELLY. WHAT A BLOW.

There's no easy way to say this, lads, but not only have we lost a Tory MP desperate for attention, but the internet's Laurence Fox has called us ..."Ball-chasers".

The London mayoral candidate who barely got as many votes as England have won major tournaments ?!

Yes, if you include Le Tournoi.

BUT LISTEN, YEAH, IT'S NOT *REALLY* ABOUT THE FIGHT FOR RACIAL EQUALITY; YOU SEE IT'S ACTUALLY ALL PART OF A **MARXIST PLOT** TO OVERTHROW THE STATE AND TURN BURTON-UPON-TRENT INTO A REEDUCATION CAMP. AND GUYS, WEMBLEY IS IN LONDON, WHICH IS IN **DAS KAPITAL!** YOU CAN'T EVEN WATCH ENGLAND AWAY WITHOUT SUNBURNT MARXISTS TAKING OVER THE TOWN SQUARE AND INTIMIDATING THE LOCALS WITH THEIR BEERY SONGS OF CLASS STRUGGLE.

AS MARX ONCE SAID: 'HISTORY REPEATS ITSELF, FIRST AS TRAGEDY, SECOND DURING A SLIGHTLY FARCICAL WARM-UP GAME AGAINST ROMANIA', SO IT WAS INEVITABLE THAT GARETH SOUTHGATE'S POLITE REQUEST FOR EMPATHY WOULD BE IGNORED. BUT HEY, IT'S HARD TO ARGUE WITH THE LOGIC OF HUMAN THUMBS WITH BRAINS AS BIG AS A GREALISH SHINPAD.

Wem-ber-lee, Wem-ber-lee, From each according to his ability, to each according to his needs.

No surrender, no surrender no surrender to the bourgeoisie!

Keep politics out of football tournaments comprising representative teams from territories defined by political borders!

We don't want political messages rammed down our throats, restricting our ability to sing about the IRA, or the war, or Britain's former Imperial might!

YOU TELL 'EM, MATE. TEENAGE LADS PEACEFULLY DEMONSTRATING FOR THEIR RIGHTS TO BE TREATED AS EQUAL HUMAN BEINGS ? **BOO, MATE; BOOOOO!**

BLOODY MARCUS RASHFORD TOO! HE'S SPENT THE LAST YEAR WORKING TO FEED THE NATION'S HUNGRY CHILDREN, BUT IT'S NEVER ENOUGH FOR YOU, IS IT MATE? HE'S EMBARRASSING THE GOVERNMENT YOU VOTED FOR! BOO, MATE, BOOOO!

TYRONE MINGS, MATE? TYRONE BLOODY MINGS? ONE OF THE PLAYERS SUBJECTED TO BAD RACISM IN BULGARIA ? NOT LIKE THE MORE SUBTLE, NUANCED RACISM OF JEERING HIS RADICAL LEFTIST POSITION THAT HIS LIFE HAS VALUE. YOU TELL HIM, MATE.

YOU WON'T BE MADE TO FEEL BAD BY TRILLIONAIRE FOOTBALLERS WHO'VE RUN THEMSELVES INTO THE GROUND FOR THE LAST YEAR, RISKING THEIR HEALTH FOR YOUR ENTERTAINMENT, ONLY TO ROUTINELY BE THE OBJECT OF RACIST BILE EVERY TIME THEY OPEN THEIR DMS.

Well this is *highly* motivating.

Sigh.

Sigh.

THIS OUTPOURING OF HUMAN EMPATHY DIDN'T OCCUR IN ISOLATION. FOOTBALL GROUNDS SIMPLY REFLECT A BROADER SOCIETY IN WHICH A NATIONAL NEWSPAPER PRINTS A STORY ABOUT NO-GO-ZONES FOR WHITE PEOPLE THAT EVEN THE EDL NEWSLETTER WOULD REJECT FOR BEING A BIT FAR-FETCHED, AND A SITTING MP LIKENS PLAYERS TAKING THE KNEE TO THEM GIVING NAZI SALUTES. THANK RUDDY GOD THEN THAT WE CAN RELY UPON HEAD THUMB BOJ TO SET THE TONE WITH SOME TEXTBOOK MORAL LEADERSHIP

Well, look, I think certainly. Listen. Both sides. I think. Well. Indubitably. We have to. Look. *Tres Leones.* Jolly good.

Sigh.

AND SO, ENGLAND GO INTO THE TOURNAMENT WITH SEVERAL UNANSWERED QUESTIONS:

HOW'S MAGUIRE'S ANKLE?

HOW DID JAMES WARD-PROWSE TAKE THE NEWS HE HADN'T MADE THE CUT ?

KENNY G INTENSIFIES

WHAT DOES IT MAKE YOU IF YOU'RE ANTI-ANTI-RACISM ?

WILL THE MARXIST-SOCIALIST REVOLUTION OCCUR BEFORE OR AFTER THE GROUP STAGE ?

It's coming home. It's coming home. It's coming. Proletarian utopia's coming home.

ERIKSEN'S LIFE WAS SAVED ON SATURDAY THANKS TO THE SWIFT INTERVENTION OF SOME EXCEPTIONAL PEOPLE, ONE OF WHOM HAS HIS OWN PANINI STICKER, MOST OF WHOM DON'T...

FOOTBALL MEANS NOTHING. NOTHING STOPS FOR FOOTBALL. THE MATCH RESUMED, FINLAND SECURED THE MOST SIGNIFICANT HOLLOW WIN IN THEIR HISTORY, THE TOURNAMENT RUMBLED ON. AS A RESULT, SO DOES THIS CARTOON. I'M AS TRAPPED IN THE CYCLE AS ANYONE.

YOU MIGHT THINK THIS STARK REMINDER OF THE FRAGILITY OF HUMAN LIFE WOULD INSTIL PEOPLE WITH A BIT OF EMPATHY FOR THEIR FELLOW MAN, BUT A FEW HOURS LATER, THE WHISTLES RANG AROUND THE KRESTOVSKY STADIUM AS BELGIUM'S PLAYERS TOOK THE KNEE BEFORE FACING RUSSIA. PERFECTLY, IT WAS ERIKSEN'S FRIEND ROMELU LUKAKU WHO SHUT THEM UP.

THANKFULLY, APPLAUSE DROWNED OUT THE RACIST GRUNTS AT WEMBLEY ON SUNDAY. BUT AFTER A BRIGHT START, ENGLAND BEGAN TO SHRIVEL LIKE A JAM SANDWICH IN THE SUN, SLOWING TO A WOOZY GSTQ-TEMPO, ALLOWING MODRIC MORE TIME ON THE BALL. UH-OH...

BUT LASHINGS OF HALF-TIME BLUE DRINK REVITALISED ENGLAND, AND A RAHEEM STERLING GOAL SEALED AN OKAYISH WIN! AT FULL-TIME, GARETH SOUTHGATE COULDN'T HAVE LOOKED MORE RELAXED IF HE'D GONE THE FULL LINGARD.

IT ALREADY FEELS SO LONG SINCE THE TOURNAMENT STARTED THAT IT COULD BE THE SUBJECT OF ITS OWN NOSTALGIC CLIP SHOW. HERE, REMEMBER THAT LITTLE CAR? AND THE EMOTION OF THE OPENING CEREMONY? DID WE EVER FIND OUT WHAT CRIME THAT WOMAN WAS ACCUSED OF THAT LED TO SUCH A DRACONIAN PUNISHMENT?

ITALY LOOKED GOOD, DIDN'T THEY? NOT LEAST ROBERTO MANCINI WITH HIS ENZO BEARZOT-INSPIRED 1960s ALITALIA CABIN CREW UNIFORM. HOWEVER, EVEN HE MAY BE INFLUENCED BY THE REAL STYLE ICON OF GROUP A: KIEFFER MOORE.

WE'VE ALREADY SEEN SOME CRACKING GOALS TOO. ANDRIY YARMOLENKO'S ROCKET AGAINST THE NETHERLANDS, STEFAN LAINER'S LEGGY, FAR-POST VOLLEY AGAINST NORTH MACEDONIA, WHICH WAS PURE ÖSTERREICH...

AND OF COURSE, PATRIK SCHICK'S HOLE-IN-ONE THAT SCHAT ON SCOTLAND'S RETURN FROM THE INTERNATIONAL WILDERNESS. THEIR AFTERNOON BEGAN WITH DISCO BANGERS, BUT SOMETHING FROM THE RADIOHEAD GLOOM CANON MAY HAVE BEEN MORE APPROPRIATE AS DAVID MARSHALL TWISTED IN THE NET HELPLESSLY.

IT WAS A SENSATIONAL STRIKE THAT TOOK EVERYONE BY SURPRISE.

THE EUROS ALSO PRESENT A CHANCE TO LEARN ABOUT OTHER CULTURES. FOR EXAMPLE, IN SPAIN THEY STAY UP REALLY LATE AND ARE STILL TRYING TO SCORE A GOAL LONG AFTER THE REST OF US HAVE GONE TO BED. THE LOCAL MEDIA CAN BE RELIED UPON TO TAKE SPAIN'S GALLESS DRAW WITH SWEDEN IN THEIR STRIDE. HOW LONG WERE THEY KNOCKING IT ABOUT HARMLESSLY, MATE?

AH WELL, THERE'S STILL A LOT OF FOOTBALL LEFT TO BE PLAYED, AND CAN A TOURNAMENT TRULY BE SAID TO HAVE STARTED UNTIL A KID HAS BEEN SUSPENDED FROM SCHOOL FOR TURNING UP WITH A KALVIN PHILLIPS HAIR-DO?

WE'RE INTO THE LAST ROUND OF GROUP MATCHES AT EURO 2020? AND AS IS TRADITIONAL WE'VE REACHED THE POINT AT WHICH ENGLAND ENJOY AN EXISTENTIAL MELTDOWN. THEIR PERFORMANCE AGAINST SCOTLAND WAS AS FLAT AS A MASON MOUNT CORNER, AS DEAD AS THE MOVING DRINKS BANTER. THE PLAYERS WERE ACCUSED OF LACKING PASHUN BUT AT LEAST CAPTAIN HARRY PLAYED AS IF HE WAS WEARING A SUPPORTER'S COSPLAY OUTFIT...

With this authentic steel chain mail, I vow to do battle as if I were playing in a cup final for Spurs!

WALTHAMSTOI

MISSION ACCOMPLISHED, SIR! ALTHOUGH THE REST OF EUROPE WAS DOUBTLESS CAPTIVATED BY THE DISPLAY OF INVENTIVE FOOTBALL ('BUNDLES'!) SOME QUESTIONS REMAIN FOR ENGLAND. FOR EXAMPLE, WHY CAN'T THESE PLAYERS WHO GET BOOED BEFORE THEY'VE EVEN STARTED PLAY WITH A FREEDOM OF EXPRESSION? AND HOW COME SOUTHGATE STILL DOESN'T KNOW HIS BEST COAT?! THERE ARE BOUND TO BE CHANGES FOR THE CZECH REPUBLIC GAME...

OUT — THE CLAMOUR FOR GREALISH

Already?

ALREADY.

IN — THE CLAMOUR FOR SANCHO

HOPE... HE CAN RECREATE HIS CLUB FORM.

SOON TO BE REPLACED BY...

THE CLAMOUR FOR SOMEONE ELSE WHO HASN'T HAD A GO YET.

RAMSDALE! RAMSDALE IS THE CHOSEN ONE.

COOLING BREAK

PHEW. EVERYONE TAKE A BREATHER AND HAVE A DEEP GULP OF PERSPECTIVE. IT WAS ONLY THE SECOND GAME. ITALY ARE GOING TO WIN IT ANYWAY. WE'RE ALL JUST SPINNING ON AN INSIGNIFICANT ROCK IN THE INFINITE VOID OF SPACE AND WE SHOULD BE GRATEFUL THAT WE EXIST IN THE SAME SNAPSHOT IN TIME AS GIROUD'S HAIR. IN A FEW WEEKS, WHEN WE'RE ARGUING ABOUT VAR DENYING BRENTFORD A GOAL AGAINST ARSENAL, WE'LL BE PINING FOR THESE LONG SUMMER NIGHTS.

HAPPIER TIMES FOR SCOTLAND, WHO NOW ONLY NEED TO BEAT CROATIA TO QUALIFY FOR THE LAST 16. THE ANCIENT TEXTS HAVE TAUGHT US THIS IS A TASK THEY WILL ACCOMPLISH WITH THE MINIMUM OF CATASTROPHE. THEIR FUTURE LOOKS AS BRIGHT AS A GRAEME SOUNESS SMILE.

AS IF TO PROVE THE POINT, THE INK WAS BARELY DRY ON THAT PANEL WHEN THE NEWS BROKE THAT BILLY GILMOUR HAD TESTED POSITIVE FOR COVID. EVEN THE BEST LAID PLANS CAN RUN AWRY, AS DEMONSTRATED BY THE BREAKOUT STAR OF THE TOURNAMENT SO FAR: **HUNGARY'S EDIT SZALAY!**

Notepad, pens, Gábor Király novelty mug, desk calendar with a different Jonathan Wilson quote about Hungarian football for each day, spongy microphone stress-relief toy. All set for this unusual assignment to tally all the uncritical mentions of the great atmosphere created by the black-shirted Viktor Orbán ultras!

KÖTEGEK!

FIOLA 5

"BUNDLES!"

I'd already lost count!

WALES ARE THROUGH, DESPITE A 1-0 LOSS TO ITALY IN THE FRIENDLY-WITH-BENEFITS. AS THEY EDGED TOWARDS FULL-TIME, ROBERT PAGE TYPIFIED THE CHILLED-OUT MOOD IN THE WELSH CAMP BY SCREAMING AT KIEFFER MOORE TO CALM DOWN, SUGGESTING A POST-FOOTBALL CAREER IN THE HEALTH SPA INDUSTRY MAY AWAIT.

RELAX!

TURKEY ARE OUT, THOUGH. FAR FROM BEING THE DARK HORSES MANY PREDICTED, SENOL GUNES' SIDE WERE THE INFLATABLE UNICORNS OF GROUP A, SPREADING GOOD VIBES TO EVERYONE THEY PLAYED. IT WON'T HAVE GONE UNNOTICED...

Fancy a job?

No, I...

I wasn't talking to you...

WALES WILL NOW FACE DENMARK, WHO THRASHED THE GREAT BEAR OF RUSSIA IN AN EMOTIONAL MIDSOMMAR FESTIVAL IN SCANDINAVIA. IT WAS A LONG NIGHT FOR STANISLAV CHERCHESOV.

STILL, AS ONE DOOR CLOSES...

Fancy a job?

Now isn't the time to—

I wasn't talking to you...

ETC.

HAVING PLAYED 36 GAMES TO ELIMINATE EIGHT TEAMS, WE'RE NOW INTO **THE BUSINESS END OF THE EUROS.** SADLY, WALES WERE THE FIRST SIDE TO FALL IN THE KNOCKOUT STAGE AFTER DENMARK FOUND THEIR UNDERBELLY TO BE AS SOFT AS THE FIRST 'I' IN MARTIN BRAITHWAITE'S SURNAME. ATTENTION SOON TURNED TO THE FUTURE OF GARETH BALE, WHICH HE TOOK ABOUT AS WELL AS HIS PENALTY AGAINST TURKEY...

If I told you what my plan was, it'd blow your bloody mind, mate.

Going into business with Ian Woosnam to sell 'Live, Laugh, Golf' mugs and tea towels?

THE DANES WILL FACE THE CZECH REPUBLIC, WHO OVERCAME THE NETHERLANDS AFTER MATTHIJS DE LIGT SACRIFICED HIMSELF SO FRANK DE BOER WOULD BE FORCED TO ABANDON THE DREADED 5-3-2. FOR DUTCH FANS, IT WAS A HELLISH SCENE WORTHY OF A HIERONYMUS BOSCH SPECIAL.

ITALY ARE ALSO THROUGH, BUT NEEDED EXTRA-TIME TO BEAT ROTHERHAM. THEY DID CONCEDE THEIR FIRST GOAL SINCE THE FALL OF THE ROMAN EMPIRE THOUGH, AND EVEN MANCINI LOOKED FLUSTERED.

THERE WAS EVEN SOMETHING IRONICALLY ITALIAN ABOUT SASA KALAJDZIC'S STOOPING NEAR-POST HEADER...

PORTUGAL ARE OUT AFTER BEING PORTUGALLED BY BELGIUM. HOWEVER, SUCH IS THE CORINTHIAN SPIRIT OF SOME PORTUGUESE PLAYERS THAT THE RESULT IS OF SECONDARY IMPORTANCE. FOR EXAMPLE, PEPE SEEMS TO BE PLAYING A DIFFERENT SPORT ENTIRELY...

YES... HA HA HA... YES!

PEPE
YELLOW CARD

BELGIUM'S WINNER CAME VIA A THUNDERBOLT FROM THORGAN HAZARD. HIS OLDER BROTHER EDEN WOULD HAVE ENJOYED IT AS MUCH AS ANYONE RELISHES BEING UPSTAGED BY A SIBLING.

Dos años... dos años...

That's how long I'm gonna have to hear about this.

MONDAY'S GAMES BOTH LOOKED PRETTY STRAIGHTFORWARD, SO ONLY LEAVING SPACE FOR TWO PANELS IN WHICH TO COVER THEM SHOWED AS MUCH FORESIGHT AS UNAI SIMÓN DEALING WITH A BACKPASS.

Wait until they get a load of that 'Bale likes golf' material...!

AFTER AN EARLIER SCARE, IT WAS PARTY TIME FOR FRANCE WHEN PAUL POGBA CURLED A SHOT INTO THE TOP CORNER TO GIVE THEM AN UNASSAILABLE 3-1 LEAD AGAINST SWITZERLAND.

I can't think of a single example from, say, the last three hours that suggests it's not safe to kick back and chill for the last 15 minutes...

BUT, MY GOD, IF THERE'S ONE THING YOU SHOULD NEVER DO IN FOOTBALL IT'S WRITE OFF SWITZERLAND, WHO FOUGHT BACK TO PULL OFF THE BIGGEST SHOCK OF THE TOURNAMENT SO FAR AND SEND THEIR FANS WILD. WHAT ELSE OTHER THAN FOOTBALL CAN INSPIRE THIS KIND OF RAW EMOTION...?

Please let it happen. I promise to remain completely neutral for the rest of the year if this one thing just happens...

YEEEAAARGH! XHAKA'S DOING HIS ANECDOTE ABOUT HIS PARENTS GIVING HIM RESPONSIBILITY FOR THE HOUSE KEY EVEN THOUGH HE HAS AN OLDER BROTHER!

BUT YOU DON'T CARE ABOUT ANY OF THIS, DO YOU? IT'S ALL JUST KILLING TIME UNTIL THE BIG ONE: SWEDEN V UKRAINE. BY THE TIME THEY KICK OFF, YOU'LL HAVE HAD YOUR FILL OF NOSTALGIA PIECES ABOUT THEIR PAST ENCOUNTERS. AS IF YOU NEED REMINDING OF UKRAINE'S PENALTY SHOOT-OUT WIN IN THE CYPRUS INTERNATIONAL TOURNAMENT FINAL OF FEBRUARY 2011!

Don't worry about it, sson.

No. Really.

EVERY TIME YOU WATCH IT, YOU THINK ANDERS SVENSSON'S GOING TO GET HIS TOE TO THAT CROSS, RIGHT?!

ARGHH!

FRUSTRATINGLY, YOU'LL HAVE TO SIT THROUGH ENGLAND V GERMANY BEFORE YOU CAN SING YOUR SONGS ABOUT THE BATTLE OF POLTAVA (1709) INVOLVING THE SWEDISH EMPIRE AND COSSACK HETMANATE. AT LEAST IT MIGHT BE ENLIVENED BY ANOTHER HALF-TIME UPDATE FROM THE UKRAINIAN CAMP, WITH EVERY LAST ASPECT OF THEIR PREPARATIONS DETAILED, INCLUDING EXCITING NEWS ABOUT A LIVE PERFORMANCE BY AN INEXPLICABLY POPULAR REALITY STAR - A SINGING STEPPE MARMOT DOING ACOUSTIC COVERS FOR THE LADS. NOT LONG TO WAIT NOW...

One disputed territory on our shirts, Cyprus International Tournament Cup still gleaming...

Wow...

There really is no avoiding the little f

YES, ENGLAND REALLY DID JUST OLÉ THEIR WAY TO A 4-0 WIN AGAINST UKRAINE IN THE QUARTER-FINAL OF A MAJOR TOURNAMENT. THEY'RE NOW JUST TWO HOME WINS AWAY FROM BEING CROWNED EUROCHAMPS, AND THEIR FIRST OBSTACLE - DENMARK- HAVEN'T WON AT WEMBLEY SINCE LAST OCTOBER! IT'LL TAKE SOMETHING PRETTY SPECTACULAR TO STOP THEM NOW...

THE VICTORY WAS ALSO NOTABLE FOR THE CONTINUED RESURRECTION OF HARRY KANE. SUCH WAS HIS IMPROVEMENT YOU'D THINK THAT WHILE IN ROME HE'D BEEN INSPIRED BY A VISIT TO SEE THE RENAISSANCE TRIPTYCH CELEBRATING THE MIRACLE OF ST CIRO - THE PATRON SAINT OF SH*THOUSERY WHO WAS SMOTE BY THE ANCIENT HORDES OF BELGAE, ONLY TO RISE FROM BEING IMMOBILE TO SUDDENLY VERY BLOODY MOBILE...

EVEN JORDAN HENDERSON SCORED FOR ENGLAND. HAD THE REFEREE ALLOWED ANY STOPPAGE TIME, WE MAY ALSO HAVE SEEN GOALS FROM FRED STREET, WORLD CUP WILLIE AND AT LEAST ONE SUGARBABE. SUCH ARE THE POSITIVE VIBES THIS TEAM INSPIRES THAT EVEN THE EVERTON FANS THE CAMERAS PICKED OUT SEEMED DELIGHTED FOR THE LIVERPOOL CAPTAIN.

ITALY'S WIN AGAINST BELGIUM SETS UP A SEMI-FINAL WITH SPAIN, WHO WERE SIMULTANEOUSLY DOMINANT AND JAMMY IN BEATING SWITZERLAND ON PENALTIES. THE SWISS MIGHT EVEN HAVE WON IF REMO FREULER HADN'T BEEN SENT OFF BY MICHAEL OLIVER, THE SIGHT OF WHOM WAS AS UPLIFTING AS SEEING SOMEONE FROM WORK WHEN YOU'RE ON HOLIDAY.

WITH A RED CARD AND MULTIPLE SUBSTITUTIONS, SWITZERLAND ENDED THE GAME WITH ONLY THREE OF THE OUTFIELD PLAYERS WHO STARTED IT, IN A SYSTEM CALLED 'PETKOVIC'S BROOM'.

DENMARK WITHSTOOD A SECOND-HALF ALL-OUT FRENZY ATTACK FROM THE CZECH REPUBLIC TO ADVANCE AND BRING JOY TO THEIR SUPPORTERS, WHO - MORE THAN ANY OTHER GROUP OF FANS AT EURO 2020- LOOK THE MOST LIKE KEYNOTE SPEAKERS AT A SALES CONFERENCE FOR DENTAL EQUIPMENT.

SOME DENMARK FANS WERE PREVENTED FROM DISPLAYING RAINBOW FLAGS IN BAKU, WHICH MAKES YOU WONDER HOW SECURITY STAFF WOULD HAVE REACTED TO A VISIT FROM ENGLAND.

THE DANES FACE THE DAUNTING TASK OF TAKING ON ENGLAND - THE NEUTRALS' FAVOURITES - AT WEMBLEY. IF THE GERMANY GAME WAS ANY INDICATION, MOST OF THE HOME CROWD WILL HAVE APPEARED ON LIVE AT THE APOLLO. BACKED BY A WALL OF NOISE CREATED BY OBSERVATIONAL COMEDY, KLOPPELGÄNGERS, AND THAT PARPING BRASS BAND, GARETH SOUTHGATE WILL BE CONFIDENT OF SUCCESS.

THE COLD, CRUEL REALITIES OF LIFE.

YOUR HOPES, DREAMS, ASPIRATIONS.

AH WELL, THE FIRST TWENTY MINUTES WERE GOOD, EH? BUT DISAPPOINTED ENGLAND FANS NEED NOT CLIMB DOWN FROM THEIR BUS SHELTER ROOFS JUST YET, BECAUSE THERE ARE STILL PLENTY OF REASONS TO BE CHEERFUL...

EURO 202? WAS A GREAT TOURNAMENT. IT CAPTURED THE IMAGINATIONS OF PEOPLE WHO'D NEVER PREVIOUSLY EXPRESSED AN INTEREST IN FOOTBALL, BE THEY RELATIVES IN THE GROUP CHAT EXTOLLING THE VIRTUES OF A THREE, JERRY MAGUIRE, OR BANDWAGON-CLAMBERING POLITICIANS WHO WEEKS EARLIER HAD CONDONED THE RACIST BOOING OF THE ENGLAND PLAYERS.

I'm not a fan of gesture politics.

THE VILE, DISMALLY PREDICTABLE RACIST ABUSE DIRECTED AT ENGLAND'S BLACK PLAYERS IN THE AFTERMATH OF DEFEAT IN THE FINAL LED TO A DISPLAY OF BACK-PEDALING NOT SEEN SINCE PATRIK SCHICK SPOTTED DAVID MARSHALL OFF HIS LINE.

TRYING TO CONDEMN RACISM.

THE INEVITABLE CONSEQUENCES OF DRAGGING FOOTBALLERS INTO YOUR STUPID CULTURE WAR.

IF ONLY THE RACISTS AND THEIR ENABLERS HAD A SHRED OF THE HUMANITY, INTELLIGENCE AND TALENT OF THE ENGLAND PLAYERS WHO SPENT THE LAST MONTH CREATING LIFELONG MEMORIES FOR US ALL. THE DIZZYING BRILLIANCE OF STERLING, THE LEADERSHIP OF KANE, THE RELENTLESS TWISTING ENERGY OF PHILLIPS, THE GALLOPING RICE. PICKFORD'S SAVE FROM JORGINHO. GREALISH'S MESMERIC PINS. MOUNT DONATING HIS SHIRT. ALL OF THEM DONATING THEIR FEES. FODEN'S HAIR TRIBUTE TO CHRISTOPHER BIGGINS. SHAW BREAKING JOSÉ'S BRAIN. WALKER'S CHARGING RUNS. MAGUIRE'S PENALTY. THAT DEFENCE - TO THINK WE (I) DOUBTED THAT DEFENCE. AND SAKA, BEAUTIFUL, BRAVE SAKA - THE BREAKOUT STAR AND A KID WITH SO MUCH POSITIVE ENERGY THAT INFLATABLE VERSIONS OF HIM COULD BE USED TO CHEER UP UNICORNS.

AND THEN THERE'S GARETH SOUTHGATE, THE MAN WHO CHANGED THE CULTURE OF THE TEAM AND LED ENGLAND TO THEIR FIRST MAJOR MEN'S FINAL SINCE YOU-KNOW-WHEN. HIS ACHIEVEMENTS ARE AN EXAMPLE TO YOUNG SAKA THAT YOUR FUTURE ISN'T DEFINED BY ONE PENALTY. AFTER ALL HE'S DONE, SOUTHGATE CAN BE FORGIVEN FOR REACTING TO THE SHOCK OF SCORING SO EARLY IN A STYLE REMINISCENT OF PREVIOUS REGIMES...

Do you think we should change it, Gareth?

One moment, Dutch, Lembit Öpik's trying to FaceTime me.

Lembo!

TYPICALLY, SOME INGERLUND FANS REACTED TO DEFEAT WITH A STIFF UPPER LIP, MAKING IT EASIER TO VACUUM UP BAGS OF CLASS A DRUGS OR BRAY FROM ATOP A PHONE BOX. DON'T IT MAKE YOU PROUD? * SNIIIIIFFFFFF * VIOLENT DISORDER WAS NOT LIMITED TO WEMBLEY ON A NERVOUS NIGHT FOR PROPRIETORS OF PIZZA RESTAURANTS OR OWNERS OF FOREIGN CARS / ACCENTS. NO WONDER FOOTBALL DECIDED TO CLEAR OFF TO ITALY.

Nope.

♪ Hey Mambo! Mambo Italiano... ♪

OH YEAH, ITALY WERE IN THE FINAL TOO. THEY WERE WORTHY WINNERS, HAVING BEEN THE BEST TEAM AT THE TOURNAMENT AND REMAINING UNBEATEN SINCE THE DAYS MANCINI AND VIALLI WERE ZIPPING ROUND THE STREETS OF GENOA ON A VESPA, THE WARM AIR RUSHING THROUGH THEIR LUSTROUS HAIR. ITALY HAVE BEEN A JOY TO BEHOLD RIGHT FROM THE MOMENT THEIR SQUAD WAS ANNOUNCED ON A LIGHT ENTERTAINMENT TV SHOW. THEY EVEN LET THE HOST JOIN THEM ON THE TRIP, IT SEEMS.

Nice Geri Halliwell linguini highlight you got there. Be a shame if it got gunged...!

G...?

OK, you can come with us. Jesus!

FOR ENGLAND, THE WAIT CONTINUES, BUT THE FUTURE LOOKS BRIGHT. UNTIL THE FINAL HURDLE, THEIR YOUNG SQUAD SEEMED UNBURDENED BY THE FAILURES OF PREVIOUS GENERATIONS. THERE'S STILL TIME FOR THEM TO REWRITE THE NARRATIVE, AND WHEN ENGLAND NEXT REACH A MAJOR FINAL (ROLL ON 2076!) MAYBE OPPOSITION TEAMS WILL BE RILED BY SONGS ABOUT THIS BITTERSWEET EURO SUMMER.

Two balls on the grass, laser pen still beaming. Smoke bomb up the arse, Leicester Square needs cleaning...

GAH!

BADDIEL

SKINNER

2021–22:
BAD EGGS AND WEST HAM

You think you've seen it all in football, and then a West Ham player films himself abusing a cat. Kurt Zouma's Cruyff turn of animal cruelty was just one story in a wildly unpredictable season that saw football touched by war, geopolitical power plays and Watford sacking their manager(s)!

The big news at the start of the season was the return of Cristiano Ronaldo to Ole Gunnar Solskjær's animatronic museum of nostalgia at Old Trafford. Much like Zouma's cat, Solskjær was eventually rehoused so that no one could hurt him any more and replaced, on an interim basis, by future safe *Pointless* answer Ralf Rangnick.

As with Alexis Sánchez before him, Ronaldo had been on the verge of joining Manchester City until United's late intervention, leaving you wondering just how often they'd fall for that one. When CR7 to City looked like a Done Deal, some United fans reacted in the now-customary way: filming themselves destroying their own belongings – in this case, their Ronnie merch.

It was a trend that continued later in the season, when one Chelsea fan filmed himself stomping on his Wi-Fi router after rumours began circulating that Three were about to cancel their shirt sponsorship as a result of Roman Abramovich and the other oligarchs having their assets frozen once Vladimir Putin began raining bombs down upon the civilian population of Ukraine.

Ronaldo v.2 started with two goals against Newcastle, slapping them down like they were a fourteen-year-old child's phone, but the Magpies' fortunes were about to change. Once the Premier League had received 'legally binding assurances' that there were no links between their prospective new owners, the Saudi Public Investment Fund, and the state of Saudi Arabia, the famous old club was free to become the latest vessel through which an oppressive kleptocracy could wield power and influence. Ha'way the lads! Like blood swirling down the drain in an interrogation room, information about how the deal transpired came in slow drips. There were allegations of political pressure, but the marmalade-smeared fingerprints of Boris Johnson were a cast-iron guarantee of unimpeachable rectitude. As with Manchester City, critics of the takeover were jealous fools, guilty of elitism against underdog clubs now owned by princes and high-ranking officials of the world's richest states. If the Saudis had chosen another club, Newcastle fans would doubtless have congratulated them warmly and vowed never to do any jokes about it.

In fairness, the way English football has structured itself means fans have little control over who buys their clubs. All you can do is campaign for months for the takeover to happen, then act as a credulous mouthpiece for the new owner, dressing up like them, singing their name and slating their critics online. As a fan of a club in the doldrums, I also dream of a financial saviour, preferably in the form of a football illustrator who becomes a billionaire off the back of sales of a book containing a collection of cartoons that people had already read in the newspaper.

While Chelsea's mid-season change of circumstances provided a timely cautionary tale about the source of your sugar daddy's wealth, there was happier news for one of their former club legends up at Everton. Rafa Benítez secured 19 points in the first six months of the season, which would prove invaluable in the club's relegation battle. Frank Lampard took over in mid-January, and by the end of the season Everton's grasp on their Premier League status was as firm as Lampard's on his hairline. Their safety was secured with an emotional win against Crystal Palace, which led to a spontaneous pitch invasion, the highlight of which was Palace boss Patrick Vieira swinging his telescopic legs at piss-taking fans. It was a narrow escape for the Toffees, and everyone vowed that they should never be allowed to be in this position again for at least another twelve months.

A few weeks earlier, a Just Stop Oil protester had fastened his neck to a goalpost with a zip tie, prompting a member of the Goodison Park ground staff with Ken Dodd teeth to use a pair of comically oversized bolt cutters to set him free. (Honestly, this whole book could have been about Everton.)

Watford burned through some more managers. Xisco was fired before I had a chance to reference all the lyrics of 'Thong Song' – ooh, that mess was scandalous. His replacement, 2016's Claudio Ranieri, didn't even last four months before Roy Hodgson was coaxed out of retirement for one last job. Their relegation was confirmed with a defeat at Crystal Palace, a distraught Hodgson waving and smiling to the Selhurst Park crowd from behind his sunglasses, cleverly hiding his disappointment by doing a passable impression of someone who could not give one solitary shit.

Manchester City again pipped Liverpool to the title on the final day, even if they had trailed Aston Villa 2–0 at one point, providing a brief reminder of a time when they knew how to have a laugh.

THE EFL RETURNS THIS WEEKEND, AND AS IF TO UNDERLINE THE STRATOSPHERIC GULF BETWEEN THE PREMIER LEAGUE ELITE AND THE FOOTBALL LEAGUE UNDERWORLD, WHILE ONE SUPERSTAR TAKES THE NUCLEAR OPTION TO TRY AND FORCE A TRANSFER...

...HUNDREDS OF OUT-OF-CONTRACT FOOTBALLERS ARE JUMPING AT ANY OPPORTUNITY TO PROVE THEIR WORTH.

Barrow's mascot's done its glutes?

I'm on my way.

SOME EFL PLAYERS ENJOYED MORE EXCITING SUMMERS, THOUGH. NONE MORE SO THAN BLACKBURN'S BEN BRERETON, WHO BECAME A HUGE STAR IN CHILE THANKS TO HIS PERFORMANCES AT THE COPA AMÉRICA

FRANKLY, IT COULDN'T HAVE BEEN MORE SURPRISING IF IT TURNED OUT THAT TONY MOWBRAY'S COMEDY STYLINGS MADE HIM A HUGE STAR OVERSEAS TOO.

AFTER A LONG, ENFORCED ABSENCE, THE WEEKEND PRESENTS A CHANCE FOR MANY FANS TO RETURN TO THEIR SECOND HOMES, WITH ALL ITS IDIOSYNCRATIC, MISMATCHING SECTIONS OF ARCHITECTURE THAT WOULD SET YOUR TEETH ON EDGE IN ANY OTHER SETTING. MOST OF ALL, IT'S AN OPPORTUNITY TO ONCE AGAIN JOIN IN A SHARED EXPERIENCE THAT UNITES A BROAD SECTION OF SOCIETY, INCLUDING SOME OF ITS MOST ECCENTRIC CHARACTERS...

Ee-ar, darlin'.

Right, who else wants one? You two, get here!

Um...

NO MATTER THE STATE OF YOUR CLUB, CHERISH THESE LAST FEW DAYS BEFORE THE SEASON STARTS, AND THE PRECIOUS OPPORTUNITIES THEY OFFER TO DREAM, DREAM, DREAM...

Wayne, having won the Championship with Derby, we want you to become player-manager at Manchester United. We don't even mind if you continue as England manager and we're happy to work around your modelling commitments. Just name your price, son.

I'll do it, old timer; but on one condition: I'm allowed to pick my own backroom staff.

Ta for picking me up, Wayne.

No problem, Rio pal.... Hang on... is that...?

WHITNEY! I can't believe it. I wanna run to u. @

You're the world's greatest pianist. Won't you play for me, Wazza, Wazza, Wazza....

WAZZA!

Huh?!

I'll put you to sleep!

You were sleep walking and you absolutely nailed our best young midfielder!

Oh no, I believe the children are the future as well. What are we gonna do now?

Don't worry. I've got an idea.

The famous Derby County, you say?!

TRIALIST ?

Absolutely not.

A RIDICULOUS TRANSFER WINDOW DRAWS TO A CLOSE WITH THE NEWS DOMINATED BY CRISTIANO RONALDO'S RETURN TO MANCHESTER UNITED! THE DEEP SPIRITUAL CONNECTION HE FEELS TOWARDS THE CLUB TRANSCENDS THE TRIVIALITY OF HIS £500K-A-WEEK SALARY. I CAN'T BELIEVE YOU'D BE SO VULGAR TO EVEN BRING IT UP. HONESTLY.

SOME KILLJOYS HAVE QUESTIONED WHETHER UNITED ACTUALLY NEED AN AGEING STRIKER WITH LESS MOBILITY THAN THE TRAFFORD CENTRE, BUT THINK OF **THE SHIRT SALES!** THEY'RE GUARANTEED TO SELL AT LEAST ONE...

AND **HIS** ARRIVAL PROVIDES UNITED'S YOUNG PLAYERS WITH A CHANCE TO LEARN FROM A GENUINE FOOTBALL LEGEND.

THERE'S ALWAYS THE OLD MAXIM THAT YOU SHOULD NEVER GO BACK, ALTHOUGH SOME PLAYERS ARE ABLE TO AVOID THIS PITFALL BY NEVER LEAVING IN THE FIRST PLACE.

BIG RONNIE'S TRANSFER COMES HOT ON THE HEELS OF LIONEL MESSI'S MOVE TO PSG, WHICH MAY BE AS CLOSE AS 'CR7' GETS TO A PRESSING RUN ALL SEASON. IT'S WIDELY ACCEPTED THAT PSG HAVE **MONSTERED** THE TRANSFER WINDOW, THE ABSOLUTE **LADS**, WITH MESSI JOINING DONNARUMMA, WIJNALDUM AND RAMOS AS THE LATEST BIG STAR TO SIGN FOR **FREE** (ASTERISK SIZE TO SCALE:)

MESSI   EIFFEL TOWER   ASTERISK

PSG ANNOUNCED HIS ARRIVAL WITH A SWOOPING DRONE SHOT OF THE PARC DES PRINCES THAT SUBTLY LINGERED IN THE GIFT SHOP, ALLOWING US TO MARVEL AT THEIR RANGE OF MESSI MOUSE MATS AND KEY FOBS. IT'S A PITY THEY DIDN'T FOLLOW THE EXAMPLE OF BESIKTAS, WHOSE UNVEILING OF PERMA-LOANEE MICHY BATSHUAYI INVOLVED DRESSING HIM UP LIKE A FATHERS 4 JUSTICE PROTESTER.

MESSI MADE HIS PSG DEBUT ON SUNDAY AND WAS GIVEN AN IMMEDIATE TASTE OF THE KIND OF ROUGHHOUSING HE CAN EXPECT IN LIGUE 1 AS THE REIMS GOALKEEPER ASKED FOR A PHOTO OF HIM WITH HIS SON, MAKING YOU WISH THEY'D SIGNED ROY KEANE INSTEAD (THAT KID WOULD STILL BE AIRBORNE). THE GAME WAS SETTLED BY A DOUBLE FROM KYLIAN MBAPPÉ, HIMSELF THE SUBJECT OF A HUGE TRANSFER BID FROM REAL MADRID, WHICH WAS SURPRISING TO ANYONE WHO COULD REMEMBER AS FAR BACK AS F✱✱✱ING APRIL...

HOWEVER, IT HAS SINCE EMERGED THAT IT WAS ALL A SMOKESCREEN CREATED BY THE 4D CHESS MASTER FLORENTINO PÉREZ TO CAPTURE THE PSG TARGET EDUARDO CAMAVINGA!

ONE STORY DOMINATED THE LAST ROUND OF PREMIER LEAGUE MATCHES - THE RETURN TO OLD TRAFFORD OF A GENUINE MANCHESTER UNITED LEGEND:

SIIIIIIIIIIGH!!

SO ADORED IS STEVE BRUCE IN NEWCASTLE THAT EVERY PLAYER WEARS THE NUMBER FOUR ON THE FRONT OF THEIR SHIRT IN REFERENCE TO HIS PLAYING CAREER.

IS THIS FUN?? IS THIS FUN??

...AND THERE WOULD BE NO TEAM MORE LIKELY TO SPOIL THE SECOND COMING OF CRISTIANO THAN BRUCE'S *WOR* SHINGTON GENERALS. BRUCE WOULD HAVE BEEN CONFIDENT AS HE SENT HIS LADS OUT TO BE SACRIFICED IN THE GLADIATORIAL ARENA, BUT...

There were lots of positives to take from the slaughter and we were right in it until they released the armoured leopards.

Bloody hell, what happened to him?

Nothing, boss; it's Allan Saint-Maximin.

Where you hiding all the strapping, big guy?

NEWCASTLE WERE ABLE TO SCORE, HOWEVER, WHEN MIGUEL ALMIRÓN DARTED THROUGH A DEFENSIVE-MIDFIELDER-SHAPED HOLE TO SET UP JAVIER MANQUILLO. BUT WITH TWO GOALS TO HIS NAME, THIS WAS RONALDO'S DAY AND NOTHING COULD DISTRACT FROM THE MOOD OF CELEBRATION. NOT THE CLUB SHOP RUNNING OUT OF NUMBER SEVENS; NOT TWO FURTHER STRIKES FROM HIS UPSTART BACKING SINGERS; APPARENTLY NOT EVEN...

Ooh look, an aeroplane!

THIS IS THE FIRST TIME RONALDO'S BEEN COACHED BY ONE OF HIS FORMER TEAMMATES, WHICH WILL UNDOUBTEDLY ADD AN EXTRA LAYER OF RESPECT TO HIS WORKING RELATIONSHIP WITH SOLSKJÆR.

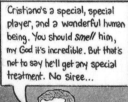

Cristiano's a special, special player, and a wonderful human being. You should *smell* him, my God it's incredible. But that's not to say he'll get any special treatment. No siree...

SOLSKJÆR! Stop your incessant blethering and get back to work.

And get right in there with the digging stick this time. Them old footballer toes are banged up good.

I can't believe I get to do this for free!

SUDDENLY THOSE FAN PROTESTS CALLING FOR GENUINE CHANGE SEEM LIKE A DISTANT MEMORY. AVRAM GLAZER WAS EVEN PRESENT AT OLD TRAFFORD ON SATURDAY, LIKE AN ABSENTEE PARENT WHO TURNS UP EVERY FEW YEARS WITH SOME EXPENSIVE GIFTS.

Wow, a Ronaldo! And a Varane! A Sancho too! Oh, batteries not included. Still, a Varane and a RONALDO!

See you in 2026, kid.

Off on another "space mission"?

Sure.

BUT RONALDO'S ARRIVAL IS A GIFT NOT ONLY TO MANCHESTER UNITED BUT ENGLISH FOOTBALL AS A WHOLE, AS IT ALLOWS EVERYONE TO PARTICIPATE IN THE ONLINE WAR BETWEEN YOUR RONFAN3000s AND YOUR MESSIGOATLORD32142019s (SEE YOU IN THE REPLIES, LADS), A BATTLE THAT WILL LAST UNTIL THE END OF TIME.

CR7's Insta-stories are the pinnacle of human achievement.

How many Copa Américas has Fraudnaldo won?

WHICH IS SILLY, BECAUSE WE ALL KNOW WHO THE GREATEST PLAYER IN THE WORLD IS...

Dwmn stwwt.

A SAD FEATURE OF MODERN FOOTBALL IS PLAYERS ISSUING SELF-FLAGELLATING APOLOGIES FOR HONEST MISTAKES, IN THE FUTILE HOPE OF PACIFYING THE MORE RABID CORNERS OF THE INTERNET"🏷️. ONE SUCH EXAMPLE CAME AT THE WEEKEND, WHEN BRUNO FERNANDES LAUNCHED A LATE PENALTY INTO ORBIT, CONDEMNING MANCHESTER UNITED TO A HOME DEFEAT TO ASTON VILLA. IN THE AFTERMATH, HE ISSUED A LENGTHY STATEMENT IN WHITE TEXT ON A BLACK BACKROUND, TO REFLECT THE GRAVITY OF THE SITUATION...

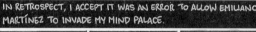

IN RETROSPECT, I ACCEPT IT WAS AN ERROR TO ALLOW EMILIANO MARTÍNEZ TO INVADE MY MIND PALACE.

SURE, THE DEFEAT WAS UNITED'S THIRD IN THE LAST FOUR MATCHES, BUT FANS CAN TAKE SOLACE IN THE KNOWLEDGE THAT OLE'S AT THE WHEEL. NO, REALLY, THERE'S A HGV DRIVER SHORTAGE.

INCIDENTALLY, IT'S YET TO BE SEEN WHAT IMPACT THE FUEL CRISIS WILL HAVE ON FOOTBALL. THE GOVERNMENT IS APPARENTLY CONSIDERING SENDING IN THE ARMY, WHICH MAY HAVE PARTICULAR CONSEQUENCES FOR BRIGHTON, SINCE GRAHAM POTTER'S NEW BEARD MAKES HIM LOOK LIKE AN ACTION MAN DOLL (COASTAL TOWN SPECIAL OPS EDITION).

SO UNITED LOST, BUT IT COULD BE WORSE, THEY COULD BE NORWICH, TRAPPED IN A STATE OF PURGATORY BETWEEN THE CHAMPIONSHIP AND THE PREMIER LEAGUE. THEY EVEN TRIED TO BREAK THE CYCLE AT EVERTON BY DISGUISING THEMSELVES IN A KIT THE COLOUR OF DELIA'S ROASTED SALMON FILLETS WITH CRUSTED PECORINO AND PESTO TOPPING. HOWEVER, THERE'S NO ESCAPING THE FOOTBALL JUSTICE OF DETECTIVE RAFAEL BENÍTEZ.

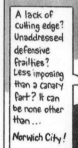

FORM IS FLEETING, THOUGH. JUST A FEW WEEKS AGO, ARSENAL WERE THE PREMIER LEAGUE'S DISASTER CLUB, BUT THEIR 3-1 WIN IN THE NORTH LONDON DERBY SAW THEM LEAPFROG TOTTENHAM AND DRAW LEVEL ON POINTS WITH BRENTFORD! MIKEL ARTETA IS SUDDENLY PUFFED UP AND DREAMING OF A GILDED FUTURE.

AS FOR SPURS, NUNO ADMITTED HE'D PICKED THE WRONG SIDE FOR THE FIRST HALF AGAINST ARSENAL. WITH FANS BECOMING RESTLESS HE MAY NEED TO EMPLOY THE ULTIMATE RECOURSE: TIME TO FIRE UP THAT NOTES APP!

SQUAD GAME

A GROUP OF DESPERATE PEOPLE GATHER AT A SECRET HERTFORDSHIRE LOCATION TO COMPETE FOR THE ULTIMATE PRIZE: THE LIMITLESS WEALTH THAT COMES WITH MANAGING WATFORD FC FOR A FEW MONTHS!

THE RULES OF THE GAME ARE SIMPLE. A GIANT ANIMATRONIC GINO POZZO SINGS...

RED AWAY KIT, GREEN THIRD KIT!

AND THE CONTESTANTS HAVE THE LENGTH OF THE PHRASE TO MOVE FORWARD AND STOP BEFORE POZZO TURNS HIS HEAD AND NOTICES WATFORD AREN'T IN THE CHAMPIONS LEAGUE SPOTS. THOSE WHO DON'T FREEZE ARE FIRED. WHO WILL MAKE IT TO THE END?!

Right, let's not mess about here. It's time to abandon my famed fancy footwork and charge headlong towards the big robot bas-

SEAN DYCHE ELIMINATED.

♫ RED AWAY KIT GREEN THIRD KIT ♪

GIANFRANCO ZOLA ELIMINATED.

They fired him! In broad daylight! That's brutal. I'm out of here, who's with me? Sannino? Garcia? Jokanovic?

Yeah, yeah.

BILLY McKINLAY ELIMINATED.

QUIQUE SÁNCHEZ FLORES MUTUALED.

WALTER MAZZARRI ELIMINATED.

YESSS!

WATFORD
GOOD BYE, GOOD BYE MAZZARRI
DON'T GET OFF THE COACH
OUT YES OUT YES OUT
YES NOW
GOOD BYE WE DON'T WANT YOU
GOOD BYE
WATFORD

Excuse me, I think there's been some sort of a mistake. I'm supposed to be at Everton you see...

Yeah, and I was this close to winning Watford an FA Cup...

MARCO SILVA ELIMINATED.

JAVI GRACIA ELIMINATED.

QUIQUE, YOU CAME BACK!

Heh, yeah. They say you should never go back, but I got this card and I thought why not –

WFC

QUIQUE SÁNCHEZ FLORES ELIMINATED.

Mr Pozzo, Nigel Pearson. Listen, it's time for a frank exchange about the way you're running this game.

Cool, sounds good. Let me just grab a cup of ELIMINATED.

AND VLADIMIR IVIC? I DON'T EVEN REMEMBER INVITING YOU. YOU'RE SO ELIMINATED.

Xisco is the last one standing! I win! Let me see that Won!

♫ RED A

Dilly ding, dilly wrong.

Old man?!

THIR KIT ♫

XISCO MUÑOZ ELIMINATED.

CR

CONGRATULATIONS, CLAUDIO RANIERI. YOU ARE THE WINNER. SEE YOU AGAIN FOR THE NEXT ROUND DURING THE NOVEMBER INTERNATIONAL BREAK.

Yipee! Wait, what?

SQUIRES

SPORTS WOR-SHING

NEWCASTLE UNITED HAVE BEEN FLOGGED - SORRY, SOLD - TO THE PUBLIC INVESTMENT FUND OF SAUDI ARABIA! WHO CARES ABOUT FOOTBALL CLUBS BEING USED AS MARKETING VESSELS FOR MURDEROUS REGIMES WHEN TRANSFER GOSSIP IS AFOOT? BESIDES, THE PREMIER LEAGUE HAS LEGAL ASSURANCES THAT THE PIF IS COMPLETELY UNCONNECTED TO THE STATE, AND GOOD LUCK FINDING A LAWYER IN SAUDI ARABIA WILLING TO CONTRADICT MOHAMMED BIN SALMAN HAHA HA...

ONCE THOSE PIRACY ISSUES WERE RESOLVED, ALL MORAL OBJECTIONS TO THE DEAL WERE REMOVED. NEWCASTLE FANS MET THE NEWS WITH GLEE, AS WOULD FANS OF MOST OTHER CLUBS. REMEMBER, THEY DIDN'T ASK FOR THIS, APART FROM ALL THE ONES WHO'VE SPENT THE LAST 18 MONTHS ASKING FOR EXACTLY THIS. THEY'VE GOT THEIR CLUB BACK (80% OWNED BY AN AUTOCRACY THAT ROUTINELY HOLDS PUBLIC BEHEADINGS) SO IT'S UNDERSTANDABLE THAT SOME FANS WOULD DON MBS MASKS AND ROLL OUT THE RED CARPET.

OTHER FANS TOOK THINGS A STEP FURTHER, WAVING THE SAUDI FLAG AND BERATING THE GRIEVING FIANCEE OF JAMAL KHASHOGGI WHOSE CRITICISM OF THE DEAL WAS CLEARLY MOTIVATED BY JEALOUSY THAT NEWCASTLE MIGHT GET FRANKY FRANK LAMPARD AS THEIR NEXT MANAGER. LIFE WAS SIMPLER WHEN FOOTBALL CLUBS WERE RUN AS VANITY PROJECTS BY WEALTHY INDUSTRIALISTS WHO GOT RICH EXPLOITING THE LABOUR OF LOW PAID WORKERS, BUT THAT WAS LAST WEEK...

MAYBE THE NEW OWNERS CAN RETURN THE CLUB TO ITS RIGHTFUL POSITION (14TH), BUT THE NATURE OF THIS FAUSTIAN PACT MEANS THAT, LIKE MANCHESTER CITY AND PSG BEFORE THEM, ANY SUCCESS NEWCASTLE ACHIEVE WILL COME WITH A FILTHY GREAT ASTERISK. CRITICISM OF THE TAKEOVER HAS LED SOME PEOPLE TO PERFORM THE KIND OF MENTAL GYMNASTICS THAT WOULD MAKE FAUSTINO ASPRILLA PROUD.

IT'S UNCLEAR WHAT LEVEL OF INVOLVEMENT THE UK GOVERNMENT HAD IN THE DEAL, AS IT'S REFUSING TO REVEAL WHAT THE FOREIGN OFFICE TOLD THE PREMIER LEAGUE IN A MEETING ABOUT THE PROPOSED TAKEOVER FOR FEAR OF HARMING RELATIONS WITH ONE OF THE FEW STATES WITH WHICH IT STILL HOPES TO HAVE A TRADE DEAL. THE MEETING MINUTES, ACQUIRED BY THE BBC, WERE SO REDACTED THEY COULD FORM THE PATTERN ON NEWCASTLE'S NEXT HOME SHIRT.

THE OTHER PREMIER LEAGUE CLUBS ARE UNHAPPY ABOUT THE SALE, WHICH IS ABOUT AS BLOODY RICH AS A THOUSAND SAUDI PRINCES, BUT ELITE-LEVEL FOOTBALL SOLD ITS SOUL LONG AGO. IT'S NOW DISTANTLY REMOVED FROM THE GAME THAT PROVIDED PEOPLE WITH A SENSE OF IDENTITY AND A CONNECTION TO THEIR LOCAL COMMUNITY; THE BEAUTIFUL, GLOBAL GAME WE ALL FELL IN LOVE WITH THAT YOU COULD PLAY ANYWHERE AND FORGET ALL YOUR TROUBLES...

REPULSED BY THE MORAL CESSPIT OF TOP-FLIGHT ENGLISH FOOTBALL BUT ARE TOO FAR INVESTED TO PACK IT IN NOW? MADE A SORT-OF-CAREER OF COVERING IT AND ARE CONSEQUENTLY UNEMPLOYABLE IN ANY OTHER PROFESSION? OH, I HEAR YOU BUDDY. EVEN LOVELY OLD CLAUDIO RANIERI MAY HAVE BEEN RUEING SOME OF HIS LIFE CHOICES AS HE WATCHED LIVERPOOL HAND OUT A 5-0 DRUBBING TO HIS NEW CLUB, WATFORD.

THE GAME PRODUCED MOMENTS OF EXQUISITE SKILL AND JOYOUS CALAMITY THAT SERVED AS A REMINDER FOR WHY WE'RE ALL HOPELESSLY ADDICTED TO THIS STUPID, WONDERFUL, IMMORAL SPORT. TAKE, FOR EXAMPLE, THE SIMPLE BEAUTY OF MOHAMED SALAH SETTING UP SADIO MANÉ WITH AN INCH-PERFECT PASS THAT FOLLOWED THE EXACT TRAJECTORY OF THE SENEGALESE STRIKER'S BLONDE STREAK.

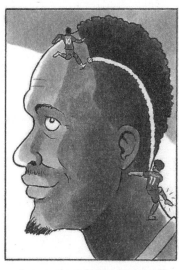

THERE WERE SOME THRILLING MATCHES ELSEWHERE TOO: WOLVES' LATE COMEBACK AT ASTON VILLA, SEALED BY A RÚBEN NEVES FREE-KICK THAT WAS OFF-TARGET UNTIL IT WENT IN OFF TARGETT; AND LEICESTER'S NOISY 4-2 WIN AGAINST MANCHESTER UNITED. THEIR UNBEATEN AWAY RUN MAY BE OVER, BUT OLE'S JOB IS SAFE SO LONG AS THE RONALDO MERCH KEEPS FLYING OUT THE DOOR OF THE UNITED MEGASTORE.

OH FOR THE JOB SECURITY OF STEVE BRUCE. IT SEEMED CERTAIN HE'D BE SACKED BY NEWCASTLE BEFORE HE MANAGED HIS THOUSANDTH PROFESSIONAL GAME, BUT SOMETHING IN THE WAY HE HOPED SOME JOURNALISTS GOT SLAPPED MUST HAVE IMPRESSED THE NEW OVERLORDS, AND SO HIS ROLLING CONTRACT GROUNDHOG DAY EXISTENCE CONTINUES.

BRUCE WAS IN THE DUGOUT FOR NEWCASTLE'S FIRST MATCH UNDER THE EYE OF THE NEW REGIME. BLESSED DAY! SOME FANS TOOK THIS AS AN EXCUSE TO RAID THE TEA TOWEL DRAWER AND CREATE A GHOULISH NATIVITY SCENE - A CHAOTIC JONJO SHELVEY CAMEO ADDING TO THE SCHOOL PLAY AESTHETIC. BUT IF YOU THOUGHT THE BROADCASTER WHO'D PAID GAZILLIONS FOR THE TV RIGHTS WOULD PROVIDE AN UNCRITICAL ANALYSIS OF PROCEEDINGS THEN YOU HADN'T ACCOUNTED FOR THE FORENSIC INTERVIEW SKILLS OF JAMIE REDKNAPP. POOR OLD JAMIE REUBEN DIDN'T KNOW WHAT HIT HIM!

BUT ALL THE BLOOD MONEY IN THE WORLD MIGHT NOT BE ENOUGH TO SAVE NEWCASTLE'S SEASON; A REALISATION THAT MAY HAVE DAWNED UPON HIS MOST WISE AND BEAUTEOUS EXCELLENCY AS THEY SLUMPED TO A 3-2 DEFEAT.

HOWEVER, THE FINAL WORD THIS WEEK GOES TO DR TOM PRICHARD AND THE MEDICAL STAFF WHO HELPED SAVE THE LIFE OF A STRICKEN FAN IN THE EAST STAND. THEY ARE THE VERY DEFINITION OF 'LOCAL HEROES'.

THEIR SWIFT ACTIONS PROVIDED THE FAN WITH THE ONLY REWARD ANY OF US NEED: THE GIFT OF ANOTHER DAY.

ARE YOU NOT ENTERTAINED?
SOLSKJÆR'S SHOWMEN STRIKE AGAIN!

GRANTED, *THE COMEBACK KINGS* ARE LEAVING IT LATE IF THEY'RE GOING TO REEL IN LIVERPOOL'S FIVE-GOAL LEAD. BY THE TIME MOHAMED SALAH COMPLETED HIS HAT-TRICK, MANY MANCHESTER UNITED FANS WERE ALREADY BREAKING OUT OF OLD TRAFFORD IN A REVERSAL OF THE ANTI-GLAZER PROTESTS THAT SAW THE FIXTURE POSTPONED LAST SEASON. IT WAS A SCENE WORTHY OF ONE OF STRETFORD'S MOST FAMOUS ARTISTS.

LS Lowry - 'Binning off the match after 50 minutes' (2021)

OLE'S NOSTALGIA PROJECT MAY BE FAITHFULLY REENACTING THE BARREN EARLY YEARS OF SURALEX'S REIGN, BUT THERE'S APPARENTLY A GROWING FEELING FROM WITHIN THE UNITED DRESSING ROOM THAT HE MAY NOT BE UP TO THE JOB. MUCH AS THEY WERE AGAINST LIVERPOOL, THE PLAYERS ARE MERE BYSTANDERS. AT LEAST LUKE SHAW ADMITTED THEY NEED TO LOOK IN THE MIRROR (WHICH WILL COME MORE NATURALLY TO SOME THAN OTHERS); ON SUNDAY THEY PLAYED LIKE THEY WERE IN A HALL OF THEM.

IT CAN'T BE EASY TO MANAGE AN ILL-FITTING GROUP OF SUPERSTARS, BUT SOLSKJÆR HAS DONE SO WITH THE CONFIDENT ENERGY OF AN OUT-OF-HIS-DEPTH SUPPLY TEACHER.

...AND THE DEFEAT WASN'T NEARLY THE WORST ACT A FORMER UNITED LEGEND HAS BEEN RESPONSIBLE FOR OF LATE.

SOLSKJÆR WASN'T THE ONLY MANAGER TO SUFFER A HUMILIATING DEFEAT AT THE WEEKEND. NORWICH CONCEDED SEVEN (SEVEN) AT CHELSEA. AND IT'S HARD TO IMAGINE A MORE NIGHTMARISH TRIP TO LONDON FOR DANIEL FARKE.

BUMPS IN TO SOMEONE FROM BACK HOME.

Farkeface! What are you doing here? Hilarious!

Sigh–

FLEECED £12 FOR A BAGUETTE

No filling. This is what you have to accept when you come here.

TIM KRUL SAVES A PENALTY!

The season starts here!

HE MOVED OFF HIS LINE BEFORE IT WAS KICKED. MASON MOUNT CONVERTS THE RE-TAKE.

Fine. Fine.

TRAUMATIC TUBE PLATFORM EXPERIENCE

Guys, where's Josh Sargent? Come on, this is why we have the buddy system! Seriously, I sometimes wonder if you're capable of tracking anyone at all.

OK, we must not panic in this moment. Everything is still going according to plan. He must be around here somewhere. You can't exactly miss him.

NEWCASTLE ALSO HAD AN UNCOMFORTABLE TRIP TO THE CAPITAL, WHERE CRYSTAL PALACE FANS HELD UP A BANNER THAT LISTED ALLEGATIONS OF HUMAN RIGHTS ABUSES BY THE SAUDI REGIME. HOPEFULLY THESE KIND OF SCENES AREN'T REPEATED AT EVERY GROUND NEWCASTLE VISIT. ONE MEMBER OF THE PUBLIC WAS SO OFFENDED THAT THEY REPORTED IT TO THE POLICE (**WON'T SOMEBODY THINK OF THE DESPOTS?!**) BUT THEY HAD MORE PRESSING CONCERNS...

This is Richard, a middle-aged football executive who hasn't been heard from since he permitted the takeover of one of the nation's most famous clubs by a brutal autocracy two weeks ago. He'll be dehydrated and confused about the relationship between the Saudi state and its sovereign wealth fund.

MISSING

BUT THE SITUATION AT MANCHESTER UNITED REMAINS THE WEEK'S BIG STORY, WITH STABILITY'S ANTONIO CONTE REPORTEDLY INTERESTED IN HEARING MORE ABOUT THE CLUB'S STRATEGIC PLAN, WHICH AT LEAST SHOULDN'T TAKE LONG.

A doodle of a rabbit on a napkin...?

It's a red devil. Imagine the bean juice is flames.

'Kinnel.

Sod it, if it winds up Ronaldo, I'm in (for 18 months, before an inevitable public falling-out with the board).

TOTTENHAM HOTSPUR HAVE SACKED NUNO ESPÍRITO SANTO, THE BOOS THAT ECHOED AROUND THEIR STADIUM DURING A 3-0 HOME DRUBBING TO MANCHESTER UNITED PROVING TO BE THE LAST STRAW FOR CHAIRMAN DANIEL LEVY.

THE RESULT LED TO AN EMERGENCY INQUEST WITH TOTTENHAM'S DIRECTOR OF INNOCENT BYSTANDING, FABIO PARATICI...

NO ONE CAN SAY NUNO WASN'T GIVEN EVERY CHANCE TO SUCCEED. THE CLUB GAVE HIM THEIR FULL SUPPORT, MAKING IT PUBLIC KNOWLEDGE THAT HE WAS THEIR PREFERRED CANDIDATE AFTER GENNARO GATTUSO AND A POTATO THAT LOOKED LIKE CHRISTIAN GROSS...

... AND THEY EVEN PUT HIM UP IN AN OFFICE BEFITTING HIS STATUS.

THE HAMMERS ARE FLYING HIGH, WITH THEIR STAY IN THE TOP FOUR SURE TO HAVE THE LONGEVITY OF THE VERY BUBBLES THAT FLOAT ACROSS THE LONDON STADIUM. CENTRAL TO THEIR SUPERB RUN HAS BEEN DECLAN RICE, WHOSE COMMANDING PERFORMANCES IN MIDFIELD HAVE TAKEN ON AN ALMOST MYTHIC STATUS, ACCENTUATED BY HIS UPRIGHT, GALLOPING STYLE THAT MAKES HIM LOOK LIKE A CENTAUR.

THEIR LATEST VICTIMS, ASTON VILLA, WERE DESPATCHED 4-1, MEANING THE PRESSURE IS NOW ALSO MOUNTING ON DEAN SMITH AND THE COLLECTION OF WORRIED-LOOKING GENERALS IN KHAKI ANORAKS WHO SCURRY AROUND BEHIND HIM, SCRIBBLING ON CLIPBOARDS AND PRODDING AT TABLETS.

THE STRESSES OF BEING A MANAGER ARE ILLUSTRATED BY THE CONTRASTING FACES OF THOSE RECENTLY RELIEVED OF THEIR DUTIES. CONSIDER THE BEAMING FACE OF STEVE BRUCE, PHOTOGRAPHED ENJOYING THE CRICKET IN A GULF STATE WITH AN APPALLING HUMAN RIGHTS RECORD (YOU CAN TAKE THE BOY OUT OF NEWCASTLE...)

AND YET, FOR REASONS BEST KNOWN TO HIMSELF, ANTONIO CONTE HAS THROWN HIMSELF BACK INTO THE FRAY AT TOTTENHAM, WHO ARE KEEN TO RECAPTURE SOME OF THAT FAMOUS SPURS DNA (HIRING AN EX-CHELSEA BOSS, ONLY TO PAY HIM OFF A FEW MONTHS LATER). THE FUTURE LOOKS BRIGHT AS THE TWO PARTIES REACHED AN UNDERSTANDING OVER THE FUTURE INVESTMENT IN RESOURCES.

PLAYERS RETURNING FROM INTERNATIONAL DUTY THIS WEEK WILL NOTICE A FEW CHANGES. SOME WILL BE COMING BACK TO NEW MANAGERS, OTHERS TO STRICTER DIETARY REQUIREMENTS...

THE WEEK'S BIG NEWS IS THAT **STEVIE G IS BACK IN THE PREMIER LEAGUE** (ALSO, ENGLAND QUALIFIED FOR THE WORLD CUP). GERRARD HAS JOINED ASTON VILLA, A FAMOUS OLD CLUB WITH A PROUD - BUT NOW SADLY IRRELEVANT - HISTORY.

DO YOU REMEMBER THE LAST TIME GERRARD FACED HIS NEW EMPLOYERS? HE WAS IN THE HOME STRAIGHT OF HIS LIVERPOOL FC FAREWELL TOUR IN 2015 AND **THE NARRATIVE** HAD ALREADY DECIDED THAT HE'D LIFT THE FA CUP IN HIS LAST GAME FOR THE CLUB ON HIS BIRTHDAY! HOWEVER, AGAINST ALL ODDS, HE CAME UP AGAINST A TACTICAL GENIUS IN THE SEMI-FINAL.

GERRARD'S COACHING ABILITIES REMAIN SOMETHING OF AN UNKNOWN QUANTITY, BECAUSE FOR THE LAST FEW YEARS HE'S BEEN MANAGING IN A MYSTERIOUS FARAWAY LAND. WE CAN ONLY SPECULATE AS TO WHAT GOES ON BEHIND THE IRN-BRU CURTAIN.

THE NEWS HE'D LEFT RANGERS LEFT THEIR FANS FEELING LOWER THAN GERRARD'S HAIRLINE. SOME TOOK THE NATURAL COURSE OF ACTION: FILMING THEMSELVES DESTROYING THEIR STEVIE-BRANDED POSSESSIONS. AT A TIME WHEN GLASGOW WAS THE FOCUS OF TACKLING AN ENVIRONMENTAL CATASTROPHE, IT'S GRIMLY IRONIC THAT A MOUNTAIN OF DISCARDED SINGLE-USE, LIFE-SIZED GERRARD CUT-OUTS WILL NO DOUBT END UP POLLUTING BRITAIN'S PRISTINE COASTLINE.

GERRARD MOVES INTO AN OFFICE LAST WEEK VACATED BY DEAN SMITH, WHO HAS ALREADY LANDED A NEW GIG WITH HIS CONSIGLIERE CRAIG SHAKESPEARE AT NORWICH.

IT HAD SEEMED LIKELY THAT FRANK LAMPARD WOULD GET THE NORWICH JOB, ALLOWING HIM TO DOVETAIL WITH STEVEN GERRARD IN THE RELEGATION ZONE. HOWEVER, HE ULTIMATELY DECIDED THE ROLE WASN'T FOR HIM, DESPITE NO DOUBT IMPRESSING IN THE INTERVIEW.

MANCHESTER UNITED HAVE MADE AN APPARENTLY SENSIBLE MANAGERIAL APPOINTMENT! THE ARRIVAL OF RALF RANGNICK MAY REPRESENT ANOTHER WILD LURCH IN COACHING PHILOSOPHY, BUT IT AT LEAST SUGGESTS SOMEONE WITH A BIT OF FOOTBALL KNOWLEDGE IS FINALLY CALLING THE SHOTS AT OLD TRAFFORD.

Ralf Rangnick!

≥Sigh≤ Fine, it's your turn to pick, I suppose. Kin' hipsters...

IT'S IMPOSSIBLE TO KNOW WHETHER RANGNICK WILL BE SUCCESSFUL, BUT IN A WAY HE'S ALREADY WON THE MOST COVETED PRIZE OF ALL...

THE SWEET, SWEET HONEY OF A LUCRATIVE CONSULTANCY GIG

CRISTIANO RONALDO BEING RELEGATED TO THE BENCH FOR UNITED'S DRAW AT CHELSEA PERHAPS FORESHADOWS WHAT AWAITS HIM UNDER THE NEW MANAGER FAMED FOR HIS FONDNESS OF THE COUNTER-PRESS.

Rolf...

Ralf

You'll get no arguments from me. I've been counter pressing for years. In fact, I'm completely against it.

Hah! That famous Ronaldo humour! No, of course, we'll be playing a high-intensity gegenpress, sacrificing individual glory for the good of the collective. I hope you like running, because your lungs will burn with the intensity of a thousand suns!

Sure. Right. Gegen. Cool. Cool, cool, cool. Can you just excuse me for one moment? Just need to make a very quick call...

Ronnie in the houuuse! What can I do for my favourite client?

Hi Jorge, quick question...

WHAT THE FU

Heh, he'll be fine once he's had his eighth micro-nap and a chia seed enema.

RONALDO WAS ALSO THE SUBJECT OF A HIGH-PITCHED DEBATE BETWEEN ROY KEANE AND JAMIE CARRAGHER, WHILST FELLOW PUNDIT JIMMY FLOYD HASSELBAINK TOOK THE SENSIBLE OPTION OF RETREATING TO THE RELATIVE PEACE OF HIS HAPPY PLACE.

Argument about winning cups, at a frequency only audible to bats!

Ultrasonic counterpoint that could shatter every window in a 12-mile radius!

RINGING SOUND

Oh, the weather at Turf Moor's frightful...

But Sean Dyche finds it delightful...

S'only a bit of bloody snow...

Power hose, power hose, power hose

Dyche

Sean Dyche shows no sign of stoppin'. Conte's agent's for a choppin'. Floodlights are turned way down lowwww, Let it snow, let it snow, let it snow...

CHINA 1958-1961

MAO ZEDONG'S AGRICULTURE POLICIES HAVE CREATED THE WORST MANMADE DISASTER IN HUMAN HISTORY — A BRUTAL FAMINE THAT HAS CLAIMED THE LIVES OF TENS OF MILLIONS OF DESPERATE PEOPLE.

THOSE WHO SURVIVE TRY TO MAKE SENSE OF THE HORRORS THAT SURROUND THEM...

You know what this is like?

I know what you're going to say, but go on...

It's like an independent regulator being given oversight of English football.

Thank you! That's *exactly* what it's like!

YES, IT'S ... THE ENTIRELY MODERATE AND COMPLETELY UNPREDICTABLE RESPONSE BY SOME PREMIER LEAGUE CLUBS TO THE RECOMMENDATIONS OF THE FAN-LED REVIEW OF FOOTBALL GOVERNANCE! (PULL YOUR PARTY POPPERS NOW, KIDS). LEEDS UNITED CEO ANGUS KINNEAR SET THE BENCHMARK FOR UNDER-STATED REACTIONS WITH A WELL-THOUGHT-THROUGH COMPARISON TO THE MAOIST POLICY THAT LED TO THE GREAT CHINESE FAMINE. IN FAIRNESS, HE'S CLEARLY A MAN WHO KNOWS HIS HISTORY.

LEEDS ARE SIX WHOLE POINTS CLEAR OF THE RELEGATION ZONE, SO IT'S IMPOSSIBLE TO IMAGINE THEM EVER SLIPPING BACK INTO A POSITION WHERE THEY MAY NEED THE HELP OF A MORE EQUITABLE REDISTRIBUTION OF WEALTH THROUGHOUT THE FOOTBALL PYRAMID. COME ON, GUYS, THEY DREW WITH *BRENTFORD* AT THE WEEKEND. SIMILARLY, WEST HAM ARE AN ESTABLISHED TOP FOUR CLUB NOW, SO IT'S LITTLE WONDER VICE-CHAIR KARREN BRADY WAS ALSO CRITICAL OF THE REVIEW'S RECOMMENDATIONS...

Well I can't think of a period when Leeds would have benefited from some independent intervention.

JOHNSON 20

Last time I looked, we did not live in North Korea, China or Russia!

Up the ladders!

TOO BLOODY RIGHT, BARONESS. BRITAIN ISN'T SOME CORRUPT ONE-PARTY STATE WHERE THE REGIME IS PROPPED UP BY A PARTISAN MEDIA AND THE ESTABLISHMENT PLACES ITS CRONIES IN POSITIONS OF POWER. NOR IS IT A PLACE WHERE THERE'S ONE SET OF RULES FOR THE MASSES AND ANOTHER FOR THE GLORIOUS DEAR LEADER AND HIS TOP CHUMS (EMPLOYEES).

BANTZ

DECEMBER 2020

THE REACTIONS OF ASTON VILLA'S CHRISTIAN PURSLOW AND CRYSTAL PALACE'S STEVE PARISH SUGGEST THEY MAY NOT HAVE FULLY UNDERSTOOD THE REPORT (FAIR PLAY, IT'S REALLY LONG). THIS PRESENTS A CHANCE TO SNEAK IN A FEW MORE RECOMMENDATIONS. FOR EXAMPLE, A RULING THAT ANY PREMIER LEAGUE CLUB EXECUTIVE WHO USES THAT ANALOGY ABOUT SUPERMARKETS NOT BEING EXPECTED TO BAIL OUT CORNER SHOPS SHOULD BE MADE TO WORK IN RETAIL FOR THE CHRISTMAS PERIOD.

This isn't the level of service I expect from Santa's Transient Emporium of Magical Tat!

Biological disaster in aisle two.

Got a little job for you, Purslow.

CHRISTIAN

IF NOTHING ELSE, THE REVIEW HAS SMOKED OUT RICHARD MASTERS, WHO HAS RETURNED LIKE A SOAP CHARACTER YOU THOUGHT HAD BEEN BUMPED OFF DURING A RIDICULOUS PLOTLINE ABOUT A MURDEROUS PETRO-STATE BUYING THE LAUNDERETTE.

Pint of Barclays please, pet.

Dirty Dickie, as I live and breathe...!

DOOF DOOF DOOF   DOOF   DOOF DOOF ETC

This could be worse...

How? How could it possibly be worse?

We could be a Premier League club forced to pay a stamp duty-like levy on transfer fees.

Don't.

THE PREMIER LEAGUE TITLE RACE IS OVER BEFORE THE QUALITY STREET TIN IS EMPTY, AND THAT'S ONLY BECAUSE OF THE STRAWBERRY DELIGHTS. IF YOU'RE WONDERING HOW WE'LL FILL THE ENTERTAINMENT VOID OVER THE NEXT FIVE MONTHS THEN FRET NOT, BECAUSE NOT ONLY CAN WE ENJOY THE USUAL RATIONAL COMPLAINTS ABOUT REFEREEING CONSPIRACIES AGAINST YOUR FAVOURITE CLUB, BUT NOW WE HAVE THE BOMBSHELL OF ROMELU LUKAKU OFFERING SOME MILD CRITICISM OF TACTICS TOMMY'S TACTICS ON ITALIAN TELEVISION!

THIS DEVELOPING STORY – WHICH MAY WELL HAVE BEEN SATISFACTORILY RESOLVED BY THE TIME YOU READ THIS – HAS IT ALL: INTRIGUE! BETRAYAL! A £97.5M STRIKER DROPPING **TRUTH BOMBS** WHILE WEARING THE KIND OF BEIGE SWEATPANT ENSEMBLE LAST SEEN IN THE 1983 AUTUMN / WINTER FREEMAN'S CATALOGUE!

IN TERMS OF FOOTBALLERS CONDUCTING CANDID INTERVIEWS WITH FOREIGN MEDIA OUTLETS, SAFE IN THE KNOWLEDGE THAT NO ONE BACK HOME HAS THE MEANS TO EVER FIND OUT, IT WAS AN ABSOLUTE CLASSIC OF THE GENRE.

LUKAKU'S SEARING DIATRIBE ABOUT WORKING HARD TO WIN HIS PLACE IN THE TEAM BACK WENT DOWN ABOUT AS WELL AS COULD BE EXPECTED.

... AND DID LITTLE TO CHEER UP THE INCREASINGLY GRUMPY TUCHEL.

IT'S PROBABLY COINCIDENTAL THAT HIS COMPLAINTS HAVE RAMPED UP AS WE ENTER THE TRANSFER WINDOW, BUT HE'LL NO DOUBT BE PRESENTING HIS CASE FOR NEW PLAYERS TO THE CHELSEA HEAD HONCHOS.

ONE DEVELOPMENT THAT MIGHT LIGHTEN HIS MOOD IS THE RETURN OF A CERTAIN **CAPTAIN, LEADER, LEGEND**, BACK IN A PART-TIME CONSULTANCY ROLE TO HELP SHAPE THE MINDS OF THE NEXT GENERATION OF CHELSEA LOANEES.

SHOWDOWN TALKS TOOK PLACE BETWEEN ROM AND TOM ON MONDAY, EFFECTIVELY RENDERING THIS WHOLE CARTOON REDUNDANT, SO CHEERS FOR STICKING WITH IT THIS FAR. IT SEEMS A SOLUTION WAS FOUND THAT ALLOWS THE CLUB TO MOVE ON TO ITS NEXT CRISIS AND AFFORDS TUCHEL A SENSE OF CLOSURE: A NO HOLDS BARRED INTERVIEW WITH AN OVERSEAS BROADCASTER!

MERSEYSIDE BLUES

THE PERPETUAL CRISIS THAT IS EVERTON FOOTBALL CLUB HAVE PARTED WAYS WITH THEIR BELOVED MANAGER RAFA BENÍTEZ. THE WRITING HAD BEEN ON THE WALL FOR A WHILE (AS WELL AS ON BEDSHEETS IN THE STANDS AND OUTSIDE HIS NEIGHBOURS' HOUSE). NOT EVEN A TACTICAL MASTERSTROKE COULD SAVE HIM FROM HIS FATE.

Guys, it's time to implement *Operation Save Big Dog*.

Err, I think I'll be alright actually, mate...

A DISMAL RUN OF RESULTS CULMINATED IN A LIMP DEFEAT AT NORWICH; THE TOFFEES TORN APART BY SAVED BY THE BELL'S JOSH SARGENT. FRUSTRATION BOILED OVER IN THE AWAY STAND, WITH ONE PITCH INVADER MAKING A DESPERATE ATTEMPT TO SECURE A LIFE BAN. PICTURE THE MOOD IN THE EVERTON DRESSING ROOM.

Did anyone see my overhead kick?!

Oh, right, the Norwich thing...

A DAY LATER, THE MANAGER WAS GONE. DESPITE HIS UNPOPULARITY AMONG THE FANBASE, IT'S HARD TO IMAGINE ANYONE REJOICING IN RAFA'S FAILURE.

BENÍTEZ'S REIGN WASN'T WITHOUT A FEW BRIGHT MOMENTS. EVERTON STARTED THE SEASON WELL, AND HIS WAISTCOAT DEFINITELY DIDN'T MAKE HIM LOOK LIKE HE SHOULD HAVE BEEN SELLING EGG SANDWICHES IN A TRAIN BUFFET CARRIAGE. EVEN THE INJURY CRISIS THAT CONTRIBUTED TO HIS DOWNFALL SAW THE EMERGENCE OF YOUNG TALENT LIKE ANTHONY GORDON, WHICH NO ONE CAN SAY IS ONLY MENTIONED HERE AS AN EXCUSE TO DRAW RAFA AS PRINCE VULTAN.

GORDON'S ALIVE!

SO WHERE NEXT FOR EVERTON? NEVER LET IT BE SAID THEY AREN'T A CLUB WITH A CLEAR, COHESIVE VISION, AS DEMONSTRATED BY THEIR DECISION TO SELL ONE OF THEIR BEST PLAYERS WHO'D FALLEN OUT WITH THE MANAGER, AND THEN SACKING THAT MANAGER FOUR DAYS LATER.

What you working on, Lucas?

Something to post on Instagram for my return to Goodison this Saturday...

Huh. A parody of Goya's 'Saturn Devouring His Son'. I prefer pictures about stuff, but hey ho. You know they've sacked Rafa, right? Funny, you could have stayed there after all.

FARHAD MOSHIRI AND THE EVERTON BOARD WILL BE APPLYING THEIR CHARACTERISTICALLY METHODICAL APPROACH TO APPOINTING THEIR SIXTH MANAGER IN AS MANY YEARS. AFTER ALL, THIS IS THE SCHOOL OF SCIENCE, NOT SOME CRAZED FUNFAIR TOMBOLA THAT SPITS OUT A WILD LIST OF RANDOM NAMES.

Oi! Red's a condiment!

Mourinho! Bobby M! Stevie G! Wazza! By whom I mean Mike Walker. Dyche! Potter! John bloody Oster!

Abel Xavier! Nick Barmby!

Julian Cope! Harry Cross! Sonia! That fan who wiped a bogey on a lady's head! The lady! The bogey! Steven Bilic!

For God's sake, pull yourself together, man!

AS FOR BENÍTEZ, DESPITE SOME OF THE PROBLEMS BEING BEYOND HIS CONTROL, THE EVERTON EXPERIMENT WAS HUGELY DAMAGING FOR HIS REPUTATION AND YOU WONDER WHERE HE'LL ROCK UP NEXT. LUCKILY FOR HIM, THIS IS ENGLISH FOOTBALL AND THERE'S ALWAYS ONE MORE CLUB A LITTLE FURTHER ROUND THE BEND.

These are all splendid suggestions, but I can only write so fast.

Ian Rush! The cast of Bread! A tin of Hafnia spam! Big Sam!

Welcome home, fabled Magpie Man!

Hi. Sorry... What's happening?

SEXY BEAST

ROY HODGSON IS COAXED OUT OF RETIREMENT FOR ONE LAST JOB...

Ohh yeah...

Bloody hell. I'm sweating here. Roasting. Boiling. Baking. People say, "Aren't you worried that the climate crisis means you're able to sunbathe in Purley in January?" Nah, I love it. It's hotter than Ride's first three EP releases.

I've gotta change my bench coat. It's sticking to me. I'm sweating like a Chris Brunt.

Raymond? What are you doing here?

I know a man, who knows a man, who knows a Pozzo. They want us back. It's a simple job. In. Out. No questions asked.

But I'm retired...

Roy-tirement. Nevermind. Look, let's not piss about here...

Why are you swearing? I'm not swearing.

... I'm just gonna have to turn this opportunity down...

No, you're gonna have to turn this opportunity yes.

Hmm. I suppose Watford have been on my mind lately...

Bastard hornet...!

In fact, you'll like this one, Raymond; I say I'm "enjoying Roy-tirement." Oh that always cracks them up down at the tapas bar.

Exactly. Everyone's getting back in the game. Even Big Frankie's returned, after biding his time and waiting for an opportunity to arise at a project that befits his skillset...

JT's got the Ape Kids Club FC gig, has he? Wonder if he needs an assistant?

But he missed out on that one, so enacted plan B...

Right, yeah.

Hello Sky Sports. This is Vitor Pereira. I am very bad at football management and I will make Everton run out to The Bill theme tune.

PEREIRA IN
HAH, NO,
SERIOUSLY
THOUGH,
LAMPARD IN

What this club needs is more midfielders who've had disastrous spells at big clubs. It's never worked before, but my God it'll work for me.

Just do the job, you flippin' Boxpark honkin' South-of-the-river day trippin' teddy boy flippin' hunk bubble!

What an odd thing to say.

Yeah, sorry, I'm a bit dehydrated. Look, Roy; if you won't do it for me then do it for what motivates most people in football: the holy trinity of bitterness, spite and sweet, sweet revenge.

Why didn't you just say?

Yeah, just waiting for the new gaffer. Mr Pozzo says he likes tapas, so I expect he'll be another exotic Mediterranean. Apparently he'll be wearing yellow, so um...

Harry?

Oh for...

THE CAT AND THE PRATS

BY D. SQUIRES (WITH APOLOGIES TO Dr. Seuss)

The oddest story of the season.
An act of violence without reason.
Zouma One and Zouma Two
subjecting a tabby
to kung-fu.

Displaying a lack of ingenuity,
they filmed their show of
animal cruelty.
Then put it all on social media.
Enough to trigger your ailurophilia.

West Ham didn't drop Kurt for their next game.

We were playing *The Hornets*, are you insane?!

You see in football there's one rule that's golden, a doctrine to which we are all beholden:

Nothing means more than the collection of points, not even kicking a cat round the joint.

So if you're confronted
with howls of derision,
just pass it all off
as "a football decision".
Your trip to Jeddah
caused agitation?
Your fans won't care
if you avoid relegation.

Our season's been saved, you're as bitter as lemons.

No doubt that will cheer the people of Yemen.

Our sponsors are angry, our fans less than chipper.

Because we announced we've signed Jack the Ripper.

FICTIONAL FOOTBALL CLUB

Tell them you're sorry, say that you've learned.
Then do it again, once the news cycle's turned.

The reaction to Zouma has partly been tribal,
an online debate between old football rivals.
Though some are defending the French international,
you suspect they might just be cocker spaniels.

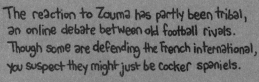

You cannot be angry about two things at once. What are you anyway, some sort of cat nonce?

I bet you eat burgers.

I bet you eat meat.

I bet those are leather shoes on your feet.

And I see there's no mention of X, y or z.

Those are ongoing cases, my flea-ridden friend.

Against Leicester City,
Kurt was a late omission.
Suddenly struck down
by a mysterious condition.
He removed himself
to seek diagnosis...

I might have a touch of the old toxoplasmosis...

Kurt Zouma's been fined and his cat's been rehoused,
with someone who won't chase it round the lounge.
There are calls for a punishment that more fits the act,
like spending some time with a much bigger cat.

I'd have found a better way to combat my boredom, if I'd known I'd be forced to hang out with James Corden!

AFTER YEARS OF COSYING UP TO VLADIMIR PUTIN, THE INTERNATIONAL FOOTBALL AUTHORITIES HAVE FINALLY DISTANCED THEMSELVES FROM THE MURDEROUS PSYCHOPATH AND ALL IT TOOK WAS THE VIOLENT INVASION OF UKRAINE. FIRST UEFA STRIPPED ST PETERSBURG OF THE CHAMPIONS LEAGUE FINAL, THEN IT ENDED ITS LONGSTANDING SPONSORSHIP DEAL WITH GAZPROM. MAYBE THEY HAVE A NEW COMMERCIAL PARTNERSHIP LINED UP TO COVER THE SHORTFALL...

GALLOP-FROM™

OFFICIAL UEFA STABLE DOOR PARTNER

- FOR WHEN YOUR HORSE HAS DISAPPEARED OVER THE HORIZON.

EVENTUALLY, UEFA AND FIFA SUSPENDED RUSSIA AND ITS CLUBS FROM ALL THEIR COMPETITIONS, BUT ONLY AFTER POLAND, SWEDEN AND THE CZECH REPUBLIC REFUSED TO PLAY RUSSIA IN THE UPCOMING PLAY-OFFS FOR A WHOLE OTHER SH*TSHOW. THIS WAS DESPITE FIFA INTRODUCING A RANGE OF MEASURES TO SHOW VLAD THEY MEANT BUSINESS, INCLUDING MAKING THEM PLAY UNDER **A SLIGHTLY DIFFERENT NAME!**

How about the "Football Union of the Cheeky Kremlin"?

OK. Or, the Football Union of Russia...?

F.U.R! Like the big hats! If that doesn't stop his Imperialist death rampage, nothing will...

AW, IT SEEMS LIKE ONLY YESTERDAY THAT GIANNI INFANTINO WAS CHILLING WITH PUTIN AND MBS AT THE 2018 WORLD CUP IN RUSSIA, AS THE TWO DESPOTS LAID WASTE TO SYRIA IN A PROXY WAR.

Well here we are now. All the lads.

GIANNI SEEMED LESS COMFORTABLE LAST WEEK WHEN THE JOURNALIST ROB HARRIS ASKED HIM ABOUT RECEIVING PUTIN'S 'ORDER OF FRIENDSHIP' IN 2019, BUT SOME CLASSIC FIFASPEAK GOT HIM OUT OF A TIGHT SPOT. UNLUCKY, HARRIS!

Sport...

...people...

football...

Sport!

ON THE DOMESTIC FRONT, THE BIGGEST ANNOUNCEMENT WAS THAT ROMAN ABRAMOVICH WAS HANDING "THE STEWARDSHIP AND CARE" OF CHELSEA TO THE CLUB'S CHARITABLE TRUST. WIDELY INTERPRETED AS A MOVE THAT COULD INSULATE THE CLUB FROM ANY POSSIBLE SANCTIONS AGAINST THE RUSSIAN OLIGARCH'S ASSETS, IT SEEMS LITTLE WILL ACTUALLY CHANGE IN TERMS OF WHO PULLS THE STRINGS.

I'll become as visible at Chelsea as Winston Bogarde. We need someone who can be the head of the organisation for the sake of appearances, but where do we find such a Junior Soprano -type figure, Bruce?

All I know is you never had the makings of a Football Union of Russia athlete..

ABRAMOVICH VEHEMENTLY DENIES THAT HE HAS LINKS TO EITHER THE RUSSIAN STATE OR PUTIN, HOWEVER, THE SITUATION HAS DRAWN ATTENTION TO THE SOURCE OF HIS WEALTH, SOMETHING PEOPLE WERE LESS INTERESTED IN WHEN HE BEGAN SHOWERING CHELSEA WITH EXOTIC OLIGIFTS BACK IN 2003.

Can you tell us again how you became so wealthy – JESUS CHRIST HE'S SIGNED NEIL SULLIVAN.

GIVEN ROMAN IS BUT A HUMBLE FOOTBALL CLUB CUSTODIAN, HE SEEMS AN ODD CHOICE FOR A PEACE ENVOY, AS ANNOUNCED BY HIS SPOKESPERSON ON MONDAY.

Thank you, Mr Abramovich. Ukraine appreciates the effort you've put in.

"Put in"? I'm not connected to "put in".

PERHAPS FOOTBALL WAS SIMPLER WHEN CLUBS WERE RUN BY LOCAL BUSINESSMEN IN SHEEPSKIN COATS WHO PLANNED TO ELECTRIFY PERIMETER FENCES. AT LEAST THEY NEVER HAD TO DENY LINKS TO A DERANGED AUTOCRAT THREATENING TO UNLEASH A NUCLEAR HELL-STORM.

I didn't realise that was an option.

THE WEEKEND'S FOOTBALL MATCHES SAW MANY DISPLAYS OF SOLIDARITY WITH THE PEOPLE OF UKRAINE. IT WAS A MESSAGE CLEARLY HEARD BY SENIOR FIGURES IN THE BRITISH GOVERNMENT, WHO RESPONDED TO THE CRISIS IN TIME-HONOURED FASHION: WAVING FLAGS, CRUELTY TO REFUGEES, AND RAIDING THE FANCY-DRESS BOX. WE'RE ON THE BRINK OF SEEING LIZ TRUSS DRESS UP AS VALERIY LOBANOVSKYI FOR THE INSTA-LIKES.

Oh this'll do some numbers, lads...

IT FEELS UTTERLY TRIVIAL TO EVEN MENTION FOOTBALL AT A TIME OF SUCH OVERWHELMING HUMAN TRAGEDY, BUT THE AGGRESSOR IN THIS CONFLICT SO OFTEN USED SPORT TO NORMALISE HIS POSITION ON THE WORLD STAGE. PERHAPS THE OUTBREAK OF WORLD WAR III WILL MAKE SOME OF SPORT'S SENIOR EXECUTIVES THINK TWICE ABOUT THE PEOPLE AND REGIMES THEY GET IN TO BED WITH. UNTIL THEN, KEEP WATCHING THE SKIES.

See you all in Qatar, guys!

THE FALL OF...

THE ROMAN EMPIRE

GRADUALLY, THEN SUDDENLY, ABRAMOVICH'S REIGN AT CHELSEA CAME TO AN END.

WITH ABRAMOVICH HIT WITH SANCTIONS BY THE GOVERNMENT, AND EVENTUALLY EVEN THE PREMIER LEAGUE, CHELSEA ARE ALLOWED TO CONTINUE UNDER A "SPECIAL LICENCE" THAT LIMITS THEIR INCOME. TICKET SALES ARE SUSPENDED, THE CLUB SHOP CLOSED, MANY QUESTIONS REMAIN, NOT LEAST...

What the Bruce Buck do we do with these?

ROSS BARKLEY FRIDGE MAGNETS

Non-MAGNET...

TRAVEL BUDGETS HAVE ALSO BEEN LIMITED, PRESENTING CHELSEA WITH CHALLENGES FOR THIS WEEK'S EURO-TRIP TO LILLE. THOMAS TUCHEL SAYS HE'LL DRIVE THE MINIBUS HIMSELF, STRETCHING THE DEFINITION OF "COACHING". IRONICALLY, IT'S A SITUATION THAT MIGHT HAVE BEEN EASIER TO RESOLVE IN THE PRE-OLIGARCH ERA AT STAMFORD BRIDGE.

Take your pick, lads!

Gaffer, I am not worthy of this lavish chariot. Three wheels!

Just treat yourself for once, N'Golo.

UNTIL A BUYER IS FOUND, CHELSEA ARE EFFECTIVELY OWNED BY THE BRITISH GOVERNMENT, WHICH MAY EXPOSE THE CLUB TO FURTHER SANCTIONS...

Mr Buck, I'm afraid your new temporary owners - us - have a history of Imperialist violence, continue to supply arms to murderous foreign powers, and have clearly established links to the Russian State.

Ugh, I smell a points deduction.

God no, you're not Derby, but we will have to use our big serious military stencil font on the socials.

ABRAMOVICH, THE FORMER GOVERNOR OF CHUKOTKA...

Or, as we say: "Chucked out, ja"?

...HAS HAD HIS BANK ACCOUNTS FROZEN, AS HAVE CHELSEA. HOWEVER, MAYBE THE CLUB CAN USE ALTERNATIVE, EDGIER FORMS OF CURRENCY...

Obviously, contract negotiations are tricky at present, César, but would you accept some of JT's precious non-fungible ape drawings?

Isn't their value tanking?

Please, for the love of God, don't mention the tanks.

SHIRT SPONSORS THREE AND HYUNDAI HAVE ALSO SUSPENDED THEIR DEALS WITH THE CLUB, PROVOKING A PERFECTLY NORMAL RESPONSE FROM SOME FANS. THE IMPACT OF THE WAR IN UKRAINE UPON YOUR PREFERRED LEISURE PURSUIT MAY NOT BE THE PRIMARY CONCERN OF THE MILLIONS OF PEOPLE FLEEING THE CARNAGE, BUT PERHAPS THEY COULD BE GIVEN A DOSE OF PERSPECTIVE BY SPENDING SOME TIME WITH THE REAL VICTIMS OF THIS ATROCITY: CHELSEA FANS.

Why is that man destroying his own modem, mother?

Mug off the Chels, will ya?!

The English have many peculiar customs, my child; but I believe that inanimate object was "taking liberties".

AND INTO THIS FESTIVAL OF EDIFICATION CAME NEWCASTLE UNITED, PART-OWNED BY THE PUBLIC INVESTMENT FUND OF SAUDI ARABIA AND OFF THE BACK OF A PROLIFIC RECENT SPELL (SIX WINS FROM THE LAST SEVEN GAMES, 81 EXECUTIONS IN THE PREVIOUS 24 HOURS). THE COACH OF THE DEATH STAR'S FIVE-A-SIDE TEAM AGAIN PUT UP THE DEFLECTOR SHIELDS WHEN ASKED ABOUT THE BARBARITY OF HIS EMPLOYERS.

What was I supposed to do, apply for a job at one of the countless other clubs without links to a brutal dictatorship? Now, can we please have some questions about our next game, against Alderaan...

Oh for...

COINCIDENTALLY, 'THE SAUDI MEDIA GROUP' ARE SAID TO BE KEEN ON BUYING CHELSEA. THE COMPANY IS REPORTEDLY UNCONNECTED TO THE RULING REGIME, WHERE IT NO DOUBT OPERATES AS FREELY AS ANY MEDIA ORGANISATION FUNCTIONING UNDER AN ABSOLUTE MONARCHY. IT'S IMPORTANT TO REMEMBER THAT THE PREMIER LEAGUE WAS ALSO GIVEN CAST-IRON LEGAL ASSURANCES THAT THERE WERE NO LINKS BETWEEN THE PIF AND THE SAUDI GOVERNMENT. OH IT'S A COMPLEX SITUATION, FOR SURE...

REGIME
CROWN PRINCE, HEAD HONCHO, MOHAMMED BIN SALMAN

PIF (CHAIRMAN)
YASIR AL-RUMAYYAN (GOVERNOR)

NEWCASTLE UNITED (CHAIRMAN)

Geopolitics, eh? Bloody hell.

THE NEWCASTLE FANS WAVING THEIR SAUDI FLAGS AND GLOATING ABOUT THEIR WEALTH DON'T SEEM TOO BOTHERED FOR NOW, BUT WHAT IF BRITAIN'S COSY RELATIONSHIP WITH SAUDI ARABIA CHANGES? WHAT HAPPENS WHEN THE UK NO LONGER NEEDS ITS FOSSIL FUELS AND THE PRIME MINISTER (WHOSE ROLE IN THE NEWCASTLE TAKE-OVER REMAINS AS CLEAR AS A BARREL OF CRUDE) DOESN'T GO BEGGING FOR OIL. WHAT IF SELLING BOMBS TO DESPOTS BECOMES POLITICALLY UNPOPULAR? THEN THOSE LADS AND LASSES OF THE GALLOW(S)GATE END MIGHT DECIDE TO CHANGE THEIR TUNE...

Sorry, old boy; we're shutting the club down. Seems selling military hardware to kill children with doesn't score too well in the focus groups.

Hah, your face! Nah, it's fine, obviously. S'only Yemen, innit.

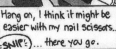

One Foot in the Algarve

TWO OF FOOTBALL'S MOST FLAMBOYANT STARS ARE RUMOURED TO BE CONSIDERING RETIREMENT. BUT HOW WILL THEY COPE WITH LIFE AWAY FROM THE BRIGHT LIGHTS?
(YEP, IT'S AN INTERNATIONAL WEEK, KIDS)

Tuesday again... :sigh:

DING DONG

Look, Michael; it's Gareth from up the road!

Oh that's all I need.

Isn't his hair lovely for a man who has the ligaments of someone twice his age?

Oh please. Anyone can grow a Nutkins strip and scrape it into a top bun.

Anyone?

Yes, but we're not all that vain.

Didn't you grow a beard because you thought it would make you look like Jason Statham?

Just answer the door.

Alright, butts!

"Butts"?

Ooh, what a treat. It's so wonderful to have a genuine superstar in our neighbourhood. How are you enjoying retirement?

Come off it. He's not even properly retired. Sure, he spends most of his time playing golf in Spain, but he still works about 10 days a year for Wales!

Golf? Michael likes golf, don't you Michael?

Oh yeah? What's your handicap, Mike?

Well...

A fastidious obsession with rules and a propensity for inserting himself in to the centre of the story. Oh, he's always been a show-off, Gareth.

Thank you. No, Bale, I prefer the noble art of caddying. Taking notes, ensuring scorecards are completed correctly in black - not blue- ink, checking the players' socks are of regulation elasticity. Sometimes, I let the ball roll through my legs, like a human crazy golf obstacle.

See? Anyway, I was sorry to hear about that anonymous post about you on the community group. I thought it was shameful, Gareth.

It was disgusting, Mrs D. Pretty ironic that anyone would call me a parasite...

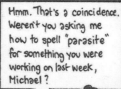

Hmm. That's a coincidence. Weren't you asking me how to spell "parasite" for something you were working on last week, Michael?

Heh, yes... we get them down at the VARden centre. I keep telling them, the whole system's riddled with bugs...!

Well I think it's lovely to have you here on the Wirral.

Yeah, it's basically Wales, innit, Mrs D? Not as nice though, obviously, hahaha.

Wot?

OFF YOU POP.

Weirdos.

And on YOU pop...

IT'S NO GREAT SECRET THAT FOOTBALL HAS LONG BEEN CO-OPTED BY THE MAN. FROM ALMOST THE OUTSET, THIS SIMPLE GAME WAS CORRUPTED BY THE GREED AND SELF-INTEREST OF POWERFUL MEN. AFTER ALL, WHAT'S THE POINT OF SOMETHING JOYOUS AND PURE IF IT CAN'T BE EXPLOITED FOR PERSONAL FINANCIAL ADVANCEMENT?

You may well have kicked the hog's head from one end of the village to the other, but according to our coefficient — this large stick — we're the real winners, so hand over your prize money and be grateful we don't crush you.

Typical big club attitude.

I swear to God, man...

LIKE NOT THINKING TOO DEEPLY ABOUT THE SOURCE OF THE SUDDEN GRISTLY BIT IN YOUR HALF-TIME SCRAN, MOST FANS TRY NOT TO LET FOOTBALL'S MORAL VOID RUIN THEIR ENJOYMENT, BUT SOME WEEKS IT'S TOO CHEWY TO IGNORE.

:CRUNCH!:

Oh God.

What's wrong?

The Qatari leadership are trotting out the line that people should "educate themselves" in a clear tactic to shut down criticism of their dire human rights record.

Just swallow it down. Hosting a major sports event will lead to democratic change - like in China and Russia!

BUT AGAINST THIS GRIM BACKDROP ARRIVES THE COMEBACK STORY OF THIS OR ANY OTHER SEASON: **THE RETURN OF CHRISTIAN ERIKSEN!**

IT'S A TALE UNTARNISHED BY SPORTSWASHING OR CORPORATE AVARICE, AND ONE THAT SHOWS THAT FOOTBALL IS STILL CAPABLE OF PRODUCING UPLIFTING STORIES WORTHY OF THE NAME ON THE FRONT OF ERIKSEN'S BRENTFORD SHIRT.

Yeah, it's an offshore betting firm.

Of course it is.

HOLLYWOOD

ERIKSEN CAPPED OFF A REMARKABLE WEEK WITH A GOAL IN BRENTFORD'S ASTONISHING 4-1 WIN AT STAMFORD BRIDGE. EVEN THE CHELSEA FANS WOULD HAVE BEEN DELIGHTED FOR THE EX-SPURS MAN.

Well *this* makes up for everything that's happened over the last month.

Joy unbridled.

THOMAS TUCHEL SEEMED QUITE PRAGMATIC ABOUT THE OUTCOME TOO.

No, I don't agree it was the most comprehensive stinging by a swarm of bees since the end of 'Mein Mädchen' but it's fine, it's fine...

CALAMINE LOTION

BEFORE THAT, ERIKSEN HAD SCORED WITH HIS FIRST TOUCH ON HIS RETURN TO INTERNATIONAL FOOTBALL, AGAINST THE NETHERLANDS. HE THEN CAPTAINED DENMARK FOR THE FIRST TIME UPON HIS RETURN TO THE STADIUM IN COPENHAGEN WHERE HE SUFFERED A CARDIAC ARREST 10 MONTHS EARLIER. HE WEIGHED IN WITH ANOTHER TYPICALLY CLASSY GOAL IN A 3-0 WIN AGAINST SERBIA, BUT YOU CAN'T IMAGINE WHAT WAS GOING THROUGH HIS MIND AS HE TROTTED PAST THE PATCH OF GRASS WHERE HIS LIFE NEARLY ENDED LAST JUNE.

IT WAS A LONG ROAD BACK FOR ERIKSEN, A PATH THAT INCLUDED HEART SURGERY, REHABILITATION, LOADS OF RUNNING, ENDLESS TESTS, AND NO DOUBT PLENTY OF THINKING. HAVING TRAINED WITH CLUBS ACROSS EUROPE, HIS JOURNEY BACK INTO ELITE FOOTBALL WAS COMPLETE WHEN HE WAS REUNITED WITH HIS OLD YOUTH COACH, THOMAS FRANK. CUE MORE DEMANDING PHYSICAL DRILLS...

STRENGTH!

So... matted...

...AND CONDITIONING!

IT IS A TALE THAT REVEALS THE BEST OF HUMANITY, NOT JUST IN THE COURAGE SHOWN BY ERIKSEN, BUT THE FRIENDS, FAMILY, COLLEAGUES, FANS, DOCTORS, MEDICAL STAFF AND CARDIOLOGISTS WHO HELPED HIM BACK. AND THAT'S EVEN BEFORE WE CONSIDER THE CENTURIES OF SCIENTIFIC ADVANCEMENT THAT LED US TO THIS POINT.

... And it is through this study of anatomy and physiology that I contend humanity shall one day achieve the unthinkable: humiliating Chelsea in their own manor, up The Bees.

THIS IS ONE GOOD NEWS STORY THAT CANNOT BE BESET BY THE MODERN SCOURGE OF **WHATABOUTERY.**

How do you think they make implantable cardioverter defibrillators anyway? They're tiny. They must use child labour, so their little hands can solder the parts together.

um...

And Eriksen's Danish. I didn't hear you moaning about human rights when the vikings were marauding the high seas. Educate yourself!

AFTER A DECADE OF DEFYING THE ODDS, SEAN "SEAN" DYCHE HAS BEEN FIRED BY BURNLEY. THERE'S STILL A CHANCE THEY CAN AVOID RELEGATION (WHERE THERE'S AN EVERTON, THERE'S A WAY), BUT IT'S THE END OF AN ERA AT TURF MOOR AND THE CLARETS FANS ARE MOURNING HIS DEPARTURE.

STOP ALL THE CLOCKS, CUT OFF THE TELEPHONE. TEAR DOWN THE PUB NAMED AFTER HIM, CREMATE IAN WOAN.

Eh?

SILENCE THE PIANOS AND INSTRUCT THE CLUB LAWYERS, TO FORWARD HIS POSSESSIONS...

TO HIS FUTURE EMPLOYERS.

And you're Ten Hag, are you...?

Yeah, if you like.

 LET AEROPLANES CIRCLE, MOANING OVERHEAD, SCRIBBLING OVER LANCASHIRE THE MESSAGE:

PRESS CONFERENCE BANTZ IS DEAD

NO MORE TALES OF EATING WORMS, TOLD IN A GRAVELLY VOICE...

GERRUM IN THE MIXER!

HE MIGHT HAVE STILL BEEN WITH US, IF CORNET HAD SHOWN MORE POISE.

There's always next week!

HE WAS OUR BURNLEY NORTH, OUR BURNLEY SOUTH, OUR BURNLEY EAST AND WEST...

HE'D RATHER PLAY A TREQUARTISTA, THAN WEAR A THERMAL VEST.

 OUR NOON, OUR MIDNIGHT, OUR TALK, OUR TUNE. GENETICALLY PREDISPOSED TO PLAYING 4-4-2.

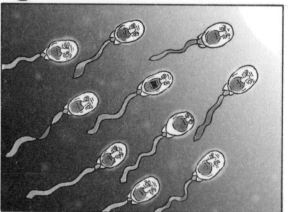

ALL THE STARS WERE SNUFFED OUT, HE CONQUERED EVERY ONE...

Guys, they make it so tough; so tough.

RECALL OUR TRIP TO EUROPE, WHEN WE ALL BAKED IN THE SUN.

ABERDEEN

What a scorcher! Grease me up, Woany.

YET THE GAME WAS ALL BUT OVER, WHEN NEWCASTLE BOUGHT CHRIS WOOD...

BUT DYCHE DID MORE FOR BURNLEY, THAN ANY MORTAL COULD.

MANCHESTER UNITED HAVE APPOINTED **ERIK TEN HAG** AS THEIR LATEST HUMAN LIGHTNING ROD! INTERIM STOOGE RALF RANGNICK MAY NOT HAVE BEEN INVOLVED IN THE SELECTION PROCESS, BECAUSE MAN UTD LOL, BUT HE HAS EARNED THAT JUICY CONSULTANCY FEE BY REPORTEDLY COMPILING AN EXTENSIVE DOSSIER THAT WILL FORM PART OF THE HANDOVER THIS SUMMER

JONG ERIK WILL DISCOVER UNITED NEED IMPROVEMENT IN A NUMBER OF AREAS, INCLUDING PLAYING FOOTBALL, TALENT RECRUITMENT, INFRASTRUCTURE, FAN SENTIMENT GRAPHS, AND THE CUMULATIVE EFFECTS OF HAVING YOUR GIZZARDS TORN AT BY VULTURE CAPITALISTS FOR 17 YEARS. AND *SURE*, THE DRESSING ROOM IS LEAKIER THAN THE OLD TRAFFORD ROOF, BUT HIS FONDNESS FOR METICULOUS PREPARATION WILL SURELY WIN OVER THE FAMOUSLY DIFFICULT PLAYING GROUP.

LUCKILY, UNITED'S TOP BRASS DON'T HAVE A REPUTATION FOR JUST (AHEM) WINDMILLING WILDLY BETWEEN COACHES WITH CONTRASTING STYLES, SOMETIMES WITHIN THE SPACE OF ONE RECRUITMENT PROCESS. SO YOU CAN GUARANTEE THEY'LL HAVE THOUGHT LONG AND HARD BEFORE LANDING ON TEN HAG.

HIS APPOINTMENT ALSO CONTINUES UNITED'S LONG ASSOCIATION WITH THE NETHERLANDS, BECOMING THE LATEST IN THE LINE OF DUTCH MASTERS...

EXCITINGLY, SHTEVE COULD POTENTIALLY RETURN AS TEN HAG'S ASSISTANT, A PROSPECT THAT WAS PERHAPS DISCUSSED WHEN A DELEGATION FROM UNITED VISITED ERIK IN OLD AMSTERDAM.

WHILE HE REMAINS AT SOMETHING CALLED "AJAX" UNTIL THE END OF THE SEASON, HE'LL BE KEEPING AN EYE ON UNITED'S PERFORMANCES. WHO KNOWS WHAT HE'LL HAVE MADE OF THEIR ENTERTAININGLY CHAOTIC 3-1 LOSS TO ARSENAL ON SATURDAY, BUT AT LEAST BRUNO FERNANDES'S FLUFFED PENALTY PROVIDED SOME USEFUL DATA FOR A FUTURE LECTURE.

RAMSDALE REACTS TO THINGS HE HAD NOTHING TO DO WITH

TEN HAG'S BIGGEST CHALLENGE WILL BE TO CONTEND WITH THE GHOSTS OF GLORIES PAST AT THE THEATRE OF GROWN ADULTS HOLDING CARDBOARD SIGNS BEGGING FOR DIOGO DALOT'S TOP. MOST NOTABLY, HE'LL NEED TO DEAL WITH THE CONSTANT PRESENCE IN THE CORRIDORS OF THE CLUB'S MOST SUCCESSFUL MANAGER. GOOD LUCK WITH THAT ONE.

THE PREMIER LEAGUE'S TWO BIG HITTERS CONTINUE TO MATCH EACH OTHER STRIDE-FOR-STRIDE IN THE ONLY BATTLE THAT COUNTS: **THE USUAL POST-MATCH BULLSH*T!** JÜRGEN KLOPP WAS GENUINELY SADDENED THAT TOTTENHAM WOULD EMPLOY TACTICS DELIBERATELY DESIGNED TO HINDER HIS BOYS IN SATURDAY'S 1-1 DRAW. WHY COULDN'T SPURS HAVE BEEN MORE ACCOMMODATING, MORE SPURSY?

Allow me, Mr Salah.

And risk muddying his shoes on your grubby shirt?! Have you lost your mind?

Boys! Let's show a bit of professionalism, yeah? Now hurry up and help form the guard of honour.

NOT TO BE OUTDONE, PEP GUARDIOLA RESPONDED TO A 5-0 FLOGGING OF NEWCASTLE IN THE WHATABOUTDERBY WITH A COMPLAINT STRAIGHT FROM THE PROVINCIAL ENGLISH CLASSROOMS OF THE 1980S: **EVERYONE SUPPORTS BLOODY LIVERPOOL!** YOU. ME. ALL OF YOUR FRIENDS AND FAMILY. YOUR PETS. GARY NEVILLE, DUNCAN FERGUSON. **ALEX FERGUSON.** ALL CLOSET LIVERPOOL FANS. THE TITLE IS IN CITY'S GRASP, BUT IT SEEMS THE ONLY TROPHY PEP CARES ABOUT IS... LOVE ☺

What is it about our relentlessly dominant sportswashing project that people don't warm to? Do they hate winners, is that it?!

Preach.

THERE IS AN OUTSIDE CHANCE THAT MOST PEOPLE COULDN'T CARE LESS EITHER WAY, BUT PERHAPS CITY'S POPULARITY COULD BE IMPROVED BY USING THEIR OWNER'S VAST MINERAL WEALTH TO SCOOP UP ANOTHER INTERNATIONAL SUPERSTAR LIKE A BASKING SHARK. MAYBE THE ADDITION OF A PLAYER WHO EXUDES WARMTH WILL WIN THE MASSES OVER.

My primary objectives are to win the Ballon d'Or, crush humanity, and make Roy Keane feel bad about kicking my previous model. Now, give me your clothes. This T-shirt is beginning to look a bit awkward.

Ooh, I can't wait to play you as a false two.

HUMAN RIGHTS
On and off the pitch

Now I know why you cry.

LIKE CITY, WEST HAM RECOVERED FROM A MIDWEEK EURO DISAPPOINTMENT WITH A RELAXING SUNDAY STROLL, IN NORFOLK. ALL THAT UNPLEASANTNESS WITH THE BALLBOYS FORGOTTEN, AT LEAST FOR NOW (THEY ALWAYS COME BACK FOR YOU IN THE END).

NORWICH (THE FULHAM OF THE EAST) WERE ALREADY DOWN, OF COURSE, AND THEY WERE JOINED BY WATFORD (THE NORWICH OF THE NOT LONDON) WHO WERE CONDEMNED TO THEIR FATE BY CRYSTAL PALACE/WEEKS OF ABJECT RESULTS. AT LEAST ROY HAD A NICE DAY OUT.

Hey, how you doin'? Looking good, Wilf. Parish in the parish! Oh am I glad all over to see you legends.

You do know we went down, right?

OH NO, DID WE?

That must sting, Harry.

Son of a...

IT'S STILL ANYONE'S GUESS WHO'LL JOIN THEM. LEEDS CURRENTLY OCCUPY THE TRAPDOOR SEAT, AND THEIR SURVIVAL CHANCES WEREN'T HELPED BY AN EPIC MELTDOWN AT ARSENAL, AS JESSE MARSCH'S TEAMTALK WENT STRAIGHT OUT OF THE WINDOW.

Guys, remember the key themes from my motivational webinar for Red Bull corporate: 'Success through Bomber Jackets.' Unlock your potential by—

He says gift them a comedy goal in the fifth minute, then go two down before most fans have even finished their pre-match pie. Luke, you fly in with a needless two-footer. And Raphers, when he gets sent off, you do your best to join him by losing it like you're a Daily Mail reader who's just been told about the new Doctor Who.

BURNLEY ARE ALSO IN DANGER OF BEING OUTCAST AFTER LOSING 3-1 TO ASTON VILLA AT TURF MOOR - THE FIRST BLOW STRUCK BY FORMER CLARETS HERO, DANNY INGS, WHO COULDN'T HAVE BEEN MORE REMORSEFUL.

I'm sorry, Mike Jackson.

Who?

I am right here!

Never meant to make the home fans cry.

Gerrard's see-through jumper's quite a sight.

BUT LOOK AT FLEVERTON GO! IN OVERCOMING LEICESTER, THEY CLAIMED THEIR FIRST LEAGUE WIN ON THE ROAD SINCE THEY BEAT BRIGHTON IN AUGUST. IMAGINE NOT BEING ABLE TO BEAT BRIGHTON, THOUGH, EH? MEANWHILE, IN AMSTERDAM...

Time to see how my next club got on at Brighton en Hove Albion!

Schips

Cruyff on a bike...!

MEXICO

FOR A FEW MINUTES, IT LOOKED **ON**. ASTON VILLA WERE LEADING AT THE ETIHAD STADIUM AND FOR ALL MANCHESTER CITY'S RECENT (DOMESTIC) SUCCESS, THE AIR WAS THICK WITH **CITYITIS**. PEP'S BRAIN MUST HAVE BEEN MELTING LIKE THE BADGE ON HIS WACKY SWEATER AS 50,000 PEOPLE ENVISIONED GERRARD GOING THE FULL DAVID PLEAT, DE BRUYNE DOING A LOMAS, OR STONES DROPPING A POLLOCK. IT WAS HAPPENING AGAIN. IT WAS HAPPENING AGAIN...

...AND IT WAS DEFINITELY ON WHEN SADIO MANÉ GAVE LIVERPOOL A 49TH MINUTE LEAD AGAINST WOLVES, AT LEAST UNTIL THE LINESMAN STOPPED THE ANFIELD CELEBRATIONS...

Manchester City are so well resourced they've probably got world class players just lounging about the place, looking like the kappa logo.

Warm up, Ilkay, it's your time to sheiiiine...

CITY BLEW VILLA AWAY IN FIVE SECOND-HALF MINUTES AND THE MOST EXCITING LEAGUE IN THE WORLD WAS WON BY THE SAME CLUB FOR THE FOURTH TIME IN FIVE YEARS! AS WAS RECENTLY ESTABLISHED, EVERYONE IN THE WORLD SUPPORTS LIVERPOOL, SO IT WAS GREAT TO SEE THE UNDERDOG PREVAIL. THE MANCHESTER CITY PROJECT CONTINUES TO ACHIEVE THE GOALS OF ITS OWNERS...

We need to buy Manchester City.

Because our fortune and power is based on the ownership of a finite mineral resource and aligning ourselves with a famous club will improve our reputation overseas and increase tourism to Abu Dhabi?

No, because I want to see the lead singer of Beady Eye call Jamie Carragher a △ end and for them both to be slapped down by the admin of a high street optician.

AS IS THE MODERN CRAZE, THOUSANDS OF FANS SPILLED ON TO THE PITCH AT THE FINAL WHISTLE, BUT A TEAM OF SECURITY OFFICERS BUNDLED THE TALENT AWAY TO SAFETY.

Um. Guys?

THE FOOTBALL AUTHORITIES ARE SAID TO BE WORKING ON A SOLUTION TO STOP THIS RECENT TREND, BUT CLONING AN ARMY OF PATRICK VIEIRAS WILL TAKE TIME.

THERE WERE MATTERS TO BE DECIDED ELSEWHERE TOO, INCLUDING THE RACE FOR THE LAST CHAMPIONS LEAGUE SPOT, WHICH WAS CLAIMED WITH CHARACTERISTIC EASE BY TOTTENHAM. ARSENAL FOUGHT TO THE LAST AGAINST AN EVERTON SIDE WHO PLAYED LIKE THEY WERE NURSING A THREE-DAY HANGOVER. MIKEL ARTETA WATCHED ON WITH A SMILE THAT LOOKED PAINTED ON, AND THE MOURNFUL EYES OF A MAN RELYING ON NORWICH.

Brendan Rodgers is right: there's no tougher place to visit than Carrow Road on a clement afternoon.

Please stop shouting. I beg of you...

Yep, 15 minutes left - ample time for the Canaries to claw back six.

AT THE OTHER END OF THE TABLE, BURNLEY WENT DOWN AFTER A HOME DEFEAT TO NEWCASTLE. THEY WERE ALWAYS CHASING THE GAME FROM THE MOMENT NATHAN COLLINS CONCEDED A PENALTY, HAVING BEEN OVERCOME BY THE NATURAL HUMAN IMPULSE TO TOUCH SOMETHING YOU'RE NOT SUPPOSED TO AND FLICKING THE BALL AWAY FROM SEAN LONGSTAFF'S MELON WITH HIS HAND.

DO NOT PRESS

Oh for... Hey, Sunderland. Long time, no see!

BURNLEY'S DEMISE MEANT A REPRIEVE FOR LEEDS, WHO SECURED THEIR SAFETY WITH AN INJURY-TIME WINNER AT BRENTFORD. MAYBE JESSE MARSCH'S HISTORIC QUOTES INSPIRED THE TEAM TO PUSH THE ENVELOPE AFTER ALL...

"Arguing with Coleen is like arguing with a pigeon. You can tell it you are right and it is wrong, but it's still going to shit on your hair."
— R. VARDY

"Guys, I've got an idea for a really good analogy about the Great Chinese Famine for this week's programme notes."
— A. KINNEAR

"Hot dang, Raphers, I haven't seen a six-pack that smokin' since I left my root beers on the hood of my Chevy on the fourth of July!"
— J. MARSCH

BUT THIS WEEK'S FINAL WORD SHOULD GO TO THE DEMONSTRATIVE, SHINY-DOMED GENIUS WHO HAS MADE SUCH AN INDELIBLE MARK ON ENGLISH FOOTBALL. YES, MIKE DEAN HAS BID FAREWELL TO THE PREMIER LEAGUE AND WILL NOW WALK THE LAND, SOLVING CRIMES, GETTING IN ADVENTURES...

WOMEN'S EUROS 2022:
SARINA SUNRISE

Regardless of gender, four decades of following the fortunes of the English national football team condition you to expect a certain level of disappointment. When Lina Magull equalised for Germany with just over ten minutes of the Women's European Championship final remaining, many thought they knew how it would end. However, this England team wasn't as emotionally fragile as their male counterparts, and, looking back, it was foolish ever to doubt them.

Under the eye of Sarina Wiegman, who against all odds was proving to be a better coach than Philip John Neville, the Lionesses played a brand of bold attacking football that was as scorching as the soaring summer temperatures. The fields of England were combusting with scintillating play and literal fire. Still, the people in your local community Facebook group said there was no need to be alarmed about it being hot enough to fry an egg on Arjan Veurink's head because it was warm in 1976 and they turned out all right, despite all evidence to the contrary.

A nervous opening win against Austria gave few hints of the goal-fest that was to follow: an astonishing 8–0 win against Norway, whose defence was as lenient as a Scandinavian prison. A tougher challenge awaited in the quarter-final against Spain, who took the game into extra time, possibly as a tactic to delay being in the company of their coach, Jorge Vilda (more of whom later). The effects of Post-Tournament Stress Disorder created the nagging doubt that England should have saved some of those group-stage goals, because that's how football works. However, Georgia Stanway again defied all learned logic by thundering in a brilliant shot from distance.

Sweden were subsequently swept aside 4–0 in a semi-final appropriately hosted at a venue intrinsically linked with flowing, inventive football: Bramall Lane. Alessia Russo's ingenious back-heel shot through the legs of goalkeeper Hedvig Lindahl was the pick of the goals the uncles in the group chat reckoned they could have saved.

Wiegman's team were also able to mix it up when necessary, and their fighting spirit was epitomised in the final by the world-class swearing of Jill Scott, the angular veteran rising elegantly from the Wembley turf like a heron from a lake to call an opponent 'a fucking prick'. The spectre of historic defeats against Germany hung heavy as the game moved into extra time, but the Lionesses were undeterred. It was almost as if Chris Waddle's penalty miss in 1990 had little relevance to the collective confidence of a group of women mostly in their twenties.

Chloe Kelly's winning goal, ten minutes from time, felt like a pivotal moment for the women's game in England; her wild, shirt-waving celebration reminiscent of Brandi Chastain, whose winning penalty in the 1999 World Cup final popularised the sport in the US. Women's football was banned in England for fifty years in the twentieth century, so there's a little catching up to do – for example, no one tried to bully their way through one of Wembley's disabled entrances or stick a flare up their bum before the final – but the achievements of the Lionesses inspired a whole generation of young girls and middle-aged cartoonists.

ENGLAND ARE TRULY OFF AND RUNNING AT EURO'22 AFTER AN EIGHT GOAL FEAST AGAINST NORWAY IN BRIGHTON THAT COULD EASILY HAVE ENDED ∞-0. NORWAY'S COACH, MARTIN SJÖGREN, TRIED TO EMPLOY SOME MIND GAMES BEFORE THE MATCH AND CONTINUED TO MESS WITH SARINA WIEGMAN'S HEAD BY WAITING UNTIL THEY WERE SIX DOWN BEFORE MAKING A SUBSTITUTION. WITH HIS SMART SUIT AND CRISP WHITE T-SHIRT, HE INCREASINGLY CARRIED THE AIR OF A SOCKLESS TECH BOSS WATCHING HIS SHARE PRICE DIVE.

I can't believe a crypto-defence didn't work!

SPEAKING OF DIVING, ONE OF THE REFRESHING THINGS ABOUT WOMEN'S FOOTBALL IS THE ABSENCE OF THE PLAY-ACTING AND S-HOUSERY THAT BLIGHTS THE MEN'S GAME. TAKE, FOR EXAMPLE, ELLEN WHITE'S HEROIC ATTEMPTS TO STAY ON HER FEET IN SPITE OF A VICIOUS FOUL FROM MARIA THORISDÓTTIR FOR THE PENALTY THAT SET ENGLAND ON THEIR WAY.

BARELY PERCEPTIBLE BRUSH WITH A SUGARY CLOUD OF PIER FRONT CANDY FLOSS.

POOR OLD NORWAY DEFENDED LIKE CHRISTMAS TREES AND WERE PUT THROUGH THE WOOD CHIPPER BY ENGLAND'S ATTACK. THEY WERE SET UP TO INVITE THE SEARING RUNS OF STANWAY, HEMP AND HAT-TRICK HERO MEAD IN A MANNER THAT SUGGESTS THEIR PRE-MATCH TALK WAS BASED EXCLUSIVELY ON NORDIC POP BANGERS.

Take on me (take on me). Take me on (take on me).

Oh she's gone.

I've scored another twooooo.

EVERYTHING IS SUNSHINE AND ROSES FOR FRANCE, THOUGH. GRACE GEYORO'S FIRST-HALF HAT-TRICK HELPED THEM TO A 5-0 LEAD AT THE BREAK AGAINST ITALY. NOT EVEN THEIR BELOVED COACH CORINNE DIACRE WOULD HAVE MINDED LOSING THE SECOND-HALF 1-0.

CONGRULATIONS, you're all dropped!

Ha ha, just one of my famous little jokes. C'est banteur, non?

But seriously, the Lyon players can pack their bags.

Disgraceful. Absolutely disgraceful.

SPAIN -AND THE EUROS AS A WHOLE- HAVE SADLY BEEN ROBBED OF THE TALENTS OF THE INJURED ALEXIA PUTELLAS, BUT SHE CELEBRATED IN THE STANDS AS HER TEAMMATES CAME FROM BEHIND TO BEAT FINLAND, 4-1. WHEN AITANA BONMATÍ LOOPED IN A HEADER TO PUT SPAIN AHEAD, SHE MADE A BEELINE FOR THE TOUCHLINE AND THE PERSON WHO COMMANDS THE MOST RESPECT.

High five!

Alexiaaaaaaaaaaa!

Right. Yep. No. Absolutely.

PEOPLE ALL OVER ENGLAND THAT ISN'T THE NORTH-EAST OR SOUTH-WEST HAVE BEEN ATTENDING MATCHES IN THEIR LOCAL AREA. THE DANISH REPUBLIC OF BRENTFORD WAS JUMPING, DESPITE A 4-0 DEFEAT TO AN OMINOUSLY GOOD GERMANY. IN SHEFFIELD, 21,000 FANS - MANY CLOAKED IN THE CALIPPO HUES OF HOLLAND AND SWEDEN - MADE BRAMALL LANE LOOK EVEN MORE TROPICAL THAN USUAL! IT ALL SEEMED TOO MUCH FOR ONE YELLOW-OUTFITTED FAN, WHO REALLY SPOILT THE CARNIVAL ATMOSPHERE WHEN ASKED HOW MANY TIMES SWEDEN HAD WON THE EUROS.

He who laughs loudest last ... no, hang on... He who lasts... nope. Oh shut up, you baying mob!

IT'S ALL BEEN TREMENDOUS FUN AND IS INFINITELY MORE EDIFYING THAN THE SUMMER'S OTHER MAJOR SPORTING EVENT - THE TORY PARTY LEADERSHIP BATTLE; A SOPHIE'S CHOICE OF PICKING THE NEXT PRIME MINISTER FROM THE BRISTOL STOOL CHART.

 LIZ LAUGH LOVE

 EYE-WATERINGLY DENSE

 WOULD DEPORT OWN NAN FOR THE LIKES

 ACTUALLY QUITE TALL, YEAH

 JEREMY HUNT

 DARLING OF THE EUROPEAN RESEARCH GROUP (ERG!)

 GENUINELY TERRIFYING

THE LEVEL OF COVERAGE THE TOURNAMENT IS RECEIVING IS UNPRECEDENTED AND INDICATIVE OF HOW FAR THE WOMEN'S GAME HAS COME. EVEN GREAT FOOTBALL THINKERS LIKE LORD SUGAR HAVE TURNED THEIR ATTENTION TO THE COMPETITION, PROVIDING THE KIND OF INSIGHT YOU'D EXPECT FROM A WALNUT WIRED UP TO AN AMSTRAD COMPUTER. **HOORAY!**

Ow come when Lord see Premiership on box they have symbolic female commentators but when Lord watch womenball they aint got bladdy male man voice send tweet

HIS LORDSHIP

THE WOMEN'S EUROS ARE HERE AND THERE'S A BUZZ OF EXCITEMENT ABOUT SOME OF THE WORLD'S MOST TALENTED FOOTBALLERS HEADING FOR MERRY OLD ENGLAND!

DISTANT RUMBLING

Is that...?

SCHÜLLER! KATOTO! HEGERBERG! PUTELLAS! MIEDEMA!

IT ALL GOES TO SHOW HOW FAR THE WOMEN'S GAME HAS COME SINCE THE TOURNAMENT'S CHAOTIC BEGINNINGS. THE FIRST UNOFFICIAL "EUROPEAN COMPETITION FOR WOMEN'S FOOTBALL" TOOK PLACE IN ITALY IN 1969. THE HOSTS BEAT DENMARK IN THE FINAL AND THE TOP SCORER WAS ENGLAND'S SUE LOPEZ – THE SOUTHAMPTON LEGEND WHO WON'T RUIN YOUR CHILDHOOD MEMORIES, AND WHO FELL IN LOVE WITH THE GAME WHEN SHE FOUND SOME OLD FOOTBALL BOOTS IN THE GARDEN SHED.

UEFA CONSIDERED THE TOURNAMENT A CAUSE FOR CONCERN. IT COULDN'T HAVE WOMEN TAKING IT UPON THEMSELVES TO ESTABLISH THEIR OWN UNSANCTIONED EVENTS LIKE SOME SORT OF VICTORIAN BACKSTREET CURIOSITY.

WALLOP

IT SET UP A COMMITTEE MADE UP ALMOST ENTIRELY OF UEFA BLOKES, THE SOLE EXCEPTION BEING SWEDEN'S KERSTIN ROSÉN. AS SUE LOPEZ LATER NOTED, BY THE TIME THE COMMITTEE WAS DISBANDED IN 1978, IT HADN'T ORGANISED A SINGLE INTERNATIONAL COMPETITION, SO IT MUST HAVE BEEN WELL BUSY.

Come on, guys; we're supposed to be organising an international tournament.

Um, hello? He's from Belgium and he's from France!

UEFA FINALLY GOT ITS ACT TOGETHER AND SET UP AN OFFICIAL TOURNAMENT IN 1984, EVEN IF THE TROPHY LOOKED LIKE AN AWARD FROM A CORPORATE EVENT FOR THE CHEESE INDUSTRY.

BEST STILTON

COMPETITION POUR EQUIPES REPRESENTATIVES FEMININES

THANKFULLY, IT HAS SINCE BEEN REPLACED BY A SLEEK MODERN DESIGN DOUBTLESS INSPIRED BY THE SINUOUS CONTOURS OF THE CONTEMPORARY FOOTBALLER AND NOT JUST SOMETHING THAT CAUGHT THE DESIGNER'S EYE AS THE DEADLINE LOOMED...

Eureka!

IN ITS PATRIARCHAL WISDOM, UEFA DECREED THAT THE GAMES SHOULD COMPRISE OF 35-MINUTE HALVES AND THAT A SIZE FOUR BALL BE USED, LEST THE LADIES' DELICATE TOES BECOME DISTRESSED BY THE FULL-SIZE VERSION.

What the hell is this ?!

Do you ever feel like they're not taking us seriously?

OF COURSE, SUCH CONDESCENDING ATTITUDES TOWARDS WOMEN'S FOOTBALL HAVE LONG SINCE BEEN ERADICATED.

NORTHERN IRELAND

Bit emotional, like.

KENNY SHIELS
MANAGER

THE FINAL WAS A TWO-LEGGED AFFAIR BETWEEN ENGLAND AND SWEDEN. THE SWEDES WON THEIR HOME LEG 1-0, BEFORE THE RETURN MATCH AT KENILWORTH ROAD ON A PITCH THAT WAS SO BOGGY IT MIGHT HAVE INSPIRED LUTON TO REPLACE IT WITH THE ASTROTURF FROM A BUTCHER'S SHOP WINDOW. ALL A FAR CRY FROM THIS SUMMER'S GLITTERING CHOICE OF VENUES : WEMBLEY ! OLD TRAFFORD ! TWO THIRDS OF LEIGH SPORTS VILLAGE ! SOME OF MANCHESTER CITY'S ACADEMY STADIUM !

Wow, we're heading to Manchester. Little old Iceland at the Theatre of Dreams !

Um, not quite, Sara...

That's OK, The Etihad is still a fine stadium.

Yeah, about that...

SWEDEN'S SHIRTS FOR THE UPCOMING EUROS HAVE INFORMATION ABOUT THEIR TACTICS AND PLAYER DATA SEWN INTO THE LABEL TO GIVE THEIR OPPONENTS A FIGHTING CHANCE OF IDENTIFYING THEIR WEAKNESSES...

AGREEING TO THIS GIMMICKY HUBRIS TO HELP FLOG SOME MERCH.

BUT DATA ANALYSIS WASN'T AS READILY AVAILABLE BACK IN '84, SO ENGLAND'S PLAYERS HAD TO WORK OUT HOW TO STOP SWEDEN FOR THEMSELVES.

100% polyester. Do not tumble dry. Iron inside out... ☒ ? What on earth is ☒ ? This doesn't help at all !

ALTHOUGH ENGLAND WON THE SECOND LEG 1-0, THEY THEN INEVITABLY LOST ON PENALTIES. THE NATION'S WOEFUL SHOOT-OUT RECORD DOESN'T DISCRIMINATE ON THE BASIS OF GENDER. WHEN PIA SUNDHAGE THWACKED IN THE WINNING KICK, COACH ULF LYFORS RACED IN TO THE VACANT END OF THE SWAMP AND SLID THROUGH SOME PRESUMABLY LOST SEAGULLS, IN THE KIND OF HOLLYWOOD SCENE YOU NATURALLY ASSOCIATE WITH LUTON.

THE SWEDES MADE IT TO THE FINAL AGAIN IN 1987, BUT WERE BEATEN BY HOSTS NORWAY. THERE THEN FOLLOWED A PERIOD OF ALMOST TOTAL GERMAN DOMINATION; AN IMPRESSIVE TIMELINE THAT SHOULD ARGUABLY WARRANT MORE THAN ONE PANEL. LET'S CALL IT A SATIRICAL NOD TO THE POOR PLANNING OF THE COMPETITION'S FORMATIVE YEARS. YES.

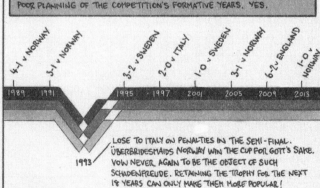

4-1 v NORWAY
3-1 v NORWAY
3-2 v SWEDEN
2-0 v ITALY
1-0 v SWEDEN
3-1 v NORWAY
6-2 v ENGLAND
1-0 v NORWAY

1989 · 1991 · 1995 · 1997 · 2001 · 2005 · 2009 · 2013

1993 LOSE TO ITALY ON PENALTIES IN THE SEMI-FINAL. ÜBERBRIDESMAIDS NORWAY WIN THE CUP FOR GOTT'S SAKE. VOW NEVER AGAIN TO BE THE OBJECT OF SUCH SCHADENFREUDE. RETAINING THE TROPHY FOR THE NEXT 18 YEARS CAN ONLY MAKE THEM MORE POPULAR !

THEIR RUN OF SUCCESS ONLY CAME TO AN END IN 2017, WHEN SARINA WIEGMAN'S NETHERLANDS TEAM SWEPT TO VICTORY PLAYING THE KIND OF VIBRANT ATTACKING FOOTBALL YOU STILL MISTAKENLY CORRELATE WITH THE DUTCH. THE GLOBALLY-RESPECTED COACH NOW HAS THE RESPONSIBILITY OF PRODUCING SIMILAR RESULTS WITH THE LIONESSES, SO STRAP YOURSELF IN FOR A SUMMER OF ENTERTAINMENT, BECAUSE THE GOOD NEWS DOESN'T END THERE...

Hey, I'm no Fizzer Neville.

HOORAY !

AS WE ENTER THE QUARTER-FINALS, THE MOOD IN THE ENGLAND CAMP IS ALSO HIGHER THAN ARJAN VEURINK'S FRINGE. THE LIONESSES' ASSISTANT COACH WAS ACTIVATED AS A MEATY CONDUIT FOR SARINA WIEGMAN WHEN SHE TESTED POSITIVE FOR BEING BRILLIANT (BUT ALSO COVID) BEFORE THE 5-0 WIN AGAINST NORTHERN IRELAND.

AN ABSORBING GROUP STAGE CONCLUDED ON MONDAY NIGHT UNDER THE KIND OF OPPRESSIVE CONDITIONS THAT ARE PROBABLY NOTHING TO WORRY ABOUT.

LUCKILY, UEFA WAS ON HAND TO SHOW ITS CARING SIDE BY PERMITTING SWELTERING FANS TO EACH BRING IN ONE OPEN VIAL CONTAINING THE SINGLE SALTY TEAR OF A CLIMATE SCIENTIST. STEWARDS WERE ON HAND TO CONFISCATE ANY LIDS.

BELGIUM CLAIMED THE LAST QUARTER-FINAL SPOT WHEN DE CAIGNY LACED IN THE WINNER AGAINST ITALY. IT SEEMS FITTING THAT A TEAM NICKNAMED 'THE RED FLAMES' WOULD QUALIFY, ESPECIALLY AT THE EXPENSE OF ICELAND (OR, AS IT WILL SOON BE CALLED, LAND). MEANWHILE, ITALY ARE LEFT ASKING THEMSELVES A BIG QUESTION: IS THERE ANYWHERE HOT ENOUGH TO MAKE COACH MILENA BERTOLINI REMOVE HER JACKET?

THE MOTHERS AND DÓTTIRS OF ICELAND EARNED A CREDITABLE DRAW WITH FRANCE BUT WERE ELIMINATED WITHOUT LOSING A GAME. THEY COULD LEAVE THE TOURNAMENT WITH THEIR HEADS HELD HIGH, SIGNING OFF WITH THEIR FAMOUS 'THUNDERCLAP', WHICH ECHOED AROUND THE SKIES OF ROTHERHAM.

FINALLY - AND NOT TO MAKE THIS ABOUT ✨ME✨ - BUT IT'S EMERGED THAT ALL THE PLAYERS FEATURED IN MY EUROS PREVIEW CARTOON HAVE EXPERIENCED SOME FORM OF SETBACK. SCHÜLLER AND MIEDEMA BOTH TESTED POSITIVE FOR COVID, KATOTO AND PUTELLAS BOTH SUFFERED SERIOUS KNEE INJURIES, AND POOR OLD HEGERBERG VANISHED COMPLETELY.

CLEARLY, THE NOTION THAT A DRAWING HAS THE SUPERNATURAL POWER TO CONDEMN THE PEOPLE IT DEPICTS TO SOME SORT OF PERSONAL MISFORTUNE (NO MATTER HOW EVIL THE ARTIST) IS UTTERLY FANCIFUL.

ENGLAND HAVE WON A MAJOR TOURNAMENT!

VICTORY OVER GERMANY HAS SECURED THE FIRST MAJOR HONOUR IN THE HISTORY OF ENGLISH WOMEN'S FOOTBALL. NOT ONLY HAS THIS TEAM ELEVATED THE PROFILE OF THE WOMEN'S GAME TO HEIGHTS PREVIOUSLY UNIMAGINABLE, THEY HAVE ALSO RECEIVED A PRIZE ALMOST AS GLITTERING AS THE FREEDOM OF MILTON KEYNES...

A LETTER FROM DE PFEFFEL!

"When people think of advocacy for ladeez, they think of THE BOJMONSTER. Alas, I can't be there in person as the amusements clash with Pimms o'clock and I don't need dem votes no more. Instead, I'm sending Viceroy Dorries for a photo-op with Tory Spice. Filly power!"

OVER THE LAST MONTH, THIS ENGLAND TEAM HAS PROVIDED TOO MANY JOYOUS MOMENTS TO FIT IN TO ONE CARTOON, BUT SOME HIGHLIGHTS HAVE INCLUDED...

RUSSO'S BACKHEEL AGAINST SWEDEN...

Daim.

AND HER ATTEMPTS TO READ THE NOTE BROUGHT ON BY THE GERMAN SUBSTITUTE, LENA LATTWEIN.

Why didn't I pay more attention in German at school?!

IN DER MIXER!

THE GOALS OF MEAD

STANWAY'S ROCKET AGAINST SPAIN

THE ANNIHILATION OF NORWAY

THE SAVES OF EARPS

REDUCING KENNY SHIELS TO HEAD-SLAPPING APOPLEXY

BIT EMOTIONAL THAT, MATE.

WALSH'S PERFECTLY-THREADED PASS TO TOONE

AND HER DELICIOUS, DINKED FINISH.

THAT DEFENCE!

AND OVERSEEING IT ALL, THE VISIONARY SARINA WIEGMAN, WHOSE CALMING INFLUENCE SHOULD BE MADE AVAILABLE TO EVERYONE AS PART OF SOME NATIONAL PROGRAMME.

No good can come of texting your ex when you're this drunk, my friend. Why not put down your phone? Arjan here has fixed you a herbal infusion.

THEN THERE WAS CHLOE KELLY'S WINNING GOAL. HAVING WON THE CORNER AND GEED UP THE CROWD, SHE OUTMUSCLED FELICITAS RAUCH TO PROD IN LUCY BRONZE'S KNOCKDOWN. THE ECSTATIC CELEBRATIONS ONLY BRIEFLY PAUSED BY A CHECK TO SEE IF @DAVE258456 RECKONS HE COULD HAVE DONE BETTER.

He's watching the Formula One!

THERE'S NOTHING RUDE ABOUT A BODY AND IF THERE'S ANY JUSTICE, THE ENGLAND BADGE WILL BE REDESIGNED TO HONOUR HER EPIC EXPRESSION OF PURE JOY.

IT IS A RARELY-MENTIONED FACT THAT THE ENGLAND MEN'S TEAM ONCE BEAT GERMANY IN A WEMBLEY FINAL TOO! THIS OCCURRED AT A TIME WHEN WOMEN WERE BANNED FROM PLAYING FOOTBALL IN BOTH COUNTRIES. BACK THEN, THE IDEA THAT A WOMEN'S GAME WOULD ONE DAY BE PLAYED AT A PACKED-OUT WEMBLEY, WITH MILLIONS MORE WATCHING AT HOME, WOULD HAVE SEEMED AS WILD AS ANY OTHER VISION OF WHAT LIFE WOULD LOOK LIKE IN 2022.

Trippy!

THE PIONEERING WOMEN WHO ENDURED DECADES IN THE WILDERNESS MAY HAVE SHED A TEAR AT HOW FAR THE GAME HAS COME, KNOWING THAT ALL OVER THE COUNTRY, FUTURE GENERATIONS OF FEMALE PLAYERS WILL HAVE BEEN INSPIRED TO RECREATE THE FINAL'S MOST EPIC MOMENTS:

F*** off, you f***ing pr***!

Wha-?!

Let's hear her out.

NOW THE CONFETTI HAS BEEN SWEPT AWAY, TALK WILL TURN TO LEGACY AND REMOVING THE OBSTACLES THAT PREVENT YOUNG GIRLS FROM EMULATING THEIR HEROES. SOD IT, I'M A 47-YEAR-OLD MAN WITH A CREAKING HIP AND A BMI SO-CALLED GPs WOULD DESCRIBE AS 'TROUBLING', BUT EVEN I HARBOUR DREAMS OF BEING FRAN KIRBY WHEN I GROW UP. WHEN WILL STRAIGHT OLD WHITE MEN GET A BREAK??

Whatever happens, if pathetic middle-aged cartoonists are not given the opportunity to follow their dreams then what are we doing?

THANK YOU.

WHILE TRIUMPHANT ENGLISH TEAMS FROM OTHER SPORTING CODES HAVE TREATED THE POST-VICTORY SESSION AS THE PINNACLE OF SUCCESS, LEAH WILLIAMSON HAS VOWED THAT THIS IS JUST THE START OF THE JOURNEY FOR A SIDE THAT HAS ALREADY PROVEN ITSELF ADEPT AT DEFYING NATIONAL STEREOTYPES. IN THE MEANTIME, THERE'S ONLY ONE WAY TO FINISH, AND THAT'S BY KEEPING THE BALL IN THE CORNER OF THE CARTOON, TO THE VOCAL FRUSTRATION OF THE GERMAN PLAYERS...

GAH! It might as well be buried beneath the messages of congratulation from Welsh, Scottish and Irish fans!

2022-23 (PART ONE):
STAMFORD BRIDGE IS DOWN

In early September 2022, Britain came to another standstill with the confirmation of historic news that people had long feared, yet which still came as a surprise: Chelsea had sacked their manager. It was a completely new experience for people born over the previous eighteen months, many of whom were unable to fully articulate their feelings and could only weep openly and point at doggies. It was a time when a great many people shat themselves in public.

Thomas Tuchel had appeared in rude health just a few weeks earlier, delighting the world as he embarked upon a bizarre mating ritual with Antonio Conte after an ill-tempered 2–2 draw with Tottenham. The two fully grown adult men had spent a late summer's afternoon pushing each other's buttons, before expressing their passions through the medium of dance, hands gripped, gums exposed, twirling one another in the sunlight. As public displays go, these alphas couldn't have appeared more dignified if they were wrestling over a supermarket parking spot.

The protocols were now enacted to crown an heir to the Chelsea throne/blue racing-car dugout seat. New Chelsea owner Todd Boehly, who had reportedly grown tired of Tuchel's weak bantz in the group chat, added a modern twist to proceedings, some blue-sky thinking: hiring whoever worked for Brighton. Graham Potter and his backroom staff duly decamped to Stamford Bridge, perhaps aware that in terms of longevity, no one could realistically hope to match his predecessor's reign.

Also around this time, in case you hadn't picked up on the analogy, the Queen died. The nation's supermarket scanners fell silent, Elizabeth II's favourite holiday destination (Centre Parcs) closed its doors and all football matches were postponed. Cynics claimed the Queen didn't even care about football, conveniently overlooking the fact that she attended three matches in seventy years.

FOOTIE FACTS

Need evidence of the Queen's passion for football? Just look at a stamp! Her portrait in profile actually shows her mugging off the away end, offering out their top boy. If the rest of her body were visible, you'd see she was dancing on the gangway steps, with her arms outstretched, as a sighing minimum-wage steward looks on.

Brighton replaced Potter with Roberto De Zerbi, whose credits included winning the Ukrainian Super Cup with Shakhtar Donetsk in 2021 and playing Beppe in *EastEnders* from 1998–2002. Under De Zerbi, the Seagulls were transformed into a free-scoring attacking force, attracting plaudits from people who don't ascribe everything that's subsequently gone wrong in their life to Brighton beating Swindon on penalties in the Second Division play-off semi-final in 2004. Bastards. Bastards. Bastards.

The Premier League was again put on hold at the end of November, but this time the only people who had to die were the migrant workers who perished while building the stadiums and infrastructure for the World Cup in Qatar. God save the Emir!

Arsenal were top of the table at the break, which came as no surprise to anyone who saw the fly-on-the-wall documentary series that revealed some of Mikel Arteta's high-performance-mindset motivational tools. One scene showed him making a point about teamwork with a cartoon drawing of a heart and brain holding hands, in a manner not unlike Tuchel and Conte. The players were as inspired as any employee forced to attend a workshop (just keep your head down and think of the buffet), further strengthening the argument that cartoonists should be given footballers' wages.

The Gunners could feel confident of maintaining their five-point cushion over Manchester City, whose top scorer, Erling Haaland, would now be forced to spend a month resting, oiling his joints and updating his targeting software.

FOOTBALL'S A FICKLE OLD BUSINESS. HOW QUICKLY PEOPLE FORGET THE GLORIES OF LIFTING THE BANGKOK CENTENARY CUP WHEN YOU LOSE YOUR FIRST LEAGUE GAME. SUCH IS THE CASE FOR THE CAPTAIN OF THE TITANIC, ERIK TEN HAG, WHOSE TEAM WERE BOOED OFF DESPITE IMPROVING ON THEIR LAST RESULT AGAINST BRIGHTON.

LUCKILY, THE ANSWER TO ALL OF MANCHESTER UNITED'S PROBLEMS IS STARING THEM RIGHT IN THE FACE: A COMPLETE RESTRUCT—

ALL OF THIS WILL BE CONSIDERED BY **THE THINK TANK** – A PANEL OF UNITED LEGENDS, SET UP AS AN INNOVATIVE NEW WAY TO UNDERMINE THE MANAGER.

Here's to swimmin' and club-branded linen.

Ugh, ish he going to be here for de whole journey, shkipper?

MARKO ARNAUTOVIĆ!

JUST £15m! 33! PROBLEMATIC! DIVISIVE!

The conclusive finding of this committee is that you didn't want to do it like that.

YOU'D USUALLY HAVE EXPECTED ARSENAL'S SEASON TO HAVE SPIRALLED BURNING TO THE GROUND BY NOW TOO, BUT THEY BEGAN WITH A SOLID 2-0 WIN AT CRYSTAL PALACE, NO DOUBT HELPED BY MIKEL ARTETA'S ATTEMPTS TO REPLICATE THE SELHURST PARK ATMOSPHERE ON THE TRAINING GROUND.

FULHAM AND LIVERPOOL PLAYED OUT THE GAME OF THE WEEKEND ON AN ARID PLAIN ADJACENT TO THE CRACKED MOSAIC OF THE EVAPORATED THAMES. MAN OF THE MATCH WAS TWO-GOAL ALEKSANDAR MITROVIĆ, WHO MAY YET WIN THE GOLDEN BOOT IF MARCO SILVA CAN CONTINUE TO TRICK HIM INTO BELIEVING HE'S STILL PLAYING IN THE CHAMPIONSHIP.

Granit, I said to draw a tifo of The Crystal Palace!

Eh?

Forget it. Bukayo, crank up 'Glad All Over'. It's track three on the playlist.

Man's talking like I'm unfamiliar with the back catalogue of The Dave Clark Five.

You sure that's Bristol City? They look a bit different to last season...

Oh, heh, yeah, they've got red shorts this year...

OK...

ENDSLEIGH MODE ACTIVATED!

'kinnel!

LIVERPOOL SALVAGED A POINT, THANKS IN NO SMALL MEASURE TO THE INTRODUCTION OF DARWIN NÚÑEZ, WHO UNSETTLED THE FULHAM DEFENCE WITH HIS CHAOTIC ENERGY.

ANOTHER IMPRESSIVE UNIT, ERLING HAALAND, SWALLOWED UP HUGE SECTIONS OF THE LONDON STADIUM WITH HIS GIANT MECHANICAL STRIDES. HIS TWO GOALS WERE CHEERED ON BY PAPPA ALFIE, WHO FAMOUSLY CREATED THE UNSTOPPABLE ROBOT BOY FROM SCAFFOLDING POLES, INDUSTRIAL SPRINGS AND LUCOZADE.

Dude. Can you do this? Dude. Look at me. Dude.

I am the very model of a modern Major-General. I've information vegetable, animal and mineral...

Dude. Look: Soul food. Dude.

REAM

ERLIN

I regret everything.

ELSEWHERE, NEWLY PROMOTED BOURNEMOUTH ARE UP AND RUNNING AFTER A 2-0 WIN AGAINST ASTON VILLA, MANAGER SCOTT PARKER ALREADY EARNING HIS STRIPES.

Cycling proficiency... Straightest parting in the regiment... Narrowest tie... Daftest jacket.

THERE ARE LOTS OF CHANGES FOR THE NEW SEASON, BUT NOT ALL OF THEM HAVE BEEN WELCOMED. THE DECISION BY BBC RADIO 5 LIVE TO REPLACE THE READING OF THE CLASSIFIED RESULTS WITH A RAP BATTLE ABOUT TEXTING OR SOMETHING HAS PROVEN UNPOPULAR. THANKFULLY, THE STORY HAS GAINED SOME TRACTION, SO YOU CAN GUARANTEE IT WILL HAVE CAUGHT THE ATTENTION OF BOTH GHOULS IN THE TORY LEADERSHIP RACE TO THE BOTTOM.

AND WE ALREADY HAVE OUR FIRST BEEF OF THE NEW TERM: BRUNO LAGE INFURIATED BY JESSE MARSCH SAYING "SOMETHING YOU CANNOT SAY" ON THE TOUCHLINE.

Good luck, Bruno. I hope we whoop your fannies, though!

I'll make assylum seekers read the results on the doorsteps of every home on their way to the deportation camps. This will allow our voter base to get their footie scores and personally abuse the sovereign trespassers for their pronunciation of 'Airdrieonians'.

Not only will I bring back football results, I'll also establish a league table system to identify the best and worst performing teams!

MOST OTHER WEEKS, MANCHESTER UNITED GETTING TONKED 4-0 BY A HOUNSLOW BUS DEPOT XI WOULD HAVE BEEN THE BIG STORY, BUT THEN TUCHEL GAVE CONTE'S PALM A LITTLE TOMMY TICKLER WITH HIS MIDDLE FINGER AND THE FOOTBALL WORLD IMPLODED. THAT WE SHOULD BE SUBJECTED TO SUCH A COMMOTION ON THE SACRED 30TH ANNIVERSARY OF RICHARD KEYS INVENTING THE PREMIER LEAGUE (AMONGST OTHER THINGS) ONLY SERVED TO MAKE IT FUNNIER.

IT ALL BEGAN FAIRLY ROUTINELY, WITH CHELSEA TAKING THE LEAD THROUGH KALIDOU KOULIBALY — THE NEW SIGNING WHO PERSONALLY RANG JOHN TERRY TO ASK HIS PERMISSION TO WEAR THE HALLOWED NO 26. NATURALLY, JT WAS MORE THAN HAPPY TO OBLIGE.

INTERESTINGLY, RUMOURED TRANSFER TARGET ANTHONY GORDON HAS ALSO CONTACTED THE SPIRIT REALM TO ASK LADY DI IF HE CAN WEAR HER HAIR.

THE TROUBLE BEGAN WHEN HØJBJERG EQUALISED FOR SPURS. TUCHEL (48) WAS SPITTING BARS AT THE FOURTH OFFICIAL ABOUT VARIOUS INFRACTIONS IN THE BUILD-UP, BEFORE HAVING HIS FLOW INTERRUPTED BY THE SCREAMING ADULT MAN, CONTE (53).

WHEN REECE JAMES RESTORED CHELSEA'S LEAD, TUCHEL CHARGED OFF DOWN THE TOUCHLINE LIKE A SET OF GOLF CLUBS SHOT OUT OF A CANNON, SOMEHOW MANAGING TO SPRINT SARCASTICALLY. FOR A MAN FAMED FOR HIS LOVE OF WATCHING PEOPLE RUN, CONTE SEEMED UNIMPRESSED.

BUT IT REALLY KICKED OFF AT THE FINAL WHISTLE. CHELSEA WERE INCENSED THAT KANE'S INJURY-TIME EQUALISER WAS ALLOWED TO STAND FOLLOWING ROMERO'S RAPUNZEL MOMENT WITH CUCURELLA. OVER 100,000 OF CHELSEA'S MOST RATIONAL FANS HAVE SIGNED AN ONLINE PETITION DEMANDING THAT ANTHONY TAYLOR BE BANNED FROM REFEREEING THEIR MATCHES. IT WOULD HAVE BEEN MORE, BUT...

TUCHEL'S BURNING SENSE OF INJUSTICE WAS FURTHER FUELLED BY CONTE'S NO-LOOK HANDSHAKE.

IT WAS A BEAUTIFULLY-CHOREOGRAPHED MOMENT OF THEATRE — TWO GROWN ADULTS WHIRLING HAND-IN-HAND LIKE NO ONE WAS WATCHING.

IF YOU THOUGHT THAT WAS FUN, WAIT UNTIL CONTE TURNS UP AT THE RETURN FIXTURE SPORTING ROMERO'S TROPHY FROM SUNDAY.

BOTH MANAGERS RECEIVED RED CARDS AND THE PLAYERS DID THEIR BEST TO HIDE THEIR AMUSEMENT — IMAGINE SEEING YOUR LINE MANAGER GETTING IN A PUBLIC DING-DONG WITH A RIVAL BRANCH SUPERVISOR AT THE NEXT REGIONAL CONFERENCE! NO ONE ENJOYED THIS DIGNIFIED SPECTACLE OF RAW MASCULINITY MORE THAN GRAEME SOUNESS. SAT IN A CRAMPED TV SET NEXT TO KAREN CARNEY (144 CAPS), THE WALKING MEME SHOWED THAT NO ROOM IS SMALL ENOUGH FOR HIM TO READ.

AND AT LEAST THE ARGIE AND/OR BARGIE TOOK THE HEAT OFF ERIK TEN HAG FOR A BIT, ALLOWING HIM TO ENJOY A PEACEFUL, POST-EMERGENCY-TRAINING-SESSION SUNDAY.

IF YOU HAVEN'T BEEN FOLLOWING THE TWITTER ACCOUNTS OF CRAZY FROG OR THE BRITISH KEBAB AWARDS THEN I HAVE SOME SERIOUS NEWS FOR YOU: THE QUEEN HAS DIED. DURING THIS TIME OF ASSUMED UNIVERSAL GRIEF, THE PREMIER LEAGUE WAS QUICK TO POSTPONE ITS WEEKEND FIXTURES. THIS FOLLOWED A CHAT WITH THE GOVERNMENT, WHO MADE IT CLEAR IT WAS THE FOOTBALL AUTHORITIES' CALL.

THE NOTION THAT A LEAGUE FULL OF FOREIGN PLAYERS WOULD BE TOO BEREFT TO PLAY FOOTBALL SEEMS ODD; AS IF, SAY, BRYAN MBEUMO, HAD GONE THE FULL WITCHELL, DONNING A VICTORIAN MOURNING VEIL AND REPEATING THE WORD "DUTY" UNTIL HIS THROAT WAS RAW. ALL THE OTHER POPULAR BRITISH SPORTS CONTINUED – RUGBY, CRICKET, MARKLE-TRASHING – BUT SOON FOOTBALL WAS CANCELLED AT ALL LEVELS, PERHAPS OUT OF FEAR THAT SOMEONE WOULD MENTION SOMETHING THAT COULD BE INTERPRETED AS CRITICISM OF EIIR.

AS EVER, FANS WHO'D ALREADY PAID FOR TICKETS, TRAVEL AND ACCOMMODATION WERE A MINOR CONSIDERATION, AS WERE THE CASUAL WORKERS RELIANT ON FOOTBALL FOR THEIR INCOME. LUCKILY, THE COST OF LIVING CRISIS HAS BEEN PUT ON HOLD DURING THIS PERIOD OF COMPULSORY BEREAVEMENT. BESIDES, THE MOUNTAIN OF WASTED FOOTY SCRAN COULD BE SET ALIGHT, GENERATING ENOUGH ENERGY TO HEAT EVERY HOME IN THE LAND. THERE'S ENOUGH SUGAR IN THOSE BURGER BUNS TO KEEP IT BURNING UNTIL SPRING!

IT'S A WIDELY-HELD VIEW THAT FOOTBALL MISSED AN OPPORTUNITY TO PAY ITS RESPECTS, PERHAPS WITH A TASTEFUL TRIBUTE ORGANISED BY WAYNE LINEKER. AFTER ALL, IT'S THE TIME FOR BIZARRE PAGEANTRY AND ANTIQUATED RITUALS, LIKE LETTING SOMEONE RULE OVER A COUNTRY ON THE BASIS OF BIRTH. WILD! SOMEONE WAS EVEN TASKED WITH INFORMING THE BEES OF THE QUEEN'S DEATH.

THE CAUTION OF THE FOOTBALL AUTHORITIES IS PERHAPS UNDERSTANDABLE. LAST WEEK, THE PRESENTER OF THE GREAT BRITISH SEWING BEE WAS SENT TO THE GULAGS FOR USING SARCASM AGAINST THE ESTABLISHMENT. OFFICERS OF THE GRIEF POLICE ARE OUT IN FORCE, LIKE INSPECTORS OF THE WOKEFINDER GENERAL, HUNTING DOWN HERETICS WHO DISPLAY ANYTHING LESS THAN 'A TOUCH OF CLASS'.

BACK IN THE REAL WORLD (SORT OF), THERE WAS ALSO A TRANSITION OF POWER AT CHELSEA. THE CODED MESSAGE 'STAMFORD BRIDGE IS DOWN' SIGNALLED THOMAS TUCHEL HAD REACHED THE END OF HIS REIGN. THE GERMAN ENJOYED A LONGER INNINGS THAN MOST, BUT WHEN HIS RELATIONSHIP WITH TODD BOEHLY BROKE DOWN, THE MAN UPSTAIRS REFUSED TO SAVE HIM.

GRAHAM POTTER SWIFTLY ASCENDED TO THE THRONE. AFTER YEARS IN OBSCURITY (SOZ, BRIGHTON), HE MUST NOW FACE THE GLARE OF A VERY PUBLIC ROLE THAT SAPS THE HAPPINESS FROM EVERY INCUMBENT. NO WONDER IF HE SEEMED A BIT STRESSED WHEN HE SIGNED HIS LIFE AWAY.

PEOPLE HAVE REACTED TO THE QUEEN'S DEATH IN DIFFERENT WAYS. IF YOU'RE SAD, THAT'S FINE. IF YOU'RE NOT SAD, THAT'S ALSO FINE AND YOU'LL BE PROCESSED IN DUE COURSE. BUT IN THESE STRANGE TIMES, THERE'S PERHAPS ONE THING WE CAN ALL ENJOY: THE THOUGHT OF MANAGERS STRUGGLING TO HOLD IN THEIR COMPLAINTS ABOUT THE FIXTURE PILE-UP THESE POSTPONEMENTS WILL CAUSE, FOR FEAR OF BEING CHASED INTO THE WOODS BY AN ANGRY MOB.

ONE LONG CELEBRATION OF THE VAST DISPARITY BETWEEN THE HAVES AND HAVE NOTS? YES, THE PREMIER LEAGUE RETURNED AT THE WEEKEND! WHAT'S MORE, EACH GAME WAS PRECEDED BY A TRIBUTE TO THE QUEEN. A STRICT FORMAT WAS FOLLOWED BY EACH CLUB, PRESUMABLY TO PREVENT ANY KIND OF 'ONE-UP MA'AMSHIP', NOT THAT IT'S IN ENGLISH FOOTBALL'S NATURE TO TREAT GRIEF AS SOME SORT OF PERFORMATIVE COMPETITION (OUT OF RESPECT, THAT IS THE ONLY JOKE IN THIS CARTOON). MANAGERS WERE ALSO ENCOURAGED TO WEAR BLACK, WHICH MARCO SILVA TOOK AS A CUE TO DRESS LIKE ALBERT SQUARE'S NEWEST BADDIE.

LAST WEEK'S NEWS WAS OF COURSE DOMINATED BY HEARTWARMING TALES FROM **THE QUEUE** OF NEW NOTTINGHAM FOREST PLAYERS (TALKING OF FAMOUS OLD INSTITUTIONS STRUGGLING FOR RELEVANCE IN THE MODERN AGE).

THE QUEEN NEVER REVEALED MUCH OF HERSELF TO THE WORLD, BUT IN THE SPIRIT OF IMPLANTING OUR OWN PERSONALITIES ONTO SOMEONE WE DIDN'T KNOW, WE CAN BE SURE THAT IN PRIVATE SHE WAS A MIDDLE-AGED SWINDON FAN WHO DREW FOOTBALL CARTOONS FOR A LIVING. IT IS HOPED THAT CHARLES WILL ENJOY A SIMILARLY POSITIVE RELATIONSHIP WITH THE GAME, ALTHOUGH THE EARLY SIGNS AREN'T PROMISING...

ON THE PITCH, MANCHESTER CITY SWATTED ASIDE WOLVES, THANKS IN PART TO THE CONTINUED DOMINANCE OF ERLING HAALAND. IT'S COOL THAT THE STRONGEST TEAM, BACKED BY LIMITLESS FINANCIAL RESOURCES, HAVE THE MOST LETHAL WEAPON; COOL, COOL, COOL. IT'S LIKE A POWERFUL REGIME PARADING ITS MILITARY HARDWARE EACH WEEK (JUST TO ADD TO THE UK'S PERVADING NORTH KOREAN VIBES).

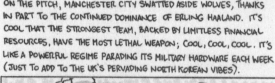

NOT EVERYONE OBEYED THE WEEKEND'S MANDATORY TONE OF DEFERENCE. IN A SYMBOLIC ACT OF REBELLION, WOLVES' IRISH DEFENDER, NATHAN COLLINS, COMMITTED A KUNG-FU KICK UPON THE CROWN JEWELS OF THAT MOST ENGLISH OF ENGLISH ROSES, JACK GREALISH (19 YOUTH CAPS FOR IRELAND). COLLINS MIGHT AS WELL HAVE TURNED HIS MORRISONS BARCODE SCANNER UP TO 11, DONE A WHEELIE THROUGH CENTER PARCS AND DESTROYED ONE OF THE REALISTIC HIGH STREET TRIBUTES TO EIIR.

LUCKILY, THE GRIEF INSPECTORS OF THE WOKEFINDER GENERAL ARE STILL OUT IN FORCE, CHECKING THAT BLACK ARMBANDS ARE OF REGULATION GIRTH AND SCANNING THE INTERNET FOR ANYONE CRITICISING THE POLICE FOR ARRESTING DISSENTERS. HOWEVER, AS THE LEAVES BEGIN TO FALL FROM THE TREES, NATURE'S INEVITABLE CYCLE MEANS THEIR FOCUS WILL SOON SHIFT...

NOTHING QUITE TYPIFIES THE LEVEL-HEADED REACTION TO THE QUEEN'S DEATH LIKE SIR LINDSAY HOYLE DESCRIBING HER FUNERAL AS "THE MOST IMPORTANT EVENT THE WORLD WILL EVER SEE", AN UNDERSTATED CLAIM THAT SUGGESTS HE COULD DO A JOB AS A SUPER SUNDAY HYPE MAN, POST-POLITICS. BUT IF YOU FIND IT A BIT BLEAK THAT ALL FUTURE ACHIEVEMENTS WILL PALE IN COMPARISON TO THE PASSING OF A 96-YEAR-OLD, AND ARE WONDERING WHERE THE HUMAN RACE GOES FROM HERE, THEN TAKE SOLACE FROM THESE 10 LITTLE WORDS...

IT'S NOTHING NEW FOR A SLICE OF FOOTBALL'S CULTURAL HERITAGE TO BE SOLD OFF TO THE HIGHEST BIDDER, BUT NEWS THAT LS LOWRY'S 'GOING TO THE MATCH' IS TO BE AUCTIONED OFF HAS BEEN MET WITH SADNESS. THE PAINTING IS FORECAST TO FETCH EIGHT MILLION KWASI KWIDS, ENABLING ITS CURRENT OWNERS, THE PFA, TO BUY A NEW PACK OF BIROS FOR ITS CHARITABLE ARM. FOOTBALL, IF NOT THE VALUE OF THE POUND, IS VERY DIFFERENT FROM WHEN LOWRY PAINTED HIS 1953 MASTERPIECE, WHICH SHOWED A LARGE CROWD FILING IN TO A BOLTON MATCH!!! SO MAYBE THE VACANT WALL SPACE AT PFA HQ CAN BE FILLED WITH AN UPDATED VERSION, DEPICTING IMAGES OF THE MODERN MATCH-GOING EXPERIENCE.

SEEMS A BOLD DESIGN CHOICE TO GIVE A GIANT DEATH ROBOT VOLUPTUOUS CRIMSON LIPS, BUT IT'S NICE THAT THE END OF DAYS WILL AT LEAST BE A BIT SEXY. ANYWAY, ARSENAL BEING GOOD AND TONY ADAMS BEING BACK IN THE SPOTLIGHT IS PROVIDING SOME REAL LATE-90s VIBES. THEY SHOULD GO THE WHOLE POG AND RELEASE A BLOATED, SUNNY DELIGHT-FUELLED ALBUM.

ARSENAL'S WIN COMPLETELY RUINED JÜRGEN KLOPP'S SEVENTH ANNIVERSARY AS LIVERPOOL MANAGER. IT'S BEEN A PERIOD OF HUGE SUCCESS, BUT NOW HE'S REACHED THE STAGE OF THE EVOLUTIONARY CYCLE ALL MANAGERS EVENTUALLY EXPERIENCE; SO WELCOME, JÜRGEN BASSETT: FUßBALLTRAINER

NEWCASTLE CELEBRATED AN ANNIVERSARY AT THE WEEKEND TOO: IT'S BEEN A YEAR SINCE THE SOVEREIGN WEALTH FUND OF SAUDI ARABIA BOUGHT THEIR CLUB/SOUL! SOME FANS MARKED THE EVENT WITH A PERFECTLY DYSTOPIAN FLAG LISTING ALL THE GREAT PLAYERS THEIR NEW OVERLORDS BOUGHT THEM WHEN THEY WEREN'T JAILING WOMEN FOR USING TWITTER. FOR THIS WAS NEWCASTLE'S 'INDEPENDENCE DAY', SPECIFICALLY THE BIT WHERE THE ALIENS USE THAT BLOKE AS A FLESHY CONDUIT TO COMMUNICATE THEIR MESSAGE.

GOOD POINT, MY PROPAGANDISING FRIEND; BUT PERHAPS ONE DIFFERENCE IS THAT WHEN YOU'RE WATCHING A DISNEY FILM, YOU DON'T GET CUTAWAYS TO THE HIGH-FIVING GOVERNOR OF THE SAUDI PUBLIC INVESTMENT FUND AFTER EVERY DRAMATIC MOMENT.

THE SAUDI REGIME'S INVOLVEMENT IN FOOTBALL WILL SURELY MAKE THEM CHANGE THEIR WAYS ANY DAY NOW, RIGHT? AFTER ALL, FOOTBALL NEVER FAILS TO SURPRISE. FOR EXAMPLE, WHO COULD HAVE GUESSED GRAHAM POTTER WOULD START TO DRESS LIKE A MEMBER OF THE CANTINA BAND FROM STAR WARS?

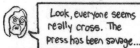
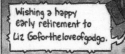

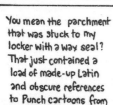

IT'S THE WACKY, DEPRESSINGLY NOT-THAT-NEW CRAZE SWEEPING ENGLISH FOOTBALL: SINGING SONGS ABOUT HILLSBOROUGH AT LIVERPOOL MATCHES. THE UNLAWFUL KILLING OF 97 PEOPLE AND A THREE-DECADE FIGHT FOR JUSTICE IS ALL GRIST TO THE BANTER MILL. BUT AS WE MOVE FURTHER AWAY FROM THE HORRORS OF 1989, PERHAPS SOME PEOPLES' MEMORIES ARE FADING THAT IT WAS A DISASTER THAT COULD HAVE HAPPENED TO ANY GROUP OF FANS...

RABID TRIBALISM

Bloody scousers. Always playing the victim! What's your problem anyway?!

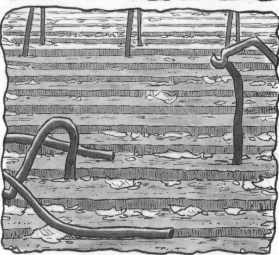

SPION KOP

LEPPINGS LANE

MEN'S WORLD CUP 2022:
TODAY I FEEL . . . NAUSEATED

Despite FIFA's long and proud history of disregarding human rights when picking World Cup hosts, there were still a *few* eyebrows raised when Qatar was awarded the gig back in 2010. There were times over the next dozen years when it seemed the nation might not even be able to follow through on its audacious plan to build the required stadiums and infrastructure on the blood of a disposable imported workforce, but nothing stops for the greatest show on Earth, especially not the deaths of an estimated 6,500 poor people. Football unites the world!

As you'd expect from a state whose wealth is based on fossil fuels, this was to be the World Cup of Gaslighting. Qatar's rulers dismissed their critics as racists, which some might argue was a tad saucy, considering they were using indentured foreign labour to build and service their vanity project. Fears about the treatment of LGBTQ+ people were also swatted away with the decisive argument that homosexuality was illegal in England when *they* hosted it, *actually*.

England hosted the World Cup in 1966.

David Beckham faced pre-tournament criticism for taking the Qatari coin to promote the country's cultural delights to heterosexuals, but no one can question his long history of allyship to money. Overseeing the football was Doha's most famous useful idiot, Gianni Infantino, he of the multiple personalities, each of them a plum. The beauty of hosting the whole tournament in one tiny state meant TV viewers were able to enjoy cutaways to his face at almost every game. The suckers who'd decided to boycott the tournament on moral grounds didn't know what they were missing!

Gianni's pre-tournament press conference speech will live long in the memory, no matter how hard you try to shake it off. You could tell that, as he practised it in front of his mirror, an assistant applying Tipp-Ex to his big white daps, he'll have thought he sounded like Martin Luther King. In reality, as he embarked on his 'Today, I feel like . . .' spiel, you were left wondering what catastrophic, life-changing trauma had befallen Shania Twain.

This set of cartoons begins with three stories about the migrant worker experience in Qatar. Firstly comes the account of Malcolm Bidali, a Kenyan who was employed as a security guard in Doha, before he was arrested and imprisoned after speaking out about the living and working conditions. The second strip is based on the reporting of *Guardian* journalist Pete Pattisson and recounts the story of a Nepalese construction worker, Rupchandra Rumba, who toiled in extreme heat before dying in the night, and his widow Nirmala's attempts to receive fair compensation. Pete also travelled to Doha and conducted the interview with 'David', the subject of the third cartoon, who went unseen by the guests of the luxury hotel he serviced to support his family back in Ghana, all while living in appalling conditions in the migrant workers' camp.

Cartoons on the plight of migrant workers were always going to provoke an emotive reaction from readers. One comment that sticks in my mind came from a man whose Twitter account was dedicated entirely to Manchester City shirts, who delivered an empathetic two-word reply to one such strip: 'Bore off.' This was obviously a heartfelt call to deactivate Qatar's mineral extraction drills. Bore off indeed, sir; bore off indeed.

Having spoken to Malcolm Bidali and seen the images of migrant workers returning to grieving relatives via the cargo holds of various South Asian airlines, I struggled to embrace the fairy-tale narrative of Saudi tourism ambassador Lionel Messi lifting the World Cup while being draped in a cloak by the Emir of Qatar, who was indirectly his boss at Paris Saint-Germain. Fair play to Emi Martínez, though, who did his best to undermine the whole spectacle by waving his Golden Glove trophy like it was his dong, while the presence of Salt Bae gave the occasion the gravitas it merited.

"Everyone told me not to do it, but I did it anyway..."

Sheikha Moza bint Nasser, Chairperson and Co-Founder of The Qatar Foundation, and mother of the Emir, often spoke of being an advocate for human rights. With multiple charitable organisations in developing nations around the globe, she was someone I respected. She was almost like a role model...

MALCOLM BIDALI

But every day I watched from the hotel security control room as she stepped from her car and walked past my co-workers stood in the 50 degree heat. The staff were instructed to stay outside for the duration of her visit, which would often be many hours. I thought she was someone who'd stand up and make people accountable for such mistreatment, but her silence made me very angry.

In the little spare time I had, I'd been writing about my experiences as a migrant worker, under the pseudonym 'Noah'. In the cramped labour camp accommodation, I'd type away on a laptop donated by a sympathetic Qatari friend.

Ignoring the advice of my friends, I decided to make Sheikha Moza the subject of my latest blog.

I don't know whether it was that particular post that got me arrested, or whether the authorities had been tracking me for a while. They didn't come for me with SWAT gear and Apache helicopters, although that would have been cool...

The reality was more mundane. The camp boss called me to his office, saying someone wanted to see me. I thought it was weird because it was Ramadan and there was no one around, but he was adamant.

He made a phone call right in front of me. I heard him use the term "MOI", meaning Ministry of Interior, which was when I knew something was really up. I messaged my contacts to say it was a possible SOS situation. Basically, the company I was working for handed me over to the authorities.

The MOI arrived and took me away. I was placed in solitary confinement in a windowless, padded cell. I can't say for sure how long I was kept there, because the guards messed with the lights, making it impossible to track the time, but I think I was in there for three days.

The guards would also turn the air conditioning up and down, making the cell either boiling hot or freezing cold.

I was regularly taken to a separate room and interrogated by two State Security Bureau agents. The walls were cushioned and presumably soundproof. I didn't see any cameras or recording devices, but they must have been there.

It was the period before the interrogations began that I really hated. Handcuffed and blindfolded, I'd be kept waiting for up to an hour. I later learned this is a standard tactic of intelligence agencies. They want to sweat you out, make you wait, make you think. In my mind, I was running through all the different scenarios, so by the time they came in, I was already messed up.

They asked me about organisations, activities, supporters...

Why did you do it? How did you do it? Who was involved?

I told them the truth, because the information was all out there already. At the end of the interrogation, they came up with a statement, typed in Arabic. They assured me it was just what I'd said, but refused my request for an English translation. Instead, one agent read it aloud, a paragraph at a time, while the other agent translated. I had to sign it and give my thumbprint.

This happened three times:

Once at the MOI   Then at a second site.

Then at the public prosecution offices.

Excuse my French, but fuck the public prosecution

As a sworn officer of the court and a member of the bar society, you're supposed to have certain limits and standards, like you're not supposed to interrogate me without my lawyer present, but that's exactly what they did!

After that, I was moved to a second cell at a "black site", away from the main prison. The cell had a small window; it was too high to see out of, but allowed enough light in that I could tell whether it was night or day.

I was given one hour of 'guard time' a day, when I was able to go outside. But it was 50 degrees out there, so I could only ever stand it for about 20 minutes.

My request for books was denied.

I asked for a Bible, but they said 'no'.

So I asked for a Qur'an, out of curiosity, and they brought one straight away.

I began to receive snippets of information from the outside world. After two weeks, I was visited by the Kenyan ambassador to Qatar, Patrick Cornel Odero Ahenda. He's since passed, and I don't want to speak ill of the dead, but he was a douchebag. He said to me:

You came here to be a security guard.   You didn't come here to be a writer or an activist.

If you feel the conditions are not up to standard, resign and go home.

So if you don't like sleeping 12 to a room, eating shitty food that I've seen people get hospitalised from, and working 13, 14, 15 hour shifts, you should just go home? That was his official position, which means it's the official Kenyan position. Embassies are supposed to be safe havens for us all. They were supposed to provide me with a lawyer and provide counsel, but they didn't do any of that. I think that everyone at the Kenyan embassy in Qatar should be fired, along with the labour attachés, because they offer no help to any Kenyan in distress. That had a very profound effect on me, the lack of empathy for fellow Kenyans. It's very painful, you're supposed to be taking care of us.

I don't think the Ambassador intended to come to the prison.

I can guarantee he was not there of his own accord.

I later discovered that my mother, who is a dual Kenyan-British citizen, had acquired a letter from the EU, signed by three member states, calling for my release, so maybe the British Foreign Office spoke to the Kenyan foreign affairs ministry...?

The Ambassador told me my story was all over the news, but not that there was an active campaign to set me free. I only discovered that after the third week, when I was visited by Max Tuñón from the International Labour Organisation of Qatar. I think it was the best news I've ever heard.

I was elated.

Euphoric.

I also discovered the National Human Rights Committee of Qatar was involved. Perhaps it was one of these things, or a combination of all of them that led to my release. Up to now, I cannot tell you what happened. All the meetings between the lawyers were held behind closed doors. I would just get the occasional update as the charges were gradually dropped:

"Hey, you remember that espionage charge? That's been dropped."

And then after a few days, or maybe a week:

"Remember that other charge? They've dropped that too."

After two months of this, they decided to settle the matter out of court, which was another relief. I'm grateful, I didn't want to go to court, as this would have meant other witnesses, and evidence being introduced, and charges being extended to others. I was ready to take the whole blame and spend years in prison.

I was fined 25,000 Riyal [about £4,750], which was unjustified. Their basis was that I was defaming Qatar.

Unusually, I was given free rein to find another job. You don't just change jobs in Qatar. I was given an NOC (No Objection Certificate), which basically means the employer doesn't object to you finding another job.

Even after everything, I was willing to work for the Qatar Foundation or Ministry of Labour, which would have been a good PR stunt for them...

But I knew I was still being monitored, and that if I said anything again, they'd just scoop me up. In the end, I went back to Kenya of my own volition.

I'm still not sure why I was really arrested, how they found me, or how I came to be released.

Maybe they let me go because my case was generating a lot of attention and bad PR.

But I do know there are many people still in prison despite similar efforts by human rights campaigners.

THE GLISTENING EDUCATION CITY STADIUM IS A STATE-OF-THE-ART CONSTRUCTION ON THE EDGE OF DOHA. WITH ITS GLASS MOSAIC EDIFICE, IT HAS BEEN NICKNAMED 'THE DIAMOND OF THE DESERT'.

INSIDE, IT OFFERS PLAYERS, FANS AND VIPS "ADVANCED COOLING TECHNOLOGIES"...

...THE LIKES OF WHICH WERE NOT AVAILABLE TO MIGRANT WORKERS LIKE RUPCHANDRA RUMBA WHO HELPED BUILD IT.

IN THE EARLY HOURS OF 23 JUNE 2019, RUPCHANDRA'S COLLEAGUES GATHERED WORRIEDLY AROUND HIS BUNK IN THE SQUALID ROOM THEY SHARED IN THE WORKERS' CAMP, HAVING BEEN AWOKEN BY THE GRIM RATTLE OF HIS BREATH.

Rumba!

Rumba!

Get help!

Rupchandra!

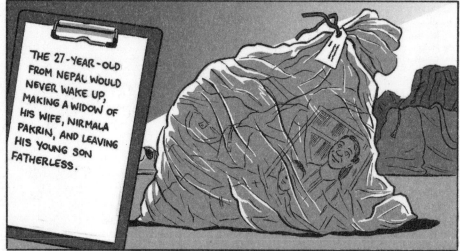

THE 27-YEAR-OLD FROM NEPAL WOULD NEVER WAKE UP, MAKING A WIDOW OF HIS WIFE, NIRMALA PAKRIN, AND LEAVING HIS YOUNG SON FATHERLESS.

RUPCHANDRA HAD ONLY BEEN IN QATAR FOR 10 MONTHS.

HE WAS EMPLOYED AS A SCAFFOLDER BY A LABOUR SUPPLY COMPANY.

HIS FRIENDS AND FAMILY SAID HE WAS IN PERFECT HEALTH.

HE DIDN'T DRINK AND ONLY SMOKED OCCASIONALLY, BECAUSE IT'S NOT EASY TO AFFORD CIGARETTES ON A MIGRANT WORKER'S WAGE, ESPECIALLY AS NIRMALA WOULD LATER SAY THAT HIS MINUSCULE WAGE WAS LONG OVERDUE.

BUT DURING HIS RELATIVELY SHORT TIME IN QATAR HE WAS EXPOSED TO LONG HOURS OF TOIL IN THE MOST EXTREME OF CONDITIONS.

PERHAPS HE'D HAVE SURVIVED IF HE'D RECEIVED MEDICAL ATTENTION SOONER, BUT HIS CO-WORKERS SAID THEY HADN'T BEEN ISSUED WITH A MANDATORY HEALTH CARD BY THEIR EMPLOYER, WHICH WOULD HAVE ENTITLED THEM TO AFFORDABLE HEALTHCARE.

NIRMALA WAS INFORMED OF HER HUSBAND'S DEATH VIA A PHONE CALL FROM THE LABOUR CAMP BOSS. CONFUSED, GRIEVING AND SCARED FOR HER FUTURE, SHE WAS UNWITTINGLY CAST IN TO THE DIZZYING MAZE OF QATARI BUREAUCRACY, WITH NO IDEA OF HOW TO GET JUSTICE.

SUCH 'SUDDEN AND UNEXPLAINED' DEATHS ARE RARELY INVESTIGATED BY THE QATARI AUTHORITIES.

DEATH CERTIFICATES ROUTINELY STATE THAT WORKERS DIED OF 'NATURAL CAUSES', BUT IN THE MAJORITY OF CASES A POSTMORTEM ISN'T CONDUCTED, MAKING IT IMPOSSIBLE TO DETERMINE HOW SOMEONE HAS DIED.

RUPCHANDRA'S SUDDEN DEATH WAS ATTRIBUTED TO "ACUTE CARDIO RESPIRATORY FAILURE DUE TO NATURAL CAUSES" AND CLASSIFIED AS A "NON-WORK-RELATED DEATH".

INITIALLY, THE ONLY FINANCIAL HELP NIRMALA RECEIVED WAS THE PROCEEDS OF A WHIP-ROUND FROM RUPCHANDRA'S CO-WORKERS, WHICH RAISED 67,000 RUPEES (£470).

HER ONLY POINT OF CONTACT WAS RUPCHANDRA'S EMPLOYER, WHO TOLD HER THAT SINCE HER HUSBAND HAD DIED IN THE CAMP, HE WAS NOT ELIGIBLE FOR COMPENSATION. QATAR'S LABOUR LAWS ONLY REQUIRE THAT EMPLOYERS PAY RESTITUTION IF A DEATH OCCURS AT WORK, OR DIRECTLY BECAUSE OF THE WORK, AND SINCE HIS DEATH WAS CLASSIFIED AS BEING DUE TO NATURAL CAUSES, ALL THEY COULD - OR WOULD - DO WAS SEND HIS BODY BACK TO NEPAL.

NIRMALA DIDN'T GIVE UP, BUT SIX MONTHS LATER SHE TOLD THE GUARDIAN SHE STILL HADN'T RECEIVED ANY COMPENSATION AND THAT THE DIRECTOR OF THE COMPANY WAS PRESSURING HER TO ACCEPT A PAY-OFF OF 7,000 QATARI RIALS (£1,460 AT THE TIME).

"I'm concerned about my safety. He is using threatening language."

WITH THE HELP OF HER SISTER, NIRMALA SENT A LETTER TO THE HEAD OF QATAR'S SUPREME COMMITTEE, HASSAN AL-THAWADI.

In the absence of my husband, who used to take care of our needs, our family is going through a serious crisis. I believe my husband's life is worth more than 7,000 rials.

IT WOULD APPEAR THE SUPREME COMMITTEE DISAGREED. AFTER SEVEN WEEKS OF SILENCE, NIRMALA FINALLY RECEIVED A REPLY. AL-THAWADI EXPRESSED "DEEP CONDOLENCES" AND SAID THE SUPREME COMMITTEE WAS WORKING TO ENSURE "OUTSTANDING AMOUNTS WOULD BE PAID", BUT CONFIRMED THERE WOULD BE NO ADDITIONAL COMPENSATION BEYOND THE 7,000 RIALS...

AL-THAWADI WROTE THAT THIS "FURTHER GOOD FAITH SETTLEMENT" WAS BEING PAID "IN LIEU OF THE FACT THAT RUPCHANDRA WASN'T ENTITLED TO THE END OF SERVICE BENEFIT AS PER QATARI LAW BECAUSE HE WAS EMPLOYED IN QATAR FOR LESS THAN THE REQUIRED 12-MONTH PERIOD",

AND WHY WAS THAT, MATE?

LIKE THE RELATIVES OF THE COUNTLESS OTHER MIGRANT WORKERS WHO HAVE DIED SINCE QATAR WAS AWARDED THE WORLD CUP IN 2010, NIRMALA WAS FORCED TO ABANDON ANY HOPE OF RECEIVING FAIR COMPENSATION.

HOWEVER, THE FOCUS HAS SINCE TURNED TO FIFA, WITH PRESSURE MOUNTING FROM A GROUP OF NON-GOVERNMENTAL ORGANISATIONS FOR FOOTBALL'S GOVERNING BODY TO PAY REPARATIONS OF AT LEAST £365M TO MIGRANT WORKERS WHOSE HUMAN RIGHTS HAVE BEEN COMPROMISED. MAYBE THOSE COOLING TECHNOLOGIES COULD COME IN HANDY AFTER ALL.

Is it getting hot in here?

MEANWHILE, NIRMALA SAYS SHE IS STILL WAITING FOR A FAIR OFFER OF COMPENSATION FROM QATAR.

IN HIS OWN WORDS, THIS IS THE STORY OF "DAVID", A GHANAIAN MIGRANT WORKER EMPLOYED AT ONE OF THE MOST LUXURIOUS HOTELS IN DOHA. THE GLITZY SURROUNDINGS OF HIS WORKPLACE ARE IN STARK CONTRAST TO HIS LIVING CONDITIONS – AN OVERCROWDED ROOM IN A DUSTY COMPOUND ON THE EDGE OF THE CITY. LIKE MANY OF HIS CO-WORKERS, DAVID GOES UNSEEN BY THE VAST MAJORITY OF VISITORS.

RECRUITMENT

"I had a very bad experience when I first came here. The agent in Ghana told us the recruitment was free, but after everything was arranged, he began to demand money. In the end, I had to pay 4,000 Ghanaian cedis (around £540 at the time). That was a huge amount for me because I was only earning 20 to 25 cedis (£3) a day back then."

IN OTHER WORDS, THE RECRUITMENT FEE WAS EQUIVALENT TO SIX MONTHS' WAGES IN GHANA.

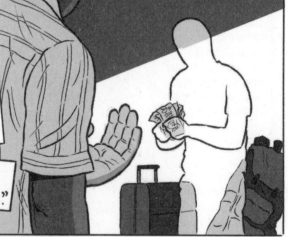

"Shortly before I was about to go to the airport to leave for Qatar, the agent demanded another 600 cedis (£81), which he said he needed to bribe the immigration officials with, so they would let us leave. He knew we were desperate to go, so he took advantage of us.

Once I got to Qatar it took me around a year to pay it all back."

ARRIVAL

"When I arrived in Qatar, I was so happy. I'll make my family proud, I thought.

When I got a day off, I went to the Khalifa Stadium. Liverpool had just played the Club World Cup final there. I had only seen it on TV, but now I could see it in real life. I just shouted out loud! This is the opportunity I had always asked for."

"After one or two months, Covid came.

We were all afraid, but not of the virus, we were scared of being sent home.

Most of us had borrowed money to come here. If we were sent home, how could we repay our debts? We were afraid to return empty-handed."

"Luckily, our company is strong [well-connected], so we were able to carry on working."

WORK

"My job is to clean swimming pools and add the right amount of chemicals. At first, we didn't really know what we were doing. We used to watch YouTube videos to learn what to do."

POOL CHLORINE

"I spent almost a year working at one of the five-star hotels that will be used at the World Cup. We worked in 12-hour shifts. At first my monthly wage was 900 rials [£210]. Now it's 1,000 rials a month [around £225], plus some extra for overtime and food. I get one day off a week and all I do is sleep."

THE MONTHLY SALARY WAS RAISED AFTER QATAR INTRODUCED A MINIMUM WAGE, WHICH CAME INTO FORCE IN MARCH 2021.

HOWEVER, IT IS STILL THE EQUIVALENT OF AROUND £1 AN HOUR.

A MONTH'S WAGE IS LESS THAN THE PRICE OF ONE NIGHT IN A BASIC ROOM AT THE HOTEL WHERE DAVID WAS WORKING.

"If I try to change jobs it will be really, really, really hard. They tell you if you want to change you will be sent back to your country..."

A NEW LAW, WHICH CAME INTO FORCE IN OCTOBER 2020, GIVES WORKERS THE RIGHT TO CHANGE JOBS, BUT IT IS WIDELY FLOUTED BY EMPLOYERS.

"Working at the hotel, you feel bad about the huge difference between us workers and the guests, but you can't do anything about it. Forget it. Just move on."

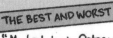

THE BEST AND WORST

"My best day in Qatar was when I got married... in Ghana! I got married online. One of my relatives stood in for me and I joined on a video call. We chose to get married during Covid, because at that time there were restrictions on large gatherings, so our wedding had to be small. That meant it would not cost much. When I saw my family, I just wished I could be there too."

"The worst thing about being here is the fear of being sent back, against my will. We have to be careful to not get into problems. It's not my country.

I wouldn't say they are taking advantage of us here. They didn't force us to come.

But in Africa our life is very hard. So that is why we are here. At last, now I can do something for my family. Now I can afford things for my family."

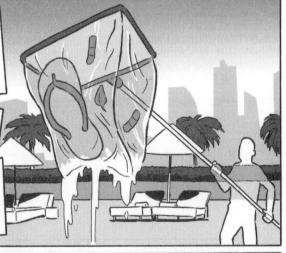

FOOTBALL

"In Ghana, everyone loves football. We're so excited about the World Cup. I might be able to see the players I've only seen on TV in real life. If Ghana don't make it out of the group stage, I will be disappointed. When we qualified everyone was so happy. We want revenge for 2010, when we were beaten by Uruguay. The tickets we can afford are sold out, so we can't watch the matches live, but we'll go and enjoy the atmosphere. We'll be happy to just stand outside the stadium!"

THE MOST SHAMEFUL WORLD CUP SINCE THE LAST ONE KICKS OFF ON SUNDAY. THE LAST 12 YEARS OF ANGER, DEATH, GRIEF AND SUFFERING COULD HAVE BEEN AVOIDED IF FIFA HAD CHOSEN A DIFFERENT PATH IN 2010...

Sure, I promised my vote to the USA, but then I saw the Australian bid had a cartoon kangaroo!

LIKE SOME SICK GAMESHOW, WE CAN ONLY GUESS AT THE NUMBER OF PEOPLE WHO HAVE DIED SINCE THE THE TOURNAMENT WAS AWARDED TO QATAR.

6,500

LUCKILY, DOHA RESIDENT AND FIFA PREZ, MR WORLD WIDE PEACE GIANNI INFANTINO, HAS BEEN ON HAND TO CALM THE WATERS WITH SOME CLASSIC FIFASPEAK. ALL TOGETHER NOW: 'QATAR, QATAR, QATAR! FIFA, FIFA, FIFA!"

Football unites us all who were born a certain way...

HE RECENTLY WROTE TO ALL 32 COMPETING NATIONS, ESSENTIALLY ASKING THEM TO 'STICK TO FOOTBALL!'. YOU GUYS, JUST SIT BACK AND ENJOY THE GOALS, THE SKILLS, THE CLEAN SHEETS - WE ALL REMEMBER HOW MUCH FIFA LIKED THOSE FROM THE FBI RAIDS IN 2015, SCENES THAT MAYBE EVEN INSPIRED THE DESIGN OF THE MASCOT FOR QATAR 2022?

POLITICAL NEUTRALITY HAS ALWAYS BEEN THE POSITION OF AN ORGANISATION WHOSE PAST HITS INCLUDE:

IL DUCE '34   JUNTA '78   VLAD '18

THERE HAVE BEEN SOME CRITICS OF THE DECISION TO AWARD HOSTING RIGHTS TO A REGIME THAT HAS RELIED UPON INDENTURED LABOUR TO BUILD THE INFRASTRUCTURE FOR ITS VANITY PROJECT AND WHOSE HOMOPHOBIA IS ENSHRINED IN LAW. HOWEVER, QATAR'S 'SUPREME COMMITTEE' MAINTAINS THAT EVERYONE IS WELCOME – A CLAIM SOMEWHAT UNDERMINED BY THE STEADY FLOW OF SENIOR FIGURES REVEALING THEIR TRUE FEELINGS.

HOWEVER, THERE ARE PLENTY OF PEOPLE WILLING TO DEFEND QATAR'S HONOUR, NOT LEAST THE NOW PRESUMABLY FORMER LGBTQI+ ADVOCATE, DAVID BECKHAM, WHO LOOKED LIKE SOMEONE HAD STAMPED ON HIS METATARSAL WHEN QATAR WON THE BID. THE NATIONAL TREASURE (HE JOINED A QUEUE, FOR GOD'S SAKE) NO DOUBT HAS 10 MILLION AND ONE REASONS FOR ACCEPTING AN AMBASSADORIAL GIG...

Everyone is welcome, to an extent!

Um, one of the lads has said the quiet bit out loud again, chief.

Homosexuality is damage in the mind.

Someone needs to fund Brooklyn's next photographic odyssey!

QATAR IS ALSO REPORTED TO HAVE RECRUITED A GROUP OF 'FAN LEADERS' FROM MULTIPLE NATIONS TO SMILE AND WAVE FOR THE CAMERAS, MAKE "A POSITIVE CONTRIBUTION", AND - IN THE FINEST TRADITION OF ALL AUTHORITARIAN STATES - RAT ON CRITICS. THESE INFLUENCERS WILL SUPPOSEDLY RECEIVE £60 A DAY, WHICH MAY NOT SEEM SUCH A GOOD RATE FOR THEIR SOUL WHEN THEY ACTUALLY ARRIVE AT THE FI-FYRE FESTIVAL...

One official FI-FYRE COMMERCIAL PARTNER™ carbonated beverage, please!

Certainly, sir. That will be the equivalent of £61, please.

QATARMY ARMY!

FI-FYRE

FI-FY

ARGUABLY, THAT ISN'T THE MOST SEVERE EXAMPLE OF HUMAN TRAGEDY AT THIS WORLD CUP.

They're paying how much for a jar of Budweiser at the fan park?! Oh, those poor souls...

USUALLY, THE EVE OF THE TOURNAMENT WOULD BE DOMINATED BY CHATTER ABOUT "WHO'S ON THE PLANE?" THIS TIME, THE ONLY FLIGHT-RELATED DISCUSSION THAT MATTERS IS HOW MANY MIGRANT WORKERS HAVE BEEN TRANSPORTED HOME IN THE CARGO HOLD.

FIFA AND THE QATARI GOVERNMENT SHOULD NEVER BE FORGIVEN FOR THIS.

ROWS ABOUT ARMBANDS, MILLENNIA-SPANNING WHATABOUTERY, U-TURNS THAT WILL FILL ANY TRAVELLING LGBTQ+ FAN WITH CONFIDENCE, YES, THE EVENT THAT BRINGS THE WORLD TOGETHER HAS BEGUN! IN CASE YOU WERE IN ANY DOUBT AS TO WHO IS CALLING THE SHOTS, JUST TWO DAYS BEFORE THE BIG KICK-OFF, QATAR'S RULERS BANNED THE PROLES FROM DRINKING BUDWEISER IN THE STADIUMS —MAYBE THEY *DO* CARE ABOUT HUMAN RIGHTS! IT WAS A CLEAR MESSAGE FROM THE AUTOCRATIC PENINSULA TO ITS WESTERN CRITICS:

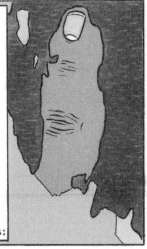

IF YOU MISSED THE OPENING CEREMONY, YOU WOULDN'T HAVE SEEN THE USUAL PARADE OF DESPOTS AND SELL-OUTS. THIS WORLD CUP MAY HAVE ITS CRITICS, BUT EVEN THE MOST CYNICAL OF HEARTS WILL HAVE MELTED AT THE SIGHT OF GIANNI COSYING UP TO MBS AGAIN. THERE WAS STATE-SANCTIONED DANCING AND SINGING AND EVEN AN ANIMATED SHARK FOR THE FIFA DELEGATION TO HURDLE AT THE AFTERPARTY. THERE WAS PROBABLY A GOOD REASON FOR MORGAN FREEMAN TO BE THERE TOO!

I need someone with freckles to play me in the biopic of my struggle against discrimination.

INFANTINO HAD A FEW WORDS TOO, BECAUSE WE HADN'T HEARD ENOUGH FROM *HIM*. A WHOLE DAY HAD PASSED SINCE HIS ATTEMPT TO FILIBUSTER HIS WAY THROUGH TO THE SAUDI ARABIA 2030 WORLD CUP. FROM THE GRAVITAS OF THE DELIVERY, YOU COULD TELL HE THOUGHT HIS BIZARRE SPARTACUS (GATARTACUS?) SPEECH WOULD ADORN THE POSTERS OF CLASSROOM WALLS FOR GENERATIONS TO COME. HE MIGHT EVEN BE RIGHT!

YOU DON'T NEED TO TELL GIANNI ABOUT DISCRIMINATION—HE HAD RED HAIR AND WAS THE SON OF MIGRANT WORKERS WHO LEFT ITALY FOR SWITZERLAND! THERE, THE INFANTINOS TOILED IN THE TOBLERONE MINES UNTIL THE CUCKOO CLOCK SIGNALLED THE END OF THEIR SHIFT. FOR THIS, HE SAYS HE WAS PICKED ON, BUT MAYBE IT TAUGHT HIM A VALUABLE LESSON IN THE BEST WAY TO DEFEAT A BULLY: UNCONDITIONAL OBSEQUIOUSNESS!

"...Today I feel [like] a migrant worker."
— GIANNI INFANTINO, 2022

Children, this is the prong who made people pine for Sepp Blatter!

Great call on the beer thing, Your Hetero-Highness. Sure, the sponsors won't be happy, but it's worth it for you, bestie. Perhaps you may consider forgoing my atomic wedgie this evening, sire?

Another great call, boss.

GIANNI MUST HAVE FORGOTTEN HIS OWN LECTURE ON TOLERANCE BY MONDAY, WHEN FIFA TOLD THE VARIOUS EUROPEAN ASSOCIATIONS THERE WOULD BE SPORTING CONSEQUENCES FOR WEARING THEIR 'ONELOVE' ARMBANDS. WHAT WAS ORIGINALLY A TOKEN GESTURE WITH A SAFELY GENERIC MESSAGE WOULD NOW BE GIVEN POWER IF THE PLAYERS DEFIED FIFA. HOWEVER, HOLLOW CORPORATE ACTIVISM SHOULDN'T HAVE CONSEQUENCES, SO THE ASSOCIATIONS FOLDED. FUNNILY ENOUGH, DURING HIS LENGTHY BRAIN-FART, INFANTINO LET SLIP A PHRASE THAT REVEALS FIFA'S POSITION MORE HONESTLY THAN ITS OTHER VAPID ARMBAND SLOGANS:

FOOTBALL UNITES THE WORLD LOL

"DON'T CRITICISE QATAR"

THE MEEKNESS OF THIS SURRENDER WAS IN STARK CONTRAST TO THE COURAGE OF THE IRAN PLAYERS WHO REFUSED TO SING THEIR NATIONAL ANTHEM IN PROTEST AGAINST THE BRUTALITY OF THE DICTATORSHIP BACK HOME—A REGIME, INCIDENTALLY, THAT INFANTINO CASUALLY SUGGESTED COULD HOST A TOURNAMENT. IT'S ALMOST AS IF HE HASN'T LEARNED A THING. IN A RARE MOMENT OF GENUINE HUMAN EMOTION AT THIS CURSED WORLD CUP, AN IRANIAN WOMAN COULD BE SEEN TEARFULLY APPLAUDING THE PLAYERS, KNOWING THEIR BRAVERY COULD HAVE A SEVERE COST.

SQUIRES

It's like they're not scared of getting a yellow card!

AFTER ALL THOSE PLEAS TO FOCUS ON THE FOOTBALL, FIFA AND THE QATARI LEADERSHIP MIGHT WANT TO CHAT A BIT MORE ABOUT ALL THE POLITICS STUFF AFTER A TEPID DISPLAY FROM THE HOST NATION IN THE OPENING GAME. DESPITE THE UNPRECEDENTED ADVANTAGE OF ALL THOSE GUEST SPOTS IN OTHER CONTINENTS' COMPETITIONS, ON THEIR BIG DAY QATAR WERE AS IMPOSING AS THEIR FAMOUS GAS. THE TEAM PLAYED IN A DAZE, LIKE THEY'D SEEN A HUGE GHOST BEFORE THE KICK-OFF.

AS THE PERSON WHO SEWED THAT DISPLAY TOGETHER PROBABLY THOUGHT, THERE IS SUCH A THING AS TOO MUCH MATERIAL. ANYWAY, WALES ARE HAVING A NICE TIME AND SOME OF ENGLAND'S FOOTBALL WAS AS CREATIVE AS THE ATTENDANCE FIGURES, BUT THIS IS A SHAMEFUL AFFAIR. ROLL ON 19 DECEMBER, WHEN WE CAN EAT ENOUGH QUALITY STREET TO TAKE THE BITTER TASTE AWAY AND LOSE OURSELVES IN CORNY BLOCKBUSTERS...

Today, I feel gay. Today, I feel a migrant worker. Today, I feel like a cup of tea and a Crunchie. Today, man, I feel like a woman.

FIFA

TWAIN INTENSIFIES

MEMORABLE MOMENTS FROM THE SECOND ROUND OF GROUP MATCHES AT QATAR 2022...

AS VIEWED BY THE PEOPLE IMPORTED TO BUILD AND SERVICE THE GREATEST SHOW ON EARTH!

MESSI
RESCUES ARGENTINA WITH A GOAL AGAINST PERENNIAL DISAPPOINTMENTS, MEXICO

NEYMAR'S ANKLE SWELLS TO PROPORTIONS THAT MAKE IT VISIBLE FROM THE MIGRANT WORKERS' FAN PARK, FAR ENOUGH FROM THE CITY THAT VISITORS DON'T NEED TO LOOK AT THEM. JOGO BONITO!

ENGLAND AND THE USA LIGHT UP THE TOURNAMENT WITH A DRAW SO CAPTIVATING THAT THE FANS BOO THE REFEREE WHEN HE ENDS THE SPECTACLE. IT FAIR LIFTS THE SPIRITS AFTER NEWS THAT SOME ENGLAND FANS IN CULTURALLY-SENSITIVE FANCY DRESS HADN'T BEEN ALLOWED TO TAKE THEIR SWORDS INTO THEIR PREVIOUS MATCH.

Bloody jobsworths.

IRAN INFLICT A LATE DEFEAT ON WALES. CARLOS QUEIROZ DEMANDS THE BBC PUNDIT JÜRGEN KLINSMANN BE FIRED FROM HIS FIFA GIG FOR HIS CRITICISM OF IRAN'S UNDERHAND TACTICS. IT'S IN THEIR CULTURE, YOU SEE; UNLIKE WALES, WHOSE COMMITMENT TO FAIR PLAY IS EVIDENCED BY WAYNE HENNESSEY RACING AN INCREDIBLE DISTANCE JUST TO BRUSH A FLY FROM MEHDI TAREMI'S CHEEK.

Caught in the moment, this might look like a foul.

UNDER EXTREME DURESS, IRAN'S PLAYERS SING THEIR NATIONAL ANTHEM AS ENTHUSIASTICALLY AS JOHN REDWOOD SINGING THE WELSH ONE. THE ANTHEM IS LOUDLY JEERED AND PROTEST FLAGS ARE SEIZED. THE GAME BETWEEN URUGUAY AND PORTUGAL IS HALTED BY A PITCH INVADER CARRYING A RAINBOW FLAG AND WEARING A T-SHIRT CALLING FOR IRANIAN WOMEN TO BE RESPECTED AND UKRAINE SAVED. IT'S THE KIND OF DIRECT ACTIVISM THE QATARI ORGANISERS NO DOUBT LOVE.

THE UNEXPECTED BEEF OF THE WORLD CUP COMES BETWEEN O CANADA AND F CROATIA. AFTER SOME PRE-MATCH TRASH-TALK AND TABLOID PHOTOSHOPPING, CROATIA WIN 4-1. FOR CANADA COACH JOHN HERDMAN, DEFEAT IS AS HARD TO SWALLOW AS A TABLESPOON OF CINNAMON.

MOROCCO PRODUCE THE SHOCK OF THE ROUND, BEATING A BELGIUM TEAM THAT EVEN KEVIN DE BRUYNE CONSIDERS TO BE TOO OLD TO WIN THE WORLD CUP. STILL, IF THIS WHOLE JAMBOREE HAS TAUGHT US ANYTHING, IT'S THAT LIVING TO SEE YOUR MID-THIRTIES IS A BLESSING.

MBAPPÉ SCORES! LEWANDOWSKI SCORES! RONALDO BRUNO SCORES!

EVERYTHING IS SET UP FOR A TANTALISING FINAL ROUND OF GROUP FIXTURES. THE TENSION MOUNTS AS WE WAIT TO SEE WHO WILL BE DEEMED SURPLUS TO REQUIREMENTS AT QATAR 2022!

By'ee

Departures

WITH THE SECOND ROUND COMPLETE, WE'RE NEARING THE END OF THE GLOBAL COMPETITION TO DECIDE WHICH FOOTBALL PERSONALITY CAN SOIL THEIR REPUTATION FROM THE GREATEST HEIGHT. BECKS CAN ONLY SQUINT ON AS FIFA COMPANY MAN ARSÈNE WENGER SCALES QATAR'S TALLEST FREUDIAN SYMBOL, FUMBLES WITH HIS PANTALONS AND MUMBLES SOMETHING ABOUT THE BEST PERFORMING TEAMS AT THE WORLD CUP BEING THE ONES WHO STUCK TO FOOTBALL. TAKE *THAT*, OVER ACHIEVING WOKEROOS!

Look out below!

Gah! Damned Zips!

- 3 PREMIER LEAGUE TITLES
- 7 FA CUPS
- WIDELY RESPECTED
- INVENTED PASTA

WENGER'S ALSO BEHIND SOME OF THE STATS APPEARING ON OUR SCREENS DURING THE MATCHES. DID YOU KNOW THAT LIONEL MESSI IS THE PLAYER WHO HAS SPENT THE MOST TIME WALKING AT THIS WORLD CUP?

IF THERE'S ONE THING WE LEARNED FROM ARGENTINA'S NARROW WIN AGAINST AUSTRALIA, IT'S THAT SOMETIMES YOU HAVE TO JUST STAND BACK AND ADMIRE THE UNSTOPPABLE GLIDING RUNS OF A PLAYER FUNCTIONING ON A HIGHER PLANE...

I don't believe in the existence of aliens, but looking at you I wonder if that's true...

BEHICH

HAVING EDGED PAST CROCODILE DUNDEE UNITED, ARGENTINA WILL NEXT FACE THE NETHERLANDS, WHO FLATTENED THE USA, 3-1. THE SCORER OF THEIR SECOND GOAL, DALEY BLIND, LATER SPOKE OF THE INSPIRATION THE PLAYERS HAVE DRAWN FROM LOUIS VAN GAAL, REVEALING THE COACH HAD KEPT HIS CANCER DIAGNOSIS FROM THE TEAM AND WOULD ATTEND HOSPITAL TREATMENTS AT NIGHT, AFTER TRAINING. WHO WOULD BEGRUDGE THIS BIG BEAUTIFUL MAN A WORLD CUP WINNERS' MEDAL?

UH-OH, TIME FOR THE OBLIGATORY CUTAWAY TO INFANTINO IN HIS BIG WHITE DAPS. THE BELOVED FIFA PREZ HAS BEEN AT EVERY GAME, EVEN THE ONES PLAYED CONCURRENTLY. IT WOULD BE MORE IMPRESSIVE IF HE HADN'T ALREADY ESTABLISHED HE'S ABOUT SIX PEOPLE.

MIGRANT WORKER
AFRICAN
QATARI
GAY
DISABLE

MAYBE THERE'S MORE TO IT THAN VAINGLORIOUS GURNING; PERHAPS HE'S TRYING TO GET THE SPONSORS BACK ONSIDE AFTER 'BUD-GATE'. THINK OF THE IMPACT ON THE ADIDAS SHARE PRICE EVERY TIME GIANNI FLASHES HIS STAN SMITHS...

MEIN GOTT!

ENGLAND AND FRANCE WILL MEET ON SATURDAY, HAVING OVERCOME

AND POLAND RESPECTIVELY. MBAPPÉ MAY HAVE GOT THE BETTER OF SZCZESNY, BUT WAIT UNTIL HE GETS A LOAD OF

Chesney...?!

ENGLAND'S STAR PERFORMER WAS JUDE BELLINGHAM, WHO PUT IN ANOTHER DISPLAY OF SUCH MATURITY THAT IT MAKES YOU WONDER IF HE'S REALLY 19.

BRAZIL ROLLED BACK THE YEARS WITH A PERFECTLY CHOREOGRAPHED 4-1 WIN AGAINST SOUTH KOREA. IT WAS A DISPLAY THAT EVEN HAD THEIR COACH DANCING LIKE A GRANDAD AT A WEDDING. NOBODY PUTS TITE IN THE CORNER. SO COMFORTABLE WAS THEIR LEAD THAT THEY WERE ABLE TO BRING ON SOME OF THE OLD STAGERS IN THE SECOND HALF.

Get your boots on, lads. Dani Alves is gonna start a conga line if we get a fifth.

Way ahead of you, chief!

Oh for fu

IF THEIR NEXT OPPONENTS, CROATIA, WERE ENRAGED BY THE HUBRIS OF THE LIGHTNING SEEDS, YOU WONDER HOW THEY'LL REACT TO THE CARNIVAL FROLICS OF BRAZIL.

CROATIA'S PROGRESS WAS SECURED WITH A PENALTY SHOOT-OUT WIN AGAINST JAPAN, AS WAS MOROCCO'S AGAINST SPAIN 24 HOURS LATER. THE SHOCK OF THE ROUND WAS AIDED BY THE HEROICS OF GOALKEEPER BONO, WHO WON THE PSYCHOLOGICAL BATTLE...

Nice tat, bro.

Not a tat.

Hey Sergio, if you score against me I'll read you some of my poetry.

MOROCCO'S REWARD IS A MEETING WITH GR26. WHATEVER ELSE HAPPENS AT THIS WORLD CUP, NOTHING WILL BE AS FUNNY AS RONALDO SITTING ON THE BENCH AS HIS YOUNG UPSTART REPLACEMENT - GONÇALO RAMOS - BANGS IN A HAT-TRICK. STILL, RONNIE HANDLED IT ALL WITH TYPICAL GRACE. THE *HATERS* WILL CRITICISE HIM FOR FLOUNCING OFF LIKE A HUMILIATED BREAKFAST SHOW HOST AS HIS SUPPORTING CAST CELEBRATED A 6-1 WIN AGAINST SWITZERLAND, BUT HE MUST HAVE HAD AN IMPORTANT APPOINTMENT TO KEEP.

Great show, king. You definitely got the last touch on at least four of those goals. You've still got it, pew, pew, pew!

Don't do that.

FOOTBALL'S COMING HOME!

YEP, ENGLAND ARE OUT OF THE WORLD CUP AFTER A NARROW DEFEAT TO FRANCE. HOWEVER, THE PLAYERS CAN LEAVE WITH THEIR HEADS HELD HIGH. AT LEAST THE PLAN TO KEEP MBAPPÉ QUIET WORKED. WELL, MOSTLY...

IT WAS A DISAPPOINTING END FOR ENGLAND, BUT DO YOU WANT TO HEAR A REALLY SAD FOOTBALL STORY? DEPARTING BRAZIL COACH TITE CAN TELL YOU ONE IN JUST SIX WORDS ...

BRAZIL WERE CROWNED WORLD CHAMPIONS JUST LAST WEEK, BUT THOSE CROATIAN SQUARES DUMPED THEM OUT AS UNCEREMONIOUSLY AS A CAT BEING REMOVED FROM A PRESS CONFERENCE.

IT LOOKED LIKE CURTAINS FOR ZLATKO DALIC'S SIDE WHEN NEYMAR SCORED A SUPERB GOAL IN EXTRA-TIME, BUT WE SHOULD ALL KNOW BETTER THAN THAT BY NOW. CROATIA'S MIDFIELD MAY MOVE WITH THE PACE OF A RIO CARNIVAL FLOAT, BUT IT SLOWLY SAPS YOUR ENERGY WITH ITS MESMERIC RHYTHMS. A LATE PETKOVIC EQUALISER AND FOUR PERFECT PENALTIES LATER AND BRAZIL WERE OUT. WE'LL NEVER KNOW WHAT ELABORATE CELEBRATION NEYMAR HAD PLANNED BECAUSE HE SELFLESSLY OPTED TO TAKE THE FIFTH SPOT KICK, ALLOWING THE UNDERSTUDIES THEIR MOMENT IN THE SPOTLIGHT.

TWO-NIL UP WITH THE CLOCK RUNNING DOWN, FAMED BEEF LOVERS ARGENTINA WERE ALSO IN COMPLETE CONTROL OF THEIR EXTENDED ARGUMENT WITH THE NETHERLANDS. HOWEVER, THE DUTCH CLAWED BACK TWO LATE GOALS THANKS TO A BRILLIANT TACTICAL INTERVENTION THAT WAS MORE EVOCATIVE OF CHARLES REEP THAN JOHNNY REP.

LVG AND HIS CREW WERE AGAIN DECKED OUT LIKE GROOMSMEN, AND THERE WAS A SENSE OF INEVITABILITY THAT THIS WEDDING WOULD END IN A PUNCH-UP. ARGENTINA EVENTUALLY PREVAILED ON PENALTIES AFTER A GRUELLING BATTLE OF END-TO-END SHITHOUSERY. THE ONLY THING THAT UNITED BOTH SIDES WAS THEIR ANNOYANCE AT REFEREE ANTONIO MATEU LAHOZ, WHO SPENT THE NIGHT REPEATEDLY BLASTING HIS WHISTLE LIKE HE WAS A CHILD WHO'D BEEN GIFTED IT FOR CHRISTMAS BY A GIT.

THEY'LL BE JOINED IN THE LAST FOUR BY THE FIRST TEAM FROM AFRICA TO REACH THE SEMI-FINALS, SURPRISE PACKAGE OF THE OFFICE SWEEPSTAKE: MOROCCO! THEIR 1-0 WIN AGAINST PORTUGAL WAS WELL-DESERVED AND INCLUDED SEVERAL STAND-OUT PERFORMANCES, NOT LEAST FROM GOALKEEPER "BONO" WHOSE INPUT WAS VITAL IN DECIDING WHICH TEAM WOULD BE CELEBRATING AT FULL-TIME.

MOROCCO'S REWARD IS A DATE WITH FRANCE, WHO PUNISHED ENGLAND FOR A LAPSE IN CONCENTRATION (WHO CAN BLAME THEM FOR BRIEFLY GETTING LOST IN GIROUD'S EYES?) AND AN UNCHARACTERISTIC ERROR FROM HARRY KANE, WHO WENT ABOUT 35 MINUTES TOO EARLY WITH THE PENALTY AGONY. WHO KNOWS WHAT GOES THROUGH A PLAYER'S MIND AT MOMENTS OF SUCH HIGH PRESSURE...?

HOPEFULLY, KANE WILL BE ABLE TO PUT THE PAIN OF DEFEAT INTO PERSPECTIVE. IN A WORLD CUP ALREADY ENTWINED WITH GENUINE HUMAN TRAGEDY, FOOTBALL LOST ONE OF ITS GREATS ON FRIDAY - THE AMERICAN JOURNALIST, GRANT WAHL. AS WELL AS BEING A PASSIONATE ADVOCATE FOR THE MEN'S AND WOMEN'S GAME IN THE US, HE NEVER SHIED AWAY FROM EXPOSING FOOTBALL'S DARKER SIDE AND WAS VOCAL IN HIS CRITICISM OF THE HUMAN RIGHTS ISSUES SURROUNDING THIS WORLD CUP, WHERE HE WAS BRIEFLY DETAINED FOR WEARING A RAINBOW T-SHIRT. BUT MOST OF ALL, GRANT WAS A GENEROUS, KIND AND BRAVE PERSON. FOOTBALL AND THE WORLD IS A POORER PLACE WITHOUT HIM.

AND THEN THE CIRCUS LEFT TOWN...

... THE STADIUMS ARE PACKED UP AND SHIPPED OFF LIKE THE DISPOSABLE PEOPLE WHO BUILT THEM. THE DROOLING CAMERA OPERATORS TASKED WITH PICKING OUT ATTRACTIVE WOMEN IN THE CROWD ARE RETURNED TO THEIR LAIRS. EMILIANO MARTÍNEZ DOESN'T EVEN TRY TO SCRUB THAT FLAG OUT OF HIS HAIR BEFORE HE STRUTS BACK INTO SCHOOL...

HAH, NO, I HAVEN'T THOUGHT ABOUT ASTON VILLA FOR A WHILE, EITHER. BECAUSE, GUYS, THERE'S BEEN A WORLD CUP ON, AND WHAT'S MORE, IT HAD A FAIRY TALE ENDING: GIANNI INFANTINO DECLARING HE WANTS TO STAY ON AS PRESIDENT UNTIL THE SEAS TURN TO DUST (2031) AND ANNOUNCING FIFA PROFITS BEYOND YOUR WILDEST DREAMS!

ANNOYINGLY, LIONEL MESSI MADE A SHAMELESS ATTEMPT TO STEAL THE LIMELIGHT FROM THE SNOOPY-FOOTED FIFA PRESIDENT. AS WELL AS SCORING TWICE AND CAPTAINING ARGENTINA TO WORLD CUP GLORY, MESSI ALSO RECEIVED A SPECIAL GIFT FROM HIS BOSS, THE EMIR OF QATAR.

CRITICS CLAIMED THE GESTURE EXPLOITED THE GOOD AND PURE TOURISM AMBASSADOR FOR SAUDI ARABIA. BUT TO QATAR'S ELITE, NOT ONLY IS THE BISHT AN ITEM OF GREAT HONOUR, IT CAN ALSO BE USED TO VEIL THINGS YOU DON'T WANT TO TALK ABOUT.

TALKING OF PRESENTATIONS, FOR A TOURNAMENT THAT HAS BEEN SO TIGHTLY STAGE MANAGED, NOT EVEN THE SUPREME COMMITTEE COULD HAVE ACCOUNTED FOR EMI MARTÍNEZ STANDING ON A PODIUM THAT PROBABLY DOUBLES AS SOME QATARI PRINCE'S SCALEXTRIC TRACK AND WAVING HIS INDIVIDUAL AWARD LIKE IT WAS A PENIS.

MARTÍNEZ'S PSYCHOLOGICAL MASTERCLASS HELPED ARGENTINA TO A PENALTY SHOOTOUT VICTORY AFTER A FINAL THAT SAW SIX GOALS — ALMOST ONE FOR EVERY THOUSAND MIGRANT WORKERS ESTIMATED TO HAVE DIED IN QATAR SINCE THEY WON THE HOSTING RIGHTS! ARGENTINA WERE CRUISING AT 2-0 WITH LITTLE OVER 10 MINUTES LEFT, BUT THEIR VIRUS-HIT FRENCH OPPONENTS FOUND A SUDDEN RESERVE OF ENERGY, AS IF ROUSED BY A MAGICAL ELIXIR.

ARGUABLY, THE EXCITEMENT OF THE FINAL DOESN'T JUSTIFY THE COST IN HUMAN LIFE, BUT PLENTY OF JOURNALISTS AND PUNDITS HAVE BEEN WON OVER. SURE, THE WHOLE SHOW WAS BUILT ON THE BLOOD OF EXPLOITED LABOUR, BUT CREDIT WHERE IT'S DUE, THEY'VE GOT THE METRO SYSTEM RUNNING ON TIME. POLITICIANS RELIANT UPON QATAR'S CONTINUED GOOD FAVOUR HAVE ALSO BEEN EFFUSIVE IN THEIR PRAISE.

THE CONTEXT-FREE TALK OF THIS BEING THE BEST EVER WORLD CUP MUST BE HUGELY UPLIFTING FOR THE GAY QATARIS LIVING IN FEAR OF PERSECUTION, THE MIGRANT WORKERS (THOSE ALLOWED TO STAY) SURVIVING ON A PITTANCE IN ONE OF THE WORLD'S RICHEST NATIONS, AND THE RELATIVES OF THE INDENTURED LABOURERS WHO PAID THE ULTIMATE PRICE FOR THIS EXTENDED SHOW OF POWER. BUT HEY, AT LEAST THERE WAS SOMEONE AT THE FINAL WHO COULD SHOW GIANNI HOW TO RUB SALT INTO THEIR WOUNDS WITH A BIT OF FLAIR.

Smashing job on the Footy Cup, lads.
Everyone says it was the best one evs.
Never mind the whinging wokerati,
David Beckham reckons the spice markets are the best he's seen!
Gary Neville will be dealt with, though.
All the best,
Sunak, Rishi ☺

2022-23 (PART TWO):
ASTERISKY BUSINESS

Some stars burn too brightly for this universe, radiant balls of energy that enrich our lives only too briefly before leaving an indelible mark that stretches through time: Jimi Hendrix, Lady Di and former Southampton manager Nathan Jones, the David Brent of Hearts. Jones's self-aggrandising press conferences showed he had the potential to become one of the Premier League's main characters, but this promise was cruelly trampled upon when the Southampton suits became scared of his truth, backed up by a run of frankly atrocious results that contributed significantly to their consequent relegation.

Jones was also the manager who denied Manchester City a clean sweep of silverware, eliminating them from the only trophy they truly craved, the Carabao Cup. That honour instead went to Manchester United, who beat Newcastle in the final, heralding a glorious new dawn for Erik ten Hag's side, a gilded, Fergie-esque era that endured for a whole week, until they lost 7–0 to Liverpool at Anfield.

As ever, much attention was focused on the boardroom at Old Trafford. The Glazers continued to care for the club with the love and attention of a deadbeat dad, putting in an appearance every few years and leaving behind empty promises and a smashed piggy bank. However, they were finally willing to relinquish a few crumbs of power at a vastly inflated price, and two bidders were eventually revealed as their preferred marks: cuddly old environmental vandal Sir Jim Ratcliffe and the son of a former Qatari prime minister, Sheikh Jassim, who famously had no links to the state of Qatar. As many as two photographs were produced to prove the actual existence of the shy sheikh, emphatically silencing cynics.

Manchester United faced stiff competition for the title of the most chaotic club in the Premier League from traditional banter powerhouse Everton and the KLF-style, money-burning, anarcho-art performance piece that was Todd Boehly's Chelsea. Frank Lampard was let go by Everton, despite overseeing a run of results that made him look like Valeriy Lobanovskyi by comparison to the coach who ended up taking over at Chelsea when they sacked Graham Potter: Frank Lampard.

Lampard's replacement at Everton illustrated the effects of the climate crisis on the natural world: a confused Sean Dyche emerged from a period of hibernation (spent watching Challenge TV with a family pack of Chilli Heatwave Doritos in hand) and exposed his milky white thighs to Everton's training ground in January, the winter air cut through with the unmistakable cry of bleep tests and ragamuffin MC Ian Woan's boombox.

Tottenham also had a disappointing season, but Antonio Conte produced one of the great post-match press conferences of recent years after watching his team concede two late goals to draw at Southampton. His extended rant earned him the sack, showing he could at last manage something successfully. Conte's interim replacement, Cristian Stellini, generated almost as much energy as any potato battery, but was thrown out before he could even start sprouting shoots.

Arsenal's title bid eventually succumbed to the relentless Terminator march of Manchester City. Nothing could stop them from claiming the Treble – not United, not Inter, not even 115 charges of alleged historical breaches of the Premier League's financial rules. However, whenever Pep Guardiola closes his eyes, he'll see the face of the maverick who denied him true footballing immortality: Blaenrhondda's most famous son, Nathan Jason Jones.

TWO LOCAL DERBIES AT THE TOP OF THE PREMIER LEAGUE SET PULSES RACING ALMOST AS MUCH AS THE PROSPECT OF PEP DEPLOYING SOME OF THE "RIDICULOUS" IDEAS HE SAID HE WAS MULLING LAST WEEK. WHAT COULD WE EXPECT; PAUL DICKOV IN NETS? DAVID JAMES UP TOP? MORE FAT-SHAMING OF KALVIN PHILLIPS? IN THE END, CONTROLLING POSSESSION FOR LONG SPELLS BUT FALLING TO A LATE COMEBACK COULD BARELY HAVE BEEN LESS WACKY...

So I told Phil to lie down on the floor... he actually did it, the absolute madman hahahahahahaha!

ONE-NIL UP WITH 10 TO PLAY, CITY LOOKED AS SNUG AS MASTER GREALISH'S BRITCHES, BUT THE GAME WAS TO SPIN ON ITS BUCKET HAT. FIRSTLY, BRUNO FERNANDES'S EQUALISER WAS ALLOWED TO STAND, AFTER THE OFFICIALS DECIDED THE OFFSIDE MARCUS RASHFORD WAS AS INVISIBLE AS HE WAS LAST SEASON, AND THEN THE RESURGENT STRIKER HIMSELF POKED IN THE WINNER. MANY A LAZY PUNDIT HAD ATTRIBUTED HIS DROP IN FORM TO HIS CHARITABLE WORK, WHICH MAKES YOU WONDER IF HE'S NOW GONE TOO FAR THE OTHER WAY...?

Yoink! I'll take those Frubes, you little punks!

Huzzah! You need the goals more than we need the calcium, Mr Rashford!

A WIN AGAINST CRYSTAL PALACE IN MIDWEEK WOULD EVEN MOVE THE RED DEVILS UP TO SECOND PLACE! FOR A BIT! THE RECENT UPSURGE IN FORM OF RASHFORD AND UNITED IS MADE ALL THE MORE REMARKABLE BY THE FACT IT HAS BEEN ACHIEVED WITHOUT A CERTAIN INSPIRATIONAL FIGURE TO LIFT MORALE AND EDUCATE HIS SUBORDINATES...

What did you learn from the Jordan B Peterson podcast I told you to listen to?

To always stay humble. To respect your manager and eat your greens. And most importantly, to regrout your bathroom tiles once a year.

What? Show me that.

JORDAN B HENDERSON

RULES FOR LIFE

EP. 127 - WE GROUT AGAIN ☺
Rules For Life with Jordan B Hen

Screw this. I'm off to a place where they truly respect freedom of speech!

Before you embark upon your grouting journey, we need to talk scrapers...

HOWEVER, THE SCENES OF JUBILATION THAT MET THE FINAL WHISTLE CAUGHT THE ATTENTION OF THAT MOST FEARED OF LAW ENFORCEMENT AGENCIES: THE PROPER FOOTBALL MEN OF THE CELEBRATION POLICE...

Punching the air and roaring at the crowd after winning a local derby in dramatic fashion, when there's still half a season left? Who does he think he is, Arsenal?! Wait until the guv'nor hears about this. Where is he, anyway?

Working on some big case, apparently...

DCI KEYS' OBSESSION WITH MIKEL ARTETA REACHED NEW LEVELS OF HEALTHINESS ON SUNDAY, WHEN HE DREW A LINK BETWEEN THE ARSENAL MANAGER'S TOUCHLINE THEATRICS AND AARON RAMSDALE GETTING KICKED BY A PROFESSIONAL JAY CARTWRIGHT IMPERSONATOR AFTER THE GUNNERS' 2-0 WIN AT SPURS.
SURE, IT'S EASY TO DISMISS THE SWEATY RAMBLINGS OF THE EMIR OF BANTZ, BUT MAYBE THERE'S A LOT MORE THAT CAN BE BLAMED ON THE LEGO-HAIRED MISCREANT...

ALEKSANDAR MITROVIĆ'S PENALTY AGAINST NEWCASTLE

The 'teta Fly Effect'
A manager flaps his arms in London

... and 282 miles away, a sudden gust of wind causes the Fulham striker to kick a penalty against his own foot.

LIVERPOOL'S LETHARGIC 3-0 DEFEAT AT BRIGHTON

How can we be expected to maintain our high levels of energy in the knowledge that a man refuses to stay within the confines of a white oblong painted on the ground? What is the point of anything?!

THE TERMINAL DECLINE OF EVERTON

Chang

The case has not 'slammed shut', it has simply closed.

IT WAS A BRIEF BUT PASSIONATE AFFAIR (MOSTLY WITH HIMSELF), BUT NATHAN JONES' 94-DAY FLING WITH SOUTHAMPTON HAS BURNED OUT IN THE FASHION OF MANY A ROMANTIC TRAGEDY: A 2-1 HOME DEFEAT BY 10-MAN WOLVES. JONES MAY BE GONE UNTIL THE LUTON JOB BECOMES AVAILABLE AGAIN, BUT WE'LL ALWAYS HAVE HIS QUOTES, LIKE THAT ONE ABOUT NOT WANTING TO MAKE DO WITH BEING A PE TEACHER IN A MINING VILLAGE AND SETTLING DOWN WITH A NICE WELSH GIRL. GOD KNOWS, THOUGH, IT WOULD HAVE BEEN FASCINATING TO SEE HOW HE'D HAVE FARED ON THE BLAENRHONDDA SPEED-DATING SCENE...

AT LEAST PEP'S STILL AROUND TO GIVE GOOD MEDIA DUTIES. LAST WEEK HE WENT THE FULL KENNETH WILLIAMS, REFERENCING JULIUS CAESAR WHEN BEMOANING THE CHARGES AGAINST MANCHESTER CITY.

THE COMPANY MAN OFFERED A STIRRING DEFENCE OF HIS OWNERS AND CLAIMED CITY WERE BEING CONDEMNED WITHOUT A TRIAL.

HE WENT ON TO SAY THE CLUB WOULD DEFEND ITSELF AS SUCCESSFULLY AS IT HAD WHEN CAS QUASHED ITS TWO-YEAR BAN FROM EUROPEAN COMPETITION FOR BREACHING UEFA'S FINANCIAL FAIR PLAY RULES. REMEMBER HOW HAPPY HE WAS WHEN CITY WERE FOUND TO BE THE PICTURE OF INNOCENCE?

PEP ALSO SPECULATED OVER WHAT ELSE WOULD BE PINNED ON CITY, WHICH MUST HAVE FURROWED AT LEAST ONE MICROSCOPIC BROW.

IT ALL FUELLED THE SENSE OF INJUSTICE AMONG CITY FANS, WHO MADE THEIR FEELINGS FELT ON SUNDAY BY BOOING A JINGLE AND UNVEILING A BANNER IN HONOUR OF LORD PANNICK KC. YOU MIGHT RECALL HIM FROM SUCH CASES AS CITY v CAS AND RECEIVING £129,700 OF PUBLIC MONEY TO SCRUTINISE THE LEGAL BASIS FOR THE PARTYGATE INQUIRY. MAD FOR IT! WHO KNOWS WHAT OTHER BIG SIGNINGS THEY MIGHT BRING IN TO BOLSTER THEIR DEFENCE? ATTICUS FINCH? KIM WEXLER? RUMPOLE OF THE BAILEY?

FOOTBALL'S DEFINITELY GETTING WEIRDER. FOR ALL THE COMPLAINTS OF AN ELITIST CONSPIRACY AGAINST SHEIKH MANSOUR'S UNDERDOGS, CITY MIGHT END UP WINNING THE LEAGUE BECAUSE ARSENAL WERE DENIED VICTORY AGAINST BRENTFORD, AS LEE MASON FORGOT TO DRAW A LINE. IT WAS ONE OF SEVERAL VAR-RELATED CLANGERS THAT LEFT YOU WONDERING WHAT WAS GOING DOWN AT STOCKLEY PARK ON SATURDAY.

IF CITY ARE FOUND GUILTY AND PUNISHED ACCORDINGLY, THEIR FANS WILL BE THE ULTIMATE VICTIMS. SWINDON'S DEMOTION FOR FINANCIAL IRREGULARITIES IN 1990 CHANGED ME AS A PERSON. I COULD HAVE BECOME A PE TEACHER IN A FORMER RAILWAY TOWN, MARRIED A LOCAL GIRL WITH LOW STANDARDS. BEAUTIFUL. BUT, NO; THE BURNING SENSE OF INJUSTICE DROVE ME TO THIS, PEDDLING PUNS FOR THE DOPAMINE HITS AND DRAWING NATHAN JONES DOING A SALSA CLASS IN AN ALTERNATIVE REALITY.

AS WE KNOW, MANCHESTER UNITED SOLD ITS SOUL LONG AGO, IN A RARE CASE OF THE DEVIL MAKING A PACT WITH SOMEONE EVEN WORSE...

BUT NOW THEY MAY BE ABOUT TO LEAP FROM THAT FRYING PAN INTO THE WARM EMBRACE OF SHEIKH JASSIM BIN HAMAD AL-THANI, CHAIR OF THE QATAR ISLAMIC BANK AND PURPORTED LONG-TIME MANCHESTER UNITED FAN.

SOME MANIACS CLAIM THERE'S A LINK BETWEEN THE STATE OF QATAR AND THE SON OF ITS FORMER PRIME MINISTER (WHO WAS ALSO HEAD OF ITS SOVEREIGN WEALTH FUND, WHICH ALSO HAPPENS TO BE THE LARGEST SHAREHOLDER IN SHEIKH JASSIM'S BANK). BUT IF THERE'S ANY CONFLICT OF INTEREST WITH QATAR ALSO OWNING PSG, YOU CAN BE SURE IT WILL BE WEEDED OUT BY THE BOSS OF THE EUROPEAN CLUB ASSOCIATION, NASSER AL-KHELAIFI!

BESIDES, WE ALL KNOW THE IDENTITY OF THE SHADOWY FIGURE WHO SET THE WHEELS OF THIS DEAL IN MOTION...

My Kingdom's wealth fund for a fine-tooth comb!

ROCK OF GIBRALTAR!

IF YOU'RE WORRIED ABOUT ANOTHER SLICE OF FOOTBALL HERITAGE BEING CO-OPTED BY AN OIL REGIME'S STATE FUND THEN FEAR NOT— THE TWIN FORCES OF THE PREMIER LEAGUE'S OWNERS AND DIRECTORS TEST AND THE GOVERNMENT'S INDEPENDENT REGULATOR (LAUNCH DATE TBC) COULD SERIOUSLY IMPEDE ANY TAKEOVER BID...

NEWS OF THE BID HAS LED TO AN OUTPOURING OF OUR OLD FRIEND, WHATABOUTERY. GUYS, DID YOU KNOW THE STATE OF QATAR OWNS OTHER THINGS YOU HAVE A DEEP EMOTIONAL CONNECTION WITH?

Careful, Your Most Excellent Excellency - the red carpet is deceptively squishy.

Yeah, I grew up in the shadow of The Gherkin, but three generations of my family were The Shard fans, so it was in my blood, you know?

Come on!

MANCHESTER UNITED'S SUPPORTERS' TRUST AND THEIR LGBTQ+ FAN GROUP, THE RAINBOW DEVILS, HAVE RAISED SERIOUS OBJECTIONS TO THE POTENTIAL DEAL THAT IS ALREADY PROVING TO BE DIVISIVE. SHOULD THE TAKEOVER GO THROUGH, MANCHESTER WOULD ALSO BECOME A PROXY BATTLEGROUND FOR MIDDLE EASTERN POWER POLITICS (THE COLD AND WET WAR?), ADDING ANOTHER DIMENSION TO A FAMOUS OLD RIVALRY THAT HAS LONG SPLIT THE CITY, AND SOMETIMES EVEN FAMILIES...

SOME SUCCESS-STARVED FANS OF THE CLUB WHO SIT THIRD IN THE PREMIER LEAGUE AND WHO ARE PLAYING BARCELONA ON THURSDAY, BEFORE A CUP FINAL ON SUNDAY, SAY THEY JUST WANT THE WORLD'S FOURTH RICHEST FOOTBALL CLUB TO COMPETE FINANCIALLY. PRESUMABLY, THIS TRANSLATES AS "BUY EVERYONE IN SIGHT" – AN APPROACH THAT'S BEEN WORKING LIKE A DREAM AT CHELSEA.

Our Kevin likes Qatar, but Steve's always gone for United (Arab Emirates).

It's murder in here come Gulf Cooperation Council Summit week!

Champions of shopping, you'll never sing that...

Where's your blockade gone? Where's your blockade gone?

I've bought you every player in that video game, Potter!

FIFA '23?

Hah, what?

Also, can you try to look a bit angrier on the bench? Danny Murphy's mentioned it, so...

Shouldn't be a problem...

GIVEN ENGLISH FOOTBALL'S WEAK PROTECTION RULES, NO MATTER IF YOU SUPPORT MANCHESTER UNITED, CHELSEA, OR HARRODS FC, CLUBS AT EVERY LEVEL ARE AT THE MERCY OF TAKEOVERS FROM SOVEREIGN WEALTH FUNDS, BLUE-SKY-THINKING CRYPTO BROS AND PUBESCENT ENTREPRENEURS. LUCKILY FOR UNITED, THERE'S AN ALTERNATIVE: CUDDLY OLD JIM RATCLIFFE!

PERHAPS THE SADDEST PART OF IT ALL IS THAT ELON MUSK DIDN'T FOLLOW THROUGH ON HIS BRAIN-FART TO BUY MANCHESTER UNITED. AT LEAST THAT SELF-DRIVING CLOWN CAR WOULD HAVE BEEN ENTERTAINING.

JUST LIKE YOUR FAVOURITE UNCLE, IN THAT HE BLOODY LOVES BREXIT.

HELPING US ALL GET CLOSER TO THE SWEET RELEASE OF DEATH WITH HIS AGGRESSIVE LOBBYING AGAINST ENVIRONMENTAL REGULATIONS. THANKS, JIM!

FRACKING GREAT HAIRLINE FOR A MAN OF HIS VINTAGE.

MONACO RESIDENT FOR YACHT REASONS (ALSO TAX REASONS).

POSSIBLY A GRANDAD ♥

That visual joke would work better if the phrase was: "Let that daft laddie with the sink in".

He says we're all fired if we don't pass to him.

(seven)

LIVERPOOL'S SUNDAY AFTERNOON ANNIHILATION OF MANCHESTER UNITED WAS FREAKISH, ESPECIALLY IF YOU DON'T WONDER WHAT THE REAL STATISTICAL OUTLIER IS IN THE SEQUENCE OF PERCH DERBY RESULTS THAT READS: 5-0, 4-0, 1-2, 7-0. THE RESULT ALSO HAD IMPLICATIONS FOR THE ONLY COMPETITION THAT MATTERS: THE PUNDIT BANTER WARS...

UNTIL CODY GAKPO GAVE LIVERPOOL THE LEAD JUST BEFORE HALF-TIME, THE GAME WAS FAIRLY EVEN, BUT UNITED'S SUBSEQUENT CAPITULATION WAS TOTAL. THE CLOSEST ANYONE GOT TO IMPEDING LIVERPOOL WAS WHEN ONE OF THEIR OWN FANS SLIPPED AND TOOK OUT ANDY ROBERTSON. IT MAKES YOU WONDER WHAT WENT DOWN IN THE VISITORS' DRESSING ROOM DURING THE BREAK.

NO ONE QUITE EPITOMISED UNITED'S COLLECTIVE MELTDOWN LIKE BRUNO FERNANDES, WHOSE EXTENDED TANTRUM WAS SO PETULANT HE MAY AS WELL HAVE ERECTED A GREEN SCREEN AND PROVIDED WATCH-ALONG COMMENTARY FOR HIS YOUTUBE CHANNEL VIEWERS.

THE RESULT WAS A BITTER PILL TO SWALLOW FOR SELF-PROCLAIMED LIFELONG MANCHESTER UNITED FANS NEAR AND FAR.

BUT THE DAY BELONGED TO LIVERPOOL. THEIR HAUL INCLUDED TWO GOALS APIECE FROM GAKPO, SALAH AND NÚÑEZ. DARWIN'S TOWERING 50p HEAD FLICK FOR 'THE REDS' FIFTH CONTINUES HIS IMPRESSIVE ASCENT FROM BEING A LAZY PUNCHLINE (SOZ) EARLIER IN THE SEASON.

THE ROUT WAS COMPLETED WITH A GOAL FROM THE DEPARTING FIRMINO, AND IF THE GAME HAD GONE ON LONGER YOU WONDER WHO ELSE WOULD WOULD HAVE PROVIDED A SENTIMENTAL MOMENT FOR THE LIVERPOOL FANS.

AS PROTOCOL DICTATES, THE STORY ENDS WITH FOOTAGE OF THE UNITED PLAYERS SOLEMNLY DRIVING THEIR CHESHIRE TANKS INTO CARRINGTON, AND FOR THEIR APOLOGIES TO FILL SOCIAL MEDIA; THEIR MINDS POURED OUT ON THE NOTES APP.

ANTONIO CONTE HAS MADE IT TO THE EXIT AT TOTTENHAM. ON SATURDAY, HE LET FLY WITH AN EXTRAORDINARY RANT, HAVING HELPLESSLY STOOD BY AND WATCHED THE TEAM HE PICKED, TRAINED AND INSTRUCTED THROW AWAY A TWO-GOAL LEAD TO DRAW 3-3 AT SOUTHAMPTON. THEY EVEN CONCEDED A GOAL WITHIN A MINUTE OF THE SECOND HALF, MAKING YOU WONDER WHAT WENT DOWN DURING THE INTERVAL...

And after they've inflated the walls of the abdomen, they can just whip out the gallbladder. Roberto is your uncle. Who wants to see it? Skipp, get your nose in here, ragazzo.

ARGH ARGH

Crumbs.

HIS POST-MATCH PRESSER EXUDED THE ENERGY OF A MAN WHO HAS DECIDED TO EFF THIS FOR A GAME OF SUBBUTEO – AS IF GRIEVING THE LOSS OF THREE CLOSE FRIENDS AND RECOVERING FROM MAJOR SURGERY GIVE YOU A HEAVY DOSE OF PERSPECTIVE. NO ONE AT SPURS WAS LEFT UNSCATHED BY HIS NOT-ENTIRELY-INACCURATE TIRADE.

IT WOULD HAVE MADE FOR A PRETTY UNCOMFORTABLE JOURNEY HOME, WHAT WITH THE ENTIRE SQUAD LOCATED BENEATH THE BUS. CONTE'S VEILED CRITICISM OF THE BOARD FELT MORE SIGNIFICANT, BUT IT WOULD SURELY BE ABSURD TO SPECULATE THAT IT WAS THE LATEST ACT OF PROVOCATION DESIGNED TO GET HIS CONTRACT PAID OUT BEFORE IT EXPIRES.

...And as for you. You're the most selfish one here! Where's the fire? Where's the passion? It's your fault Richarlison has turned into a Stars In Their Eyes Grzegorz Rasiak, and I bet it was you who sent on Davinson Sánchez when we needed a goal against Milan!

Well I hardly think that's fair...

You don't mind if I use your private stanza di merda, right, Danny boy?

Well actually–

Grazie mille.

Ey Levy; someone's blocked your crapper!

Three more months, Daniel. Three more months...

HOWEVER, CONTE HAS NOW LEFT SPURS. WHETHER IT WAS BECAUSE HE DARED TO HINT AT THE COMMON DENOMINATOR IN 20 YEARS OF UNDERACHIEVEMENT, OR SOMETHING ELSE PUSHED LEVY OVER THE EDGE WILL REMAIN AS MUCH OF A MYSTERY AS SPURS STILL BEING FOURTH.

CRYSTAL PALACE FINALLY LOST PATIENCE WITH PATRICK VIEIRA LAST WEEK TOO, AND THERE WERE ECHOES OF THE FAMOUS DISMISSAL OF TREVOR "BUT IT'S MY BIRTHDAY" FRANCIS AS BRAVELY BOLD STEVE PARISH DELIVERED THE NEWS TO VIEIRA OVER THE PHONE AS HE DROVE TO TRAINING ON HIS SPECIAL DAY.

Hmm, the Bircher muesli tastes a bit different this morning...

Son of a...

Yeah, I came in four hours early and removed all the chia seeds by hand.

Ah, good morning, Mr Parish. What have you got planned for my St Patrick's Day celebrations?

Well...

SCREECH!

REMARKABLY, ROY HODGSON HAS RETURNED TO HIS OLD HOOD UNTIL THE END OF THE SEASON, BECAUSE IF THERE'S ANYONE WHO CAN INSPIRE A GROUP OF YOUNG MEN, IT'S SOUTH LONDON'S YOUNGEST SEPTUAGENARIAN. YEAH, ROI!

IT'S A SURPRISING CHOICE, BUT SUCH IS THE UNPREDICTABILITY OF FOOTBALL, ANYTHING CAN HAPPEN. WELL, ALMOST ANYTHING...

Zip up the CD case, Raymond. It's time to relate to your dem.

LATER You need to remember the basics, Eberechi. As my old pals Embrace used to say, "come back to what you know, take everything real slow"...

CLICK CLICK

Crumbs.

Antonio, how would you feel about a contract extension?

HAHAHAHAHAHA!

Ow. Please. The doctor says I'm still not allowed to experience joy.

You're in the right place, chum.

JUST SEVEN MONTHS AFTER PAYING BRIGHTON £21.5M TO GIVE GRAHAM P45OTTER A BEARD TRIM AND A NEW ROLL-NECK, CHELSEA HAVE JOGGED HIM ON. LANGUISHING IN 11TH AND FACING A HUGE FINANCIAL DEFICIT, THE BLUES' ONLY HOPE FOR THE REST OF THE SEASON IS THAT THE INEXPERIENCED BRUNO SALTOR CAN DO A DI MATTEO, POTTER'S ASSISTANT HAVING DECIDED TO STAY ON AT THE BRIDGE...

HAVING SACKED THE PREVIOUS BLOKE, WHO MAY HAVE DELIVERED A CHAMPIONS LEAGUE, BUT OFFERED ZERO BANTS IN THE GROUP CHAT, BLUE SKY THINKER TODD BOEHLY INSTALLED POTTER AS MANAGER AND SET ABOUT PEBBLE-DASHING HIM WITH NEW PLAYERS FASTER THAN THEY COULD BE OFFLOADED, TO AN ALMOST MEME-WORTHY EXTENT.

HOWEVER, RESULTS DIDN'T IMPROVE, AND YOU HAD TO WONDER WHETHER THE SEEMINGLY INDISCRIMINATE STOCKPILING OF TALENT WAS REALLY HELPFUL. FOR EXAMPLE, SIGNING MYKHAILO MUDRYK MAY HAVE BEEN NOBLE IN ITS MOTIVATIONS (TROLLING ARSENAL LOL), BUT GIVING HIM AN EIGHT-YEAR CONTRACT FELT A BIT EXCESSIVE TO THOSE OF US WHO DIDN'T GO TO NO FANCY BUSINESS SCHOOL.

THE GENUINELY PITIFUL RUN OF RESULTS ASIDE, WE'RE TOLD POTTER NEVER QUITE VIBED WITH THE CLUB ON A SENSORY LEVEL. HE NEVER LOOKED, SOUNDED OR SMELLED LIKE HE BELONGED AT STAMFORD BRIDGE, BEGGING THE QUESTION: WHAT PHYSICAL ATTRIBUTES SHOULD A CHELSEA MANAGER HAVE?

THEN THERE WAS ALL THAT CHATTER ABOUT HIM NOT BEING ANGRY ENOUGH, SOMETHING THAT MIGHT HAVE CHANGED WHEN HE GOT THE DREADED PHONE CALL ON SUNDAY AFTERNOON...

AS FOR CHELSEA, THEIR BEST BET FOR NOW IS FOR THE FANS TO HOLD OFF ON THE DEATH THREATS FOR A BIT AND BACK THE INTERIM COACH...

...UNTIL THE CLUB HIRES A COACH WHO- UNLIKE POTTER- THE SQUAD CAN'T MOCKINGLY COMPARE TO A CHARACTER FROM CHILDREN'S FICTION.

DESPITE THE BASIC WEIRDNESS OF THIS SEASON, IT DOES SOMETIMES FEEL LIKE WE'RE EXISTING IN AN ENDLESS LOOP. IT'S A SENSATION OF HISTORY REPEATING ITSELF THAT MUST BE FELT KEENLY BY ROBERTO DE ZERBI EVERY TIME HOWARD WEBB COMES A-CALLIN' FOLLOWING ANOTHER *** UP.

THIS FEELING THAT WE'RE ALL PART OF A FAMILIAR "CLEAR AND STABLE PLAN" WAS HEIGHTENED LAST WEEK BY THE RETURN TO THE CHELSEA DUGOUT OF HALL OF FAMER, FRANK LAMPARD! SURE, THE HIPSTER HATERS WILL SAY THEY MIGHT AS WELL HAVE HIRED ONE OF JT'S CRYPTO PRIMATES, BUT IT'S REFRESHING TO SEE AN ENGLISH MANAGER FINALLY GET A (*COUNTS*) FOURTH BITE OF THE CHERRY, AND HE WAS PREDICTABLY PHILOSOPHICAL FOLLOWING SATURDAY'S INEVITABLE, LIMP 1-0 DEFEAT AT WOLVES...

FLAMPS NOW HAS THE DAUNTING TASK OF TAKING HIS/TUCHEL'S/POTTER'S/BRUNO SALTOR'S/BIG TODD'S TEAM TO PLAY REAL MADRID AT THE BERNABÉU. HOWEVER THIS IS NOTHING COMPARED TO THE CHALLENGE CARLO ANCELOTTI FACES IN TRYING TO HIDE HIS SURPRISE AT SEEING HIS OLD PLAYER BACK IN THE OPPOSING DUGOUT.

IF WE ARE ALL WHIRLING IN THE INFINITE SPACE-TIME SPIN CYCLE, WHAT WE NEED IS SOMEONE TO REINVENT THE COSMIC WHEEL. THANKFULLY, TODD BOEHLY IS HERE WITH HIS BIG IDEAS TO FIX FOOTBALL — A GAME THAT HAD SOMEHOW LIMPED ON FOR 160-ODD YEARS WITHOUT ANYONE EVER THINKING TO SEEK THE OPINION OF ONE OF THE STARS OF 'LESBIAN VAMPIRE KILLERS'. JAMES CORDEN REPORTEDLY PLAYED A ROLE IN THE LAMPARD RECRUITMENT PROCESS, THUS BREAKING THE SENSE OF DÉJÀ VU BY BEING INVOLVED IN SOMETHING FUNNY.

ADMITTEDLY, IT'S NOT EVERY DAY A LINO GETS ACCUSED OF ELBOWING A PLAYER, SO AT LEAST THE TIME CONTINUUM IS THROWING US THE ODD FUNNY BONE TO THE CHIN. THE FOOTBALL AUTHORITIES ARE INVESTIGATING TO SEE WHETHER CONSTANTINE HATZIDAKIS WENT THE FULL WW-REF ON ANDY ROBERTSON, THIS AT A TIME WHEN THEY'VE ALREADY GOT THEIR HANDS FULL ENDLESSLY REWINDING THE VIDEO TO SEE WHETHER DANIEL PODENCE FLOBBED ON BRENNAN JOHNSON THE OTHER WEEK...

ELSEWHERE IN THIS RIDICULOUS TIMELINE, EVEN FAILED MANAGERIAL APPOINTMENTS ARE REPEATING THEMSELVES, THE CIRCLE OF TIME CONTRACTING AS JESSE MARSCH FAILS TO REACH AN AGREEMENT WITH LEICESTER (AS HE DID WITH SOUTHAMPTON) OVER THE LONG-TERM AVAILABILITY OF GREY JEGGINGS. THIS LEFT THE STAR GATE OPEN FOR A RETURN TO COACHING FOR DEAN SMITH, CRAIG SHAKESPEARE AND MAGIC APE DRAWING LAD. IT'S AS YET UNCLEAR WHOSE EXPERTISE THE FOXES CONSULTED BEFORE HIRING THE (INTERIM) DREAM TEAM.

ROY HODGSON IS ALSO BACK AND IS GETTING A TUNE OUT OF CRYSTAL PALACE WITH THE HOT NEW SOUND OF ATTACKING FOOTBALL. THEIR SECOND CONSECUTIVE WIN UNDER HIS CONTROL — A 5-1 WIN AT ELLAND ROAD — LEFT LEEDS GAZING AT THEIR SHOES. IT'S INCREASINGLY CLEAR THIS IS ROY'S DIVISION AND WE'RE ALL JUST LIVING IN IT.

UNKNOWN PLEASURE CRUISES

SO MAYBE YOU CAN CHANGE YOUR DESTINY. ROB HOLDING'S PLAY-DOH MOP TOP HAIR SHOP REGROWTH SHOWS US THAT MIRACULOUS COMEBACKS ARE POSSIBLE.

OR PERHAPS WE REALLY ARE JUST HURTLING THROUGH SPACE LIKE CARLO'S ERRANT EYEBROW, PREDESTINED TO PLAY THE SAME CHARACTERS OVER AND OVER AGAIN...

GIVE YOURSELF A FULL-BODY BUNTING FLOSS AND REPORT YOUR NEIGHBOUR TO THE AUTHORITIES FOR WEARING A LIVERPOOL TOP, BECAUSE SAM ALLARDYCE HAS SECURED THE SUCCESSION TO BECOME INTERIM MONARCH AT LEEDS UNITED!

MUCH LIKE HIS MAJESTY'S GOVERNMENT, BIG SAM KNOWS THE VALUE OF A SET PIECE, AND HIS CORONATION AT LEEDS INVOLVED THE KIND OF PAGEANTRY THAT EVEN THE STAUNCHEST OF WITCHELLS MIGHT CONCEDE ARE RIDICULOUS.

... AND CHRIST KNOWS WHAT WAS HAPPENING BEHIND THAT SCREEN...

THE EVENT WAS WATCHED BY MILLIONS AROUND THE WORLD, INSPIRED BY THE HISTORIC TRADITION OF TAKING THE PISS ON THE INTERNET. OTHERS TRAVELLED FROM FAR AND WIDE TO PERSONALLY ATTEND A PARTY THAT REPRESENTS WORSE VALUE FOR MONEY THAN PAYING £24.5M FOR A STRIKER WHO PLAYED 48 MINUTES.

THIS SEASON, LEEDS HAVE RESEMBLED A CORONATION QUICHE: SOFT UP TOP, CRUMBLY AT THE BASE, AN EGGY DISAPPOINTMENT. BUT KING SAM HAS ASSEMBLED A BACKROOM STAFF THAT WILL ENABLE HIM TO RULE FOR ALL ETERNITY - OR AT LEAST UNTIL LEEDS SCRAPE TOGETHER ENOUGH POINTS TO ALLOW HIM TO DISAPPEAR OVER THE HORIZON IN A GOLDEN CHARIOT STUFFED WITH RUBIES AND SCEPTRES. HOWEVER, THERE WAS ONE SETBACK...

NO MONARCH ENJOYS INTERACTING WITH THE CITIZENS, SO A VISIT TO MANCHESTER CITY WAS DAUNTING (EVEN IF THEY DO REGULARLY SING THE NAME OF THEIR OWN CARBON PRINCE). AS BEFITS THIS FANTASY TALE OF KINGS AND SIDE-QUEENS, CITY HAVE AN ACTUAL GIANT IN THEIR RANKS! THE SCONE-HATING WOKERATI WILL CLAIM THE KING'S MEN LOST 2-1, BUT THE JOHN STONES OF DESTINY DIDN'T GET A TOUCH AND BIG SAMUEL TAMED THE NORSE COLOSSUS TO CLAIM A MORAL THREE POINTS. **HUZZAH!**

SADLY, MONDAY'S RESULTS SHOW THAT SOME TROUBLE-MAKERS ARE INTENT ON RUINING THE FESTIVITIES. MAYBE KING SAM SHOULD USE THE POLICE AS HIS PRIVATE MILITIA AND ROUND UP THE LIKES OF SEAN DYCHE AND STEVE COOPER LEST THE HORSES BOLT ON LEEDS' SURVIVAL HOPES. BUT WHILE SOME **TREASONOUS TIPPY-TAPPY HOUNDS** MAY LOOK UPON THE RECENT LINEAGE OF LEEDS MANAGERS WITH DISMAY, IF ALLARDYCE IS SUCCESSFUL WE CAN ALL LOOK FORWARD TO ANOTHER FESTIVAL OF BAKED GOODS AND ROOM-READING CELEBRATED IN THE TIME-HONOURED TRADITION.

DESPITE BEING TOP OF THE PILE FOR MUCH OF A SEASON THAT STARTED ABOUT EIGHT YEARS AGO, **ARSENAL HAVE BOTTLED IT!** CHOKED! FAILED TO ENJOY THE FINANCIAL BACKING OF A NATION STATE, HIRED THE WORLD'S BEST COACH AND SIGNED A NORDIC DEATH ROBOT CAPABLE OF SCORING 50-PLUS GOALS A SEASON! **LOSERS!** THEIR FATE WAS ALL BUT SEALED WITH A 3-0 HOME DEFEAT BY BRIGHTON, WHOSE MANAGER, ROBERTO DE ZERBI, CELEBRATED THE GOALS BY RACING OFF DOWN THE TOUCHLINE, IN STARK CONTRAST TO THE FAMOUSLY RESTRAINED MIKEL ARTETA.

I'm sorry, but I just think that's undignified.

Don't you think that's undignified?

BRIGHTON AND THEIR ENDLESS PRODUCTION LINE OF SOUTH AMERICAN PRODIGIES HAD BEEN COMPREHENSIVELY DYCHED BY EVERTON JUST SIX DAYS EARLIER, BUT THEIR RESPONSE WAS AS IMPRESSIVE AS THEIR PHYSIOS' BICEPS AND MAY HAVE BEEN INSPIRED BY DE ZERBI REPORTEDLY SHOWING THEM A MICHAEL JORDAN VIDEO AS MOTIVATION.

Guys, when the Looney Tunes gang pulled Michael Jordan into their universe and made him participate in a basketball match against some cartoon monsters, did he complain? Yes. At length. But he also employed the laws of animation physics to extend his arm to comedic lengths and slam dunk a buzzer beater!

MANCHESTER CITY NEED JUST ONE WIN FROM THEIR FINAL THREE GAMES TO SEAL THE TITLE, WHICH IS THE KIND OF SCENARIO THAT USED TO BE RIDDLED WITH JEOPARDY BACK WHEN THEY WERE MORE OF A LAUGH. THANKFULLY, OTHERS ARE WILLING TO STEP INTO THE COMEDIC VOID, AND CITY'S TROUNCING OF EVERTON FEATURED JORDAN PICKFORD FUNGING HIMSELF AT A SERIES OF LOST CAUSES FOR OUR ENTERTAINMENT.

HAALAND'S HEADER

GÜNDOGAN'S FREE-KICK

CORN SHEIKHS

THE INEXORABLE MARCH OF TIME

ARSENAL'S TITLE DREAMS

Champions

CITY'S 3-0 WIN ALSO THREW EVERTON BACK INTO THE RELEGATION MIRE. COULD THE CHEVRONS ON THEIR SHOULDERS BE A NYLON PORTENT OF THE DIRECTION IN WHICH THEY'RE HEADING? THAT WAS CERTAINLY THE CASE FOR SOUTHAMPTON, WHOSE OWN DEMOTION WAS CONFIRMED ON SATURDAY WITH A LIMP HOME DEFEAT TO FULHAM. NOT EVEN THE INSPIRING PRESENCE OF CELEBRITY FAN AND CURRENT PM RISHI SUNAK COULD RESCUE THEM!

Yes, it's suboptimal, but we've only had 36 of the results in and we're actually excited about spreading our message to the key Championship battlegrounds of Peterborough, Sandwell and Rotherham.

Now if you'll excuse me, I hear there are some boats that need to be stopped down at the docks.

Even I'm not diving for that.

SOUTHAMPTON USE A DATA-DRIVEN MODEL TO INFORM THEIR RECRUITMENT, BUT GIVEN HOW THE SEASON PANNED OUT, THE SPREADSHEET BOFFINS COULD PERHAPS HAVE BENEFITED FROM SOME ASSISTANCE.

It looks like you're trying to avoid relegation. Can I suggest not hiring the Welsh David Brent for the lols?

NATHAN JONES WAS BROUGHT IN TO REPLACE RALPH HASENHÜTTL, BUT HIS REIGN OF BANTER WAS CUT CRIMINALLY SHORT AND RUBÉN SELLÉS WAS PUT IN CHARGE UNTIL THE END OF THE SEASON, THANKS TO A WIN IN HIS FIRST GAME THAT IMPRESSED CEO MARTIN SEMMENS.

His rollneck metrics are second to none, and anyone who can beat Chelsea must be good!

...uck this.

SAINTS' EXPERIMENT OF SIGNING PLAYERS WITH LESS PREMIER LEAGUE EXPERIENCE THAN CLUB LEGEND ALI DIA MAY ULTIMATELY HAVE FAILED, BUT IT DOES PROVIDE THE BASIS FOR A FUN QUIZ: WHICH OF THESE CHARACTERS IS A LEGIT SOUTHAMPTON PLAYER?

QARLOS EQUINTÓ

SPICY ALAN

BOBSON DUGNUTT

KERWIN

ANSWER: IT'S ALL OF THEM!

WE STILL DON'T KNOW WHO WILL BE JOINING SOUTHAMPTON (AND LEICESTER?) IN **THE CHAMPIONSHIP.** FOREST HAD TO SETTLE FOR A DRAW AT FRANK LLLLLLWDAMPARD'S CHELSEA, WHILE LEEDS ALSO DREW WITH NEWCASTLE IN AN EVENTFUL LUNCHTIME FOR JUNIOR FIRPO, WHO EARNED A PENALTY BUT LATER CONCEDED ONE WITH AN IMPRESSIVELY HIGH-ALTITUDE HANDBALL, BEFORE EVENTUALLY BEING SENT OFF. SUCH A WEIRD SEASON.

Right, which one of you pillocks showed him Space Jam?

PEP. PEP HAS CLAIMED THE BARCLAYS, AGAIN. HIS MANCHESTER CITY SIDE HAVE WON THEIR THIRD TITLE IN A ROW — AN OUTCOME EVERY NEUTRAL CRAVED, AS EVIDENCED BY THE LOOK OF DELIGHT ON STEVE COOPER'S FACE WHEN NOTTINGHAM FOREST'S WIN AGAINST ARSENAL CONFIRMED CITY'S TRIUMPH. ALL THAT WAS LEFT WAS FOR A ROUTINE VICTORY AGAINST CHELSEA AND AN UNSANCTIONED PUBLIC GATHERING ON THE PITCH, THE KIND OF WHICH CITY'S OWNERS NO DOUBT LOVE. FIRE UP THE ~~WATER~~ CONFETTI CANNONS!

FOR THOSE WEIRDLY NOT INVESTED IN THE MOST DOMINANT CLUB STEAMROLLING TO ANOTHER TRINKET, PERHAPS THE BLOW COULD HAVE BEEN SOFTENED BY AN *EL CHIRINGUITO* - STYLE SEGMENT FEATURING THREE MINUTES OF A FAMOUS ARSENAL FAN SITTING IN SILENCE TO THE TRAGICOMIC SOUNDTRACK OF A SINGLE DOOM-CHORD. ACTUALLY, IT MIGHT CHEER US ALL UP.

THE CITY MACHINE DOESN'T CARE ABOUT YOUR LONGING FOR A COMPETITIVE PREMIER LEAGUE. IT CAN'T BE BARGAINED WITH. IT CAN'T BE REASONED WITH. IT DOESN'T FEEL PITY OR REMORSE OR FEAR. AND IT ABSOLUTELY WILL NOT STOP, EVER, UNTIL WE ARE ALL DEAD (A PROCESS EXPEDITED BY THEIR OWNER'S CARBON EMISSIONS). IN THE MEANTIME, IT WILL CONTINUE TO APPLY THE SAME FORMULA : GIVING PEP GUARDIOLA WHATEVER HE WANTS.

I want a Kalvin Phillips. I want a hoodie with a big "P" on it. And most of all, I want a Scandi Boy-God with thighs like a Norwegian pine tree and L'Oréal ad hair as long and golden as a summer's day in Tromsø.

So be it.

BUT POSSESSING THE COMPONENT PARTS DOES NOT GUARANTEE SUCCESS, AND GUARDIOLA'S TACTICAL INNOVATIONS WERE KEY TO CITY'S SUCCESS. KALVIN PHILLIPS WAS CONVERTED INTO A HUMAN PUNCHBAG, JOÃO CANCELO WAS DEPLOYED IN A WIDER ROLE (BY ABOUT 925 MILES), AND JOHN STONES WAS TRANSFORMED INTO A GEN Y BECKENBAUER, MAKING HIM THE SECOND MOST IMPOSING PRESENCE IN THE CITY ENGINE ROOM.

AH, YEAH, THOSE 115 CHARGES. IF YOU'RE A FAN OF CONTEXT-FREE ADULATION, LOOK AWAY NOW...

Here comes the compliance bit...

CITY HAVE REPORTEDLY BEGUN THEIR LEGAL CHALLENGE WITH THE SMOKING GUN (NER) THAT THE BARRISTER LEADING THE DISCIPLINARY PROCESS LIKES ARSENAL! WHILE IT MAY SOUND LIKE AN ARGUMENT LIFTED DIRECTLY FROM THE RIVALS.NET ARCHIVES, IT SHOWS CITY ARE GOING TO DIG IN, IN A FASHION NOT SEEN SINCE STEVE LOMAS WAS IN HIS POMP.

ON SUNDAY, WE HAD THE AWKWARD SITUATION WHEREBY THE HEAD OF THE ORGANISATION WHICH HAS BROUGHT THE CHARGES WAS THERE HANDING OUT THE WINNERS' MEDALS. CREDIT WHERE IT'S DUE TO PREMIER LEAGUE BIGWIG RICHARD MASTERS FOR TURNING UP AT THE PARTY AND BEING COMPLETELY OBLIVIOUS TO HIS OWN UNPOPULARITY.

Heh, funny to think I brought all the gifts and nibbles, but might take it all home with me in a bit. Wild, eh?

Also, someone's mashed crisps into the sofa and blocked the downstairs loo. Who? I'm afraid I can't comment, lol.

ALL THAT STANDS BETWEEN CITY AND THE TREBLE IS AN FA CUP FINAL AGAINST A TEAM THEY'VE ALREADY BEATEN 6-3 THIS SEASON, AND GETTING BOGGED DOWN IN A SEMANTIC BATTLE OVER THE CORRECT WAY TO PRONOUNCE THE NAME OF THEIR CHAMPIONS LEAGUE FINAL OPPONENTS.

Quick, Inter Milan are breaking!

Er, no such club, mate. Unless you mean simply "Inter"?

Hey, are you guys talking about Football Club Internazionale Milano — or as I call them, I Nerazzurri?

MAYBE NEXT SEASON A NEW CHALLENGER WILL EMERGE. A PLUCKY UNDERDOG WHO HAVE ALREADY QUALIFIED FOR THE CHAMPIONS LEAGUE WITH A SQUAD BUILT ON NOTHING MORE THAN THE CHARISMA OF A BOX-HEADED BOY AND THE PATRONAGE OF AN AUTHORITARIAN STATE SUGAR DADDIE WITH A FUNKY JACKET LINING AND A CHEEKY SMILE. FINALLY, SOME GOOD GUYS TO ROOT FOR. PERHAPS MODERN FOOTBALL ISN'T COMPLETELY ****ED AFTER ALL...

FOOTBALL CARTOON

WELL THAT WAS A STRANGE EPISODE. GARY LINEKER HAS BEEN REINSTATED AS MATCH OF THE DAY HOST, HAVING BEEN BENCHED FOR LIKENING THE LANGUAGE USED TO PROMOTE THE GOVERNMENT'S LATEST ACT OF IDEOLOGICAL CRUELTY TO THAT USED IN 1930s GERMANY. HOW DARE HE?! LUCKILY, WOUNDED CONSERVATIVE POLITICIANS AND THEIR MEDIA FOGHORNS EXPERTLY QUASHED THOSE COMPARISONS BY EFFECTIVELY SILENCING A CRITIC OF THE STATE.

BUT THOSE WHO FAIL TO LEARN THE LESSONS FROM HISTORY ARE DOOMED TO REPEAT THEM, AND IT SEEMS THE TORIES HAVE ALREADY FORGOTTEN WHAT HAPPENED THE LAST TIME THEY TRIED TO TAKE ON A FOOTBALLER.

UNDER PRESSURE, LINEKER WAS MADE AN EXAMPLE OF — THE BBC USING HIM BY NOT USING HIM. THE DISPUTE ALSO SHIFTED ATTENTION AWAY FROM THE BILL LINEKER WAS REFERRING TO. THERE WAS NO MENTION OF RUINING THE WEEKEND'S TERRESTRIAL FOOTBALL COVERAGE IN THE POSTER THAT ACCOMPANIED THE POLICY ANNOUNCEMENT, WHICH LOOKED LIKE A PAMPHLET YOU'D FIND IN FARAGE'S BOX O' NOSTALGIA.

IF A FOOTBALL PRESENTER IS MEAN ABOUT THE UK GOVERNMENT, YOU WILL BE...

- DENIED ACCESS TO THE VIDIPRINTER
- UNABLE TO HUM ALONG TO THE MOTD THEME TUNE AS YOU FINISH YOUR TAKEAWAY
- STOPPED FROM HEARING THE THOUGHTS OF SHEARER, WRIGHT, JENAS...
- BANNED FROM BROTHERTON
- ✓ BARGAIN HUNT WILL STILL BE AVAILABLE, YES

RISHI SUNAK WILL STOP THE POST-MATCH QUOTES

BUT THE BBC CAN'T HAVE FREELANCERS LIKE LINEKER EXPRESSING HIS POLITICAL VIEWS LIKE HE'S ALAN BLADDY SUGAR. IMPARTIALITY IS VITAL FOR AN ORGANISATION WHOSE CHAIRMAN, RICHARD SHARP, DONATED £400,000 TO THE CONSERVATIVE PARTY AND HELPED FACILITATE A MASSIVE LOAN FOR BORIS JOHNSON; JUST AS IT IS TO ITS DIRECTOR GENERAL: FORMER DEPUTY CHAIR OF THE HAMMERSMITH AND FULHAM CONSERVATIVES, TIM DAVIE. IRONICALLY, THE ADDED SCRUTINY THE STORY HAS CAUSED MUST BE STIRRING UP SOME SERIOUS ITALIA 90 VIBES FOR BOTH MEN.

I'm in listening mode, I'm in listening mode, I'm in listening mode...

ALTHOUGH VILIFYING THE VULNERABLE HAS REPEATEDLY PROVEN TO BE A VOTE WINNER, THIS FEELS LIKE THE DESPERATE FINAL THROW OF THE DICE BY A CONSERVATIVE GOVERNMENT RELYING ON A GROTESQUE SET-PIECE IN ADDED TIME.

We're drinking in the last chance private members club here, guys. Get it launched up to the big man and hope the dead cat bounces kindly.

What'd you say?

DECEIVE

VISIT RWANDA

WITH LINEKER SUSPENDED FOR THE FIRST TIME IN HIS CAREER, AND HIS BBC FOOTBALL COLLEAGUES WITHDRAWING THEIR LABOUR IN SOLIDARITY, THE CORPORATION WAS FORCED TO SERVE AN AUSTERE 20-MINUTE VERSION OF THE SHOW. YET THERE WAS STILL ENTERTAINMENT TO BE HAD IN WATCHING RIGHT-WING POLITICIANS AND COLUMNISTS TRYING TO MAINTAIN THE PRETENCE THAT IT WAS MORE ENJOYABLE THAN THE USUAL BROADCAST, BECAUSE THERE'S NO RETREATING IN THE CULTURE WARS...

MATCH OF THE DYSTOPIA OVEN-READY

Why it's as satisfying as a turnip served in a broth of good old British waterway effluent! Goals!

THANK ST GEORGE THEN FOR GB NEWS, THOSE TIRELESS DEFENDERS OF FREE SPEECH IF IT ALIGNS WITH THEIR POLITICAL VIEWS. EMPLOYING THEIR FAMED PRODUCTION SKILLS THAT WOULD PUT SOME YEAR 12 MEDIA STUDIES PROJECTS TO SHAME, THEY PUT OUT AN 'ALTERNATIVE MATCH OF THE DAY'. EXPECT TO SEE IT PROJECTED ON TO THE WHITE CLIFFS OF DOVER AS PART OF THE POLICY TO DETER REFUGEES.

Here, I bet the Tofu-eaters wish WOKING were in the Premiership!!!

Right, turn around, we're supposed to be fleeing torture...

IT'S ONE THING TO CRITICISE THE HUMAN RIGHTS ABUSES OF QATAR, BUT IT'S QUITE ANOTHER TO HIGHLIGHT THE FAILINGS OF THE BRITISH GOVERNMENT, CRISP BOY! FOR MAGGIE'S SAKE, CAN'T YOU LEAVE POLITICS TO THE INTELLECTUAL HEAVYWEIGHTS LIKE NADINE DORRIES, SUELLA BRAVERMAN AND LEE ANDERSON? IN FACT, WHY NOT LET THEM PRESENT THE SHOW? PENNY MORDAUNT'S ALREADY SHOWN SHE'S ADEPT WITH A FOOTY ANALOGY.

Wait, so they can see us, but we can't see them?

Bloody hell, Nadine, you're about as useful as a penalty throw-in on the fifth-yard hole. Trequartista!

We're not even showing the hanging? What woke tripe is this?! DEFUND THE BBC!

MEANWHILE, TO THE RELIEF OF MANIACS NO LONGER OBLIGED TO PRETEND THEY PREFERRED THE SANS-MOWBRAY SHOW, LINEKER AND HIS WOKERATI COMRADES WILL RETURN TO MATCH OF THE DAY DUTY ON SATURDAY FOR A REGULAR PROGRAMME. WELL, ALMOST...

Good evening and... um...

Good evening and ___ of ___ a ___

THE GREATEST SEASON IN SPORTSWASHING HISTORY HAS AN ENDING!

MANCHESTER CITY HAVE COMPLETED THE TREBLE AND THERE'S NO ASTE-RISK OF ANYTHING DIMINISHING THEIR ACHIEVEMENTS!

YOU SUSPECT ALL THAT CAN STOP THEM FROM WINNING THE LOT NEXT SEASON IS ANOTHER PREMIER LEAGUE CLUB PULLING THE NATHAN JONES LEVER, OR PEP DECIDING HE NEEDS A NEW CHALLENGE AND OPENING HIS OWN HEALTH SPA.

RELAX!

SATURDAY'S CHAMPIONS LEAGUE FINAL WAS A NIGHT FOR THE FANS (TO BE TREATED LIKE CATTLE, IF CATTLE HAD TO REMORTGAGE THEIR SHEDS TO PAY FOR THE EXPERIENCE). AMONG THE DIE-HARDS WERE THE LIAM AND NOEL OF PETRO-MONARCHS: SHEIKH MANSOUR AND BROTHER, UAE 'TOP BOY' MOHAMMED BIN ZAYED AL-NAHYAN. NO DOUBT THE CHATTER IN THE POSH SEATS HAD ALL THE AUTHENTICITY OF A HASTILY FILMED SOAP OPERA SCENE.

Eeh, I remember my first game like it was 2010, bruv. It was also my last game, so that makes it easier to recall. Come on you blue moons!

Oh, yeah, totally...

I was just thinking, Manchester City is an English [citation needed] professional football club based in Manchester that competes in the Premier League, the top flight of English football. Founded in 1880 as...

THIS HAS BEEN A WATERSHED SEASON FOR STATE-OWNED PR PROJECTS. CITY WILL SOON BE JOINED IN THE CHAMPIONS LEAGUE BY NEWCASTLE UNITED - A CLUB OWNED BY SAUDI ARABIA'S PUBLIC INVESTMENT FUND, WHICH EITHER IS OR ISN'T CONNECTED TO THE STATE, DEPENDING ON WHICH SPORT YOU'RE TRYING TO CONSUME. PIF CHAIRMAN MOHAMMED BIN SALMAN IS A MAN WHO GETS THINGS DONE - THE EXECUTION RATE HAS ALMOST DOUBLED SINCE HE BECAME THE KINGDOM'S DE FACTO LEADER. BUT SHUT UP AND LOOK OVER THERE: THE NEWCASTLE CHAIRMAN/PIF GOVERNOR, YASIR AL-RUMAYYAN IS DOING SOME MAD SKILLS IN A JAZZY BLAZER! WHAT A **LAD!**

THE PIF HAS ALSO RECENTLY ANNEXED GOLF, AND WHILE S'ONLY GOLF, IT PROBABLY SHOWS WHAT'S IN STORE FOR FOOTBALL. IN THE SHORT TERM, WE CAN ALL ENJOY A SUMMER SEEING WHICH OF OUR FAVOURITE PLAYERS AGREE TO DANCE FOR THE REGIME AND JOIN THE SAUDI RETIREMENT LEAGUE FOR ALREADY LUDICROUSLY WEALTHY MEN. AT LEAST SOMEONE'S WILLING TO GIVE STEVEN GERRARD A GIG. YOU CAN ONLY IMAGINE THE SIZE OF THE BID THEY'RE PREPARING FOR KYLIAN MBAPPÉ - THE ACTUAL DUDE FROM THE 'CRY MORE' GIF!

They say they'll make another crater in Yemen and fill it with luxury watches for you. Also, Steven Gerrard will be your personal roller-skating butler.

Will he be wearing a little bow tie?

I'll ask...

WHAT IS SAUDI ARABIA'S END GOAL? A SUPER LEAGUE? GLOBAL DOMINATION? AT LEAST A WORLD CUP. THEY ALREADY HAVE THE GOLD STANDARD OF REPUTATIONAL LAUNDRY AS AN EXAMPLE TO FOLLOW: THE QATAR WORLD CUP THAT WEDGED ITSELF INTO THE MIDDLE OF THE SEASON LIKE SALT BAE IN A VIP PADDOCK AND CAME AT SUCH A HIGH HUMAN COST (EXPOSURE TO SALT BAE). BUT HEY, ALL THAT SCRUTINY WILL MAKE QATAR IMPROVE ITS HUMAN RIGHTS RECORD ANY DAY NOW, PRESUMABLY ON THE SAME DAY THE GRIEVING RELATIVES OF THE DEAD MIGRANT WORKERS RECEIVE THOSE COMPENSATION PAYMENTS. AT LEAST THE SAUDI TOURISM AMBASSADOR GOT A NICE CLOAK OUT OF IT.

I've been Sports Washed!

CITY'S SUCCESS WILL ONLY INCREASE CALLS FOR MANCHESTER UNITED TO SELL ITS SOUL TO THE QATARI BANKER SHEIKH JASSIM - THE SON OF THE FORMER PRIME MINISTER WHO WE'RE ASSURED HAS NO LINKS TO THE STATE. HIS SUPPORTERS DON'T SEEM PERTURBED BY THE LIMITED PUBLIC INFORMATION ABOUT HIM, WITH ONLY A FEW PHOTOGRAPHS TO VERIFY HIS EXISTENCE, LIKE SOME SORT OF SOFT POWER SASQUATCH. IF THE DEAL GOES THROUGH, MAYBE HE'LL MOVE IN WITH THE HENDERSONS (DEAN AND FAMILY).

NO ONE IN POWER SEEMS WILLING OR ABLE TO TACKLE ISSUES OF STATE OWNERSHIP, AND BROADCASTERS RESOLUTELY IGNORE IT, BECAUSE RAISING AN OWNER'S HUMAN RIGHTS RECORD WHEN A CLUB AMBASSADOR'S ON THE PUNDIT PANEL WOULD BE **AWKWARD.** MEANWHILE, ALEKSANDER CEFERIN CASUALLY TELLS 'THE OVERLAP' HE HAS NO ISSUE WITH MULTI-CLUB OWNERSHIP, THEN DROPS THE IDEA OF PLAYING THE CHAMPIONS LEAGUE FINAL IN THE US TO 'MEN IN BLAZERS'. GOD KNOWS WHAT OTHER GENIUS IDEAS HE BOUNCED OFF THE CHELSEA SPORTING DIRECTOR WHEN HE DID HIS SHOW.

The fans will walk 500 miles. The fans will walk 500 more. Just to be the fans who walked a thousand miles. To reach the stadium doors.

A classic!

THIS IS THE NEW REALITY OF FOOTBALL. WE'VE PASSED THE TIPPING POINT. THERE'S NO TURNING BACK NOW. BUT JOY CAN STILL BE FOUND BEYOND THE PROXY POWER STRUGGLES OF THE CARBON DESPOTS. SEE, FOR EXAMPLE, HOW MUCH WEST HAM ENJOYED WINNING THE EUROPA VAUXHALL CONFERENCE. SURE, THE BLOATED FINANCIAL MIGHT OF THE PREMIER LEAGUE MEANS THEY ARE THE 15TH RICHEST CLUB IN THE WORLD, BUT ANYTHING THAT RESULTS IN AN IMAGE AS HAUNTINGLY BEAUTIFUL AS THIS CAN'T BE ALL BAD:

RC STRASBOURG ALSACE HAVE BECOME THE LATEST LUCKY CLUB TO ASCEND TO THE MULTI-CLUB-IVERSE BY BEING ABSORBED INTO THE CORPORATE STRUCTURE OF *THE CHELS*. FÉLICITATIONS! IN EXPANDING HIS SPORTING EMPIRE, TACTICS TODD IS FOLLOWING A PATHWAY ESTABLISHED BY THE OWNERS OF SOME OF FOOTBALL'S MAJOR PLAYERS: MAN CITY, MILAN, BOURNEMOUTH ETC. THE TAKEOVER HASN'T BEEN POPULAR WITH STRASBOURG FANS, BUT MAYBE THIS IS THE OUTCOME THE CLUB'S FOUNDERS DREAMED OF BACK IN 1906...

Who knows what bountiful gifts from The New World we may one day be showered with, in exchange for being reduced to the status of a potential siphon for local talent!

Pardon?

SURE, STRASBOURG HAVEN'T PRICKED THE CONSCIOUSNESS OF MOST PREMIER LEAGUE FANS SINCE THEY KNOCKED LIVERPOOL OUT OF THE UEFA CUP 26 YEARS AGO, AND FINE, THERE'S NO ROOM FOR EMPATHY IN ALPHA MARKET GROWTH, BUT *LE RACING* IS A CLUB WITH A RICH, COMPLEX HISTORY, HAVING SURVIVED TWO WORLD WARS AND ONE LIQUIDATION. THEY ARE ALSO A SOURCE OF LOCAL PRIDE FOR THE WHOLE REGION, AND FOR ENTIRE GENERATIONS OF FANS...

For example, they might one day lend us a Fatty Foulke, or one of their legend's magical ape drawings! Heh, yes, I did hit my tête quite hard.

Wow!

Some bloke!

Qu'est-ce que...?

RACING CLUB DE STRA CLEARLAKE CAPITAL

Ours now!

Yeah, they sold your kid to Al-Hilal for 80 mill, so I'm here until January.

WHILE OTHER PREMIER LEAGUE
FOOTBALLERS MIGHT CHOOSE TO
SPEND THEIR HARD-EARNED ON
BIG FANCY CARS FILLED WITH
INVESTMENT PROPERTIES,
NEWCASTLE'S CALLUM WILSON
COLLECTS ART. WITH THE
WOMEN'S WORLD CUP STILL
OVER A WEEK AWAY AND THE
'NATHAN COLLINS TO BRENTFORD'
SAGA NOT QUITE PROVIDING
ENOUGH MATERIAL FOR A FULL
STRIP, IT'S
A GREAT TIME
TO DELVE
INTO THE
GOAL-GETTER'S
ART
COLLECTION.

'The Away Fans' Section at The Tower
of Babel, Newcastle' (Bruegel)

'The Son of Scran' (Magritte)

'Thirty-six views of
Mount, Mason' (Hokusai)

'The Medical of a New Signing
for The Socials' (Rembrandt)

'The Irritating Gentleman cries
"Publicity stunt!"' (Woltze)

'Hi rio do u want picking
up in the morning pal'
(Lichtenstein)

'One dog goes one way, one dog
goes the other way, and this guy's
sayin': "Just smash into someone"'
(Scorsese)

'Game Management' (Dali)

'Making a Splash at a
Major Tournament' (Hockney)

'The French Kiss' (Klimt)

'The Birth of Jenas' (Botticelli)

'Pre-season with Nigel Pearson'
(Friedrich)

'Limited Edition Fourth
Kit Stadium shirt,
RRP £80 - £100'
(Pollock)

'The Restoration of
Chelsea' (Boehly)

'The Floodlit Night'
(Van Gogh)

WOMEN'S WORLD CUP 2023:
SE ACABÓ

You may be surprised to learn that there are *other* cartoonists, and one of the very finest was Charles Addams, creator of *The Addams Family*. One of his most celebrated drawings depicts the dastardly Uncle Fester, sat in a packed cinema, his wicked moon-face beaming with delight as all around him weep at an unseen tear-jerker. It's an image I was reminded of when, as an English football fan living in Australia, I witnessed the Lionesses crush the hopes of a nation by beating the Matildas 3–1 in the semi-final of the Women's World Cup.

Over the course of the tournament, Matildas fever had swept the nation, enchanting even the football sceptics who, just weeks earlier, had been doing brilliant and original jokes about it being a boring game played by softies and divers, Davo. The sniff of success had encouraged millions to drop their long-held prejudices, the majority of whom were almost certainly not motivated by the prospect of a day off should Australia lift the cup. Best of all, new-found enthusiasts included high-ranking politicians whose fandom dated back as far as the group stage, and who could respond to critics pointing out their historical record of underfunding football with a resounding retort of, 'Hey, I bought this bloody scarf, didn't I?'

Having lived in Australia since 2009, it was astonishing to witness the Matildas' progress from kicking about in dusty suburban grounds to selling out a vast Olympic stadium (accessible by occasionally functional transport infrastructure). Stadiums across Australia and New Zealand saw record attendances, and it was the first time since Euro '96 that I'd been in the same country as a major tournament. I was lucky enough to attend England's match against Denmark in Sydney, and it showed how much the women's game had grown that friends from all walks of life* were also dotted around the stadium.

It was a World Cup of shocks. The Philippines beating the joint hosts, New Zealand; Jamaica, South Africa and Morocco advancing to the knockout stage ahead of more illustrious opponents; Nigeria were a penalty shoot-out away from eliminating England and condemning me to at least 48 hours of retrograde SMS banter. Sweden were ranked third in the world, but winning a penalty shoot-out against the USA was still as surprising as it was funny.

So great was the tournament that Gianni Infantino even dropped in for the final in order to deliver one of his famed uplifting speeches, telling women to pick their battles in their ongoing fight for equal pay, thus producing the World Cup's second-best deflection, after Sam Kerr's goal against England that went in off Millie Bright. Sadly, poor old Gigi was about to be upstaged, just as he had been by Salt Bae, Emi Martínez and Lionel bloody Messi at the men's World Cup final the previous year . . .

---

* The media.

183

Spain's World Cup, which culminated in a deserved 1–0 win against the Lionesses in the final, was achieved against a backdrop of internal conflict alien to anyone who has observed Spanish national teams at major tournaments over the years. Eleven months earlier, fifteen players had declared themselves unavailable for selection while Jorge Vilda remained as coach. As if to prove their complaints about the Spanish Football Federation, while they celebrated their victory, its president, Luis Rubiales, grabbed midfielder Jenni Hermoso by the head and planted a kiss on her lips, thus adding the World Cup final to the list of places where women can't go without being groped by entitled men. Unluckily for Rubiales, this was one battle Spain's women players were ready to pick and win.

THE WOMEN'S WORLD CUP IS UNDER WAY. AS WELL AS RECORD ATTENDANCES, IT HAS SO FAR BEEN A TOURNAMENT OF FIRSTS...

THE TOURNAMENT HAS ALSO SEEN THE INTRODUCTION OF REFEREES EXPLAINING VAR DECISIONS, SORT OF! ANYONE FAMILIAR WITH THE WORK OF PETER WALTON WILL KNOW THE SHEER THRILL OF HEARING A REFEREE SPEAK. BUT MUCH LIKE WALTON, THIS SEEMS TO BE A PURELY SHOWBIZ DEVICE OF LITTLE PRACTICAL USE. ONCE THE REFEREE ANNOUNCES A DECISION, NOT MANY PEOPLE STRAIN THEIR EARS FOR AN EXPLANATION.

NEW ZEALAND GET THEIR FIRST WORLD CUP WIN, WITH A SHOW AS BRIGHT AS CAPTAIN ALI RILEY'S RAINBOW FINGERNAILS.

We got a Code Red... orange... yellow... ...green...

FIFA

CANADA'S QUINN BECOMES THE FIRST OPENLY TRANS, NON-BINARY PLAYER TO COMPETE AT A WORLD CUP.

PHILIPPINES RECORD THEIR FIRST WIN (AGAINST NEW ZEALAND!), BRAVELY UPSETTING THE HOME CROWD AND A SIX-FOOT PENGUIN.

No mortal will be spared Tazuni's vengeance.

After on-field review, my decision is... LIMBS. No violation of law... oh, forget it.

Wait! We need to hear why! To which specific sub-section of the laws does this refe—

ENGLAND ARE OFF AND RUNNING AFTER A 1-0 WIN AGAINST HAITI - A MORE COMFORTABLE VICTORY YOU'LL NEVER SEE! SURE, THE WELL-DRILLED HAITIAN PRESS AND LIGHTNING-QUICK COUNTER ATTACKS OF MELCHIE DUMORNAY LEFT ENGLAND FLOUNDERING AS IF THEY'VE LOST MULTIPLE KEY PLAYERS TO INJURY AND RETIREMENT, BUT SARINA HAS A PLAN. INDEED SHE COULD BE SEEN SCRIBBLING NOTES IN THE DUGOUT DURING SATURDAY'S STROLL.

THE SITUATION WOULD HAVE BEEN WORSE FOR ENGLAND IF NOT FOR MARY EARPS' BRILLIANT LATE SAVE TO DENY ROSELINE ÉLOISSANT. THE KEEPER'S HEROICS MADE A MOCKERY OF NIKE'S DECISION NOT TO SELL REPLICAS OF HER SHIRT - A CHOICE THAT PRESENTS AN OPPORTUNITY FOR ENTERPRISING INDIVIDUALS TO SELL SNIDE VERSIONS OUTSIDE THE SYDNEY FOOTBALL STADIUM FROM, SAY, 4PM ON FRIDAY (CASH ONLY, NO RETURNS).

Here, gaffer, where do you think I can get a Haiti goalie top?!

Punish Arjan

Shouldn't the badge have three lions?

EARPS

Me biro ran out. Make a decision, kid.

EARPS 1

FIFA   FIFA

AUSTRALIA HAD A NERVY START AGAINST A BATTLING IRELAND TOO. PERHAPS THEY WERE STILL REELING FROM THE NEWS OF SAM KERR'S CALF TWANG. THE MATILDAS ARE HUGELY POPULAR IN AUSTRALIA, BUT AREN'T IMMUNE TO THE HOSTILITY FOOTBALL FACES FROM FANS OF OTHER CODES, LEADING TO SOME CLASSIC #DISCOURSE CLAIMING TONY GUSTAVSSON HAD CONNED THE PUBLIC BY LEAVING IT LATE TO ANNOUNCE KERR'S "MD-1 TRAINING" GAH.

INJURIES HAVE ROBBED THE TOURNAMENT OF SEVERAL TOP PLAYERS, BUT AT LEAST SPAIN'S 3-0 WIN AGAINST COSTA RICA SAW THE RETURN OF ALEXIA PUTELLAS. THE SPANISH CAMP HAS FAMOUSLY BEEN BESET BY DISHARMONY, MOST OF IT DIRECTED TOWARDS UNPOPULAR COACH, JORGE VILDA, BUT PERHAPS THE INTRODUCTION OF "ALEXIA 2.0" ON A WET WINTER'S NIGHT IN WELLINGTON WILL BE THE CATALYST TO UNITE THE TEAM BEHIND A COMMON CAUSE.

Vera, someone on the internet who watches football once a year says it would be fraudulent if we didn't share the news of an injury to our star player. In that spirit, I present our entire game plan, all of our online banking passwords, and my teenage poetry. Anything you'd like to share with us...?

Nope.

'kinnell.

Gustavssonnets

Warm up, Alexia. I'm bringing you on...

This f***ing guy!

THE STORY OF THE WORLD CUP HAS BEEN THE PERFORMANCE OF SOME OF THE UNDERDOGS. JAMAICA DREW WITH FRANCE AND SOUTH AFRICA WERE MINUTES AWAY FROM HOLDING SWEDEN. THESE DISPLAYS ARE EVEN MORE REMARKABLE WHEN YOU CONSIDER THE FINANCIAL CONSTRAINTS MANY TEAMS ARE FORCED TO OVERCOME. INTO THIS FESTIVAL OF OVERACHIEVEMENT STEPPED MARTINA VOSS-TECKLENBURG'S GERMANY.

NOT TO MENTION THE AGE-OLD FINANCIAL DISPARITY BETWEEN THE WOMEN'S AND MEN'S GAME, HIGHLIGHTED BY SOME OF THE MIND-BENDING FIGURES BEING THROWN AROUND THIS WEEK, WHICH PROBABLY CONTRIBUTE TO THE ONGOING PARTY ATMOSPHERE.

Ah, it's a veritable feast of banana skins! For sure, our Moroccan sisters will be inspired by the funding-defying feats of other minnow nations!

Destroy them.

"MBS power-grabbing project bids €300m for Mbappé gap year."

Talking of money, I wonder if we'll get paid this year?

ZAMBIA

HAHAHAHA

It's actually costing me money to be here!

ENGLAND HAVE **BREEZED** INTO THE WORLD CUP QUARTER-FINALS AFTER A **COMPREHENSIVE VICTORY** AGAINST NIGERIA (ON PENALTIES) THAT PROVIDED A LEVEL OF ANXIETY THAT FRANKLY NO ONE NEEDS ON A MONDAY.

THE PIVOTAL MOMENT WAS LAUREN JAMES' SHREWD TACTICAL DECISION TO OPERATE IN A MORE WITHDRAWN ROLE, HER RED CARD LEADING EVERYONE TO MAKE THE SAME COMPARISON TO ANOTHER YOUNG ENGLAND STAR...

JAMES BECAME THE FIRST 21-YEAR-OLD TO EVER MAKE A MISTAKE, ALLOWING FRUSTRATION TO GET THE BETTER OF HER AND TRYING TO USE MICHELLE ALOZIE'S PELVIC BONE AS A SPRINGBOARD TO EVADE NIGERIA'S PRESS. SHE'LL GO ON TO ENJOY A FABULOUS CAREER, AND IN THE SHORT TERM CAN AT LEAST ENJOY WATCHING THE QUARTER-FINAL FREE FROM THE ATTENTION OF HER MARKER, HALIMATU AYINDE.

ENGLAND PREVAILED DESPITE NIGERIA DOMINATING FOR LONG SPELLS. UNTIL CHLOE KELLY'S ICE-COLD WINNING SPOT KICK, IT SEEMED LIKE THE LIONESSES WERE HEADING FOR THE SAME FATE AS SEVERAL OTHER BIG TEAMS AT THIS WORLD CUP, AS IF ONE OF THE GROUP HAD PICKED UP THE CURSED CROCHETED KOALA LEFT BEHIND BY THE GERMAN TEAM IN THE BRISBANE STADIUM DRESSING ROOM.

PERHAPS THE BIGGEST SHOCK OF THIS CRAZY WORLD CUP CAME ON SUNDAY WHEN LOWLY, THIRD-RANKED SWEDEN SENT THE USA SWIRLING DOWN THE PLUGHOLE IN A CLOCKWISE DIRECTION AFTER A PENALTY SHOOTOUT SO UNBELIEVABLE YOU'D THINK ALL THE SCRIPTWRITERS WERE ON STRIKE. ALYSSA NAEHER WAS LEFT AGHAST AS THE DECISIVE PENALTY SHE THOUGHT SHE'D SAVED WAS RULED TO HAVE JUST CREPT OVER THE LINE.

IT'S FINE TO ADMIRE WHAT THE USWNT HAVE ACHIEVED WHILE ALSO ENJOYING THE PUBLIC PIERCING OF THEIR HUBRIS (THAT **ADVERT!**). MEGAN RAPINOE SKIED HER PENALTY - SOMETHING YOU'D NEVER SEE A BLOODY **BLOKE** DO - UNLEASHING A TIRADE OF SCORN FROM THE CRY-LAUGHING EMOJI LADS IN THE 'FOR YOU' TAB. SHE MAY HAVE BOWED OUT AT THE TOP, BUT HER ABILITY TO PROVOKE A DERANGED REACTION FROM A CERTAIN TYPE OF MAN WILL REMAIN UNDIMINISHED...

YOU MIGHT THINK THAT LOCAL FANS WOULD BE ROOTING FOR THE TEAM WHOSE FANS HAD SPENT THE WEEK COMPLAINING ABOUT KICK-OFF TIMES, HAVING RECENTLY DISCOVERED INTERNATIONAL TIME ZONES. HOWEVER, THE USWNT HAD ALREADY LOST THE BATTLE FOR HEARTS AND MINDS WITH THE AUSTRALIAN PUBLIC BY SHORTENING "MELBOURNE" TO "MELBY". IF THERE'S ONE THING AUSTRALIANS SIMPLY WON'T ACCEPT, IT'S SUCH AN EGREGIOUS BASTARDISATION OF LANGUAGE.

SWEDEN'S REWARD IS TO ENJOY A FIRST-HAND VIEW OF THEIR OWN SURGICAL DISMANTLING AT THE HANDS OF JAPAN'S BEAUTIFULLY INTRICATE PASSING. ON SATURDAY, THE JAPANESE DELIVERED A CHILLING MESSAGE TO THE REST OF THE TOURNAMENT BY HUMBLING NORWAY WHILE RESPLENDENT IN PASTEL PINK AND PURPLE, LIKE A TERRIFYING PACKET OF LOVE HEARTS.

BUT NOT EVEN JAPAN WILL BE ABLE TO STOP AUSTRALIA, WHOSE SUCCESS HAS BEEN GUARANTEED BY THE PERFECT STORM OF MY AUSSIE FATHER-IN-LAW AWAKENING TO BOTH THE BRILLIANCE OF THE MATILDAS AND THE SMS FUNCTION ON HIS PHONE, YE GODS. THEY BREEZED THROUGH AGAINST DENMARK, 3-0 (TWO GOALS, ONE SAM KERR CAMEO) AND THE ROAR WHEN CAITLIN FOORD TUCKED AWAY MARY FOWLER'S PERFECT THROUGH-BALL COULD BE HEARD FROM AN ALMOST UNIMAGINABLE DISTANCE AWAY.

A LAZY CRITICISM OFTEN AIMED AT FOOTBALL IN AUSTRALIA IS THAT THERE ARE NO BLOODY GOALS AND IT'S BORING, MATE. AFTER A THRILLING GOALLESS DRAW AND A PENALTY SHOOTOUT WIN AGAINST FRANCE THAT WAS SO SURREAL IT EVEN FEATURED A PLAYER CALLED DALI, IT'S NOT A COMPLAINT LIKELY TO BE REPEATED FOR A WHILE. THE MATILDAS' VICTORY WAS MET WITH WILD CHEERS ACROSS THE VAST LAND, AND EVEN IN THE CLOUDS ABOVE IT.

YOU'VE NO DOUBT SEEN THE VIDEO OF COURTNEE VINE'S DECISIVE SPOT-KICK BEING WATCHED BY A PLANE LOAD OF PASSENGERS, APART FROM ONE LOTR ULTRA WHO MISSED OUT ON THE REAL FANTASTICAL TALE.

FOOTBALL FEVER HAS SWEPT AUSTRALIA, WITH MATCHES BEING SHOWN IN PLACES YOU'D NEVER EXPECT: THE SCG, THE MCG, FREE-TO-AIR TELEVISION! THE OTHER, PREVIOUSLY DOMINANT, FOOTBALL CODES ARE RUNNING SCARED. MAYBE EVEN THE PREMIER LEAGUE IS WORRIED ABOUT LOSING VIEWERS TO THE WORLD CUP, WHICH IS WHY IT INTRODUCED SOME NEW GIMMICKS ON THE OPENING WEEKEND, SUCH AS PLYING ROY "BRICK TOP" HODGSON WITH GOLD BLEND AND LETTING THE FIREWORKS ENSUE.

IT WOULD BE RECKLESS FOR ANYONE WHO PLANS TO CONTINUE LIVING IN AUSTRALIA BEYOND NEXT WEEK TO POINT OUT THAT FRANCE WERE THE BETTER TEAM FOR LONG PERIODS AND PROBABLY DESERVED TO WIN THE GAME BEFORE IT WENT TO PENALTIES, IT'S AN OPINION THAT WOULD LEAVE YOU AS POPULAR AS JORGE VILDA AFTER SPAIN'S VICTORY AGAINST THE NETHERLANDS.

JUST ONE THING STANDS BETWEEN THE MATILDAS AND THE PROMISED LAND OF DEBATING HOW LONG THE PUBLIC HOLIDAY SHOULD BE WHEN THEY WIN THE FINAL: SAZBALL.

WIEGMAN CONFESSED SHE HAS MUCH TO LEARN ABOUT THE DEPTH OF THE SPORTING RIVALRY BETWEEN ENGLAND AND AUSTRALIA. WELL HAVE I GOT AN INBOX TO SHOW YOU, SARINA!

ENGLAND CAME THROUGH A BRUISING BATTLE WITH COLOMBIA, BUT THEIR SITUATION LOOKED GRIM WHEN LEICY SANTOS LOOPED A SHOT OVER MARY EARPS, EVOKING MEMORIES OF ANOTHER PONYTAILED ENGLISH KEEPER BEING LOBBED BY A SOUTH AMERICAN IN A QUARTER-FINAL. IT LEFT FANS WONDERING WHICH VINTAGE MOMENT OF ENGLISH WORLD CUP CALAMITY THE LIONESSES WOULD PARODY NEXT...

BUT THIS SIDE IS NOT AS EMOTIONALLY FRAGILE AS THE MEN'S VERSION AND THEY FOUGHT BACK TO WIN 2-1, SHOWING A DETERMINATION TO STAY IN AUSTRALIA AS LONG AS POSSIBLE. THE MANCHESTER UNITED CONTINGENT PERHAPS HAVE THE ADDED INCENTIVE OF NOT WANTING TO RUSH BACK AND PROVIDE MORAL GUIDANCE ON THE MASON GREENWOOD SITUATION, THEIR BRAVELY BOLD EMPLOYERS HAVING MADE THEM A TARGET FOR BLUE TICK INCELS EVERYWHERE BY ANNOUNCING THEY'D BE CONSULTED ON THE MATTER.

ENGLAND FACE THE TOUGH TASK OF BREAKING DOWN A STUBBORN AUSTRALIAN DEFENCE, BACKED NOT ONLY BY THE ENTIRE NATION, BUT A LEGION OF POLITICIANS WHO HAVE UNDERFUNDED FOOTBALL FOR YEARS BUT ARE NOW DESPERATE TO ATTACH THEMSELVES TO SOMETHING POPULAR. NOT ALL OF THEM GET IT RIGHT, THOUGH — ON SATURDAY, BARNABY JOYCE MP PROVIDED MORE MATERIAL FOR HIS ALREADY COLOURFUL WIKIPEDIA ENTRY BY FILMING HIMSELF IN A PUB, WATCHING FOOTAGE OF A MONTH-OLD FRIENDLY. LUCKILY, HE'S NOT THE KIND OF GUY IN THE HABIT OF REPEATING ERRORS...

EVERYONE KNOWS THE FINALISSIMA WAS THE REAL QUIZ, BUT CONGRATULATIONS TO SPAIN FOR CLAIMING THE CONSOLATION PRIZE OF THE WOMEN'S WORLD CUP ON SUNDAY. AFTER ENGLAND'S SEMI-FINAL WIN AGAINST AUSTRALIA, SARINA WIEGMAN SPOKE OF LIVING IN A FAIRY TALE. SADLY, IT TURNED OUT TO BE ONE OF THOSE ONES THAT LEAVE YOU FEELING SLIGHTLY TRAUMATISED...

THERE'S NO DENYING SPAIN WERE WORTHY WINNERS. THEY STUCK TO ENGLAND LIKE THE WEB OF ONE OF SYDNEY'S SMALLER SPIDERS AND WERE MESMERIC IN THEIR PASSING AND MOVEMENT; CONSTANTLY CREATING SPACES, TRIANGLES, PARALLELO-GRAMS. THEIR PLAYERS SEEM GIFTED WITH A TELEPATHY INTRINSIC IN SPANISH FOOTBALL CULTURE, AN ESP. IN MIDFIELD, AITANA BONMATÍ'S ABILITY TO SCAN THE WHOLE PITCH IS PERHAPS ONLY RIVALLED BY LUIS RUBIALES' TALENT FOR READING THE ROOM.

THE GAME'S DECISIVE MOMENT CAME WHEN LUCY BRONZE MADE A DESPERATE BREAK FOR FREEDOM, RACING INTO THE UNCHARTED TERRITORY OF THE CENTRE, BUT FINDING ONLY BONMATÍ-SHAPED PERIL. THE BALL WAS WORKED BACK INTO THE SPACE SHE'D VACATED AND OLGA CARMONA EXPERTLY FINISHED. IT WAS TOUGH ON BRONZE, WHO WOULDN'T BE THE FIRST ENGLISH EXPLORER TO STRAY INTO TROUBLE IN AUSTRALIA.

NO ONE BLAMED BRONZE, OF COURSE, AND AS WE SAW SO OFTEN AT THIS WORLD CUP, IT WAS HER OPPONENTS WHO WERE QUICK TO OFFER SOME SOOTHING WORDS AT THE END.

HOWEVER, ANY TALK OF HEARTBREAK WAS LATER THROWN INTO SHARP PERSPECTIVE BY THE AWFUL REVELATION THAT OLGA'S FATHER HAD DIED BEFORE THE FINAL, NEWS SHE WAS UNAWARE OF AS SHE CONTEMPLATED THE GREATEST ACHIEVEMENT OF HER YOUNG CAREER.

ENGLAND DID HAVE THEIR MOMENTS, AND IT BRIEFLY SEEMED THE TURNING POINT HAD ARRIVED WHEN MARY EARPS SAVED JENNI HERMOSO'S SECOND HALF PENALTY. THE GOALKEEPER, WHO HAD GIVEN SO MUCH OVER THE LAST MONTH, PROVIDED ONE LAST GIFT: THE PERFECT .gif WITH WHICH TO RESPOND TO REPLY GUYS, PUB BORES AND FIFA PRESIDENTS ALIKE.

BUT SPAIN WERE NEVER TRULY TROUBLED, AND WHEN THE FINAL WHISTLE BLEW THEIR PLAYERS AND COACHES CELEBRATED WILDLY JUST 50 METRES APART. FOOTBALL UNITES THE WORLD! GIVEN JORGE VILDA'S POPULARITY, MANY WILL VIEW IT AS A PYRRHIC VICTORY.

IT'S A COMPLEX SITUATION FOR EVERYONE APART FROM THE PLAYERS WHO STAYED AT HOME AFTER SPEAKING OUT AGAINST VILDA, AND AFTER THE TROPHY PRESENTATION SOME OF THE SQUAD COULD BE SEEN GLEEFULLY THROWING HIM IN THE AIR, SO MAYBE HE'S NOT UNIVERSALLY LOATHED...

BUT THE WORLD CUP WASN'T ABOUT THAT DUDE OR HIS WEIRD BOSS, EVEN IF TEAMS ACHIEVING IN SPITE OF THEIR FEDERATIONS WAS ONE OF THE THEMES OF THE TOURNAMENT. NO, AUSNZ 23 WAS ABOUT THE CLOSING GAP BETWEEN THE TRADITIONAL POWERHOUSES™ AND THE UNDERDOGS. IT WAS ABOUT THE PACKED STADIUMS, PUBS AND LIVING ROOMS AS FOOTBALL FEVER INFECTED THE HOST NATIONS. IT WAS ABOUT DISCOVERING WHAT THE LEADER OF THE LIB DEMS LOOKS LIKE. MOST OF ALL, IT WAS ABOUT THE BEAUTIFUL, INSPIRING MOMENTS FUTURE GENERATIONS WILL REMEMBER FOREVER...

IT SPEAKS VOLUMES ABOUT THE MAN THAT LUIS RUBIALES WAS APPARENTLY PREPARED TO BURN DOWN EUROPEAN FOOTBALL RATHER THAN ACCEPT RESPONSIBILITY FOR PLANTING A KISS ON THE LIPS OF JENNI HERMOSO, BUT FINALLY HE HAS GONE.

HOWEVER, IT'S A FAST-MOVING STORY AND WE CAN ONLY GUESS WHICH MEMBER OF HIS EXTENDED FAMILY WILL HAVE SUPERGLUED THEMSELVES TO THEIR LOCAL LIDL BY THE TIME THIS IS PUBLISHED. IT'S BEEN QUITE A WEEK FOR THE GASLIGHT ENTHUSIAST.

No it hasn't.

RUBIALES HAD BEEN EXPECTED TO ANNOUNCE HIS RESIGNATION AT THE SPANISH FOOTBALL FEDERATION'S GENERAL ASSEMBLY LAST FRIDAY, BUT INSTEAD CHOSE TO REPEATEDLY HOWL, "I WILL NOT RESIGN" AND THROW OUT ACCUSATIONS LIKE THEY WERE UNSOLICITED KISSES ON THE MOUTH OF A CO-WORKER. WHILE HE RECEIVED WIDESPREAD CONDEMNATION FOR FAILING TO READ THE ROOM, HIS RANT WAS PITCHED PERFECTLY FOR THE HALL OF RFEF BIG SWINGERS, AND COULD ONLY HAVE RECEIVED MORE RAPTUROUS APPLAUSE IF HE'D INCORPORATED A GOAL CELEBRATION MIME.

FEW CLAPPED MORE GLEEFULLY THAN OLD PAL JORGE VILDA. HOWEVER, THE FEMALE MEMBERS OF THE COACHING TEAM WHO'D BEEN STRATEGICALLY SEATED AT THE FRONT OF THE HALL FOR PEAK #OPTICS WERE LESS IMPRESSED, AND ONCE THE ENTIRE BACKROOM STAFF HAD WITHDRAWN THEIR SERVICES ALONGSIDE ALMOST EVERY WOMAN ELIGIBLE TO PLAY FOR THE NATIONAL TEAM, JORGE PRODUCED A TURN AITANA BONMATÍ WOULD BE PROUD OF.

THE SUCCESS OF THE WOMEN'S TEAM - WHICH LOOKS INCREASINGLY ASTONISHING WITH EVERY FRESH RFEF STATEMENT - HAS EXPOSED THE INSTITUTIONAL SEXISM OF THE FEDERATION. AMONG THE MANY GLARING DEFICIENCIES IT SEEMS EAGER TO SHOW THE WORLD INCLUDES A SEEMINGLY WIDESPREAD INABILITY TO GRASP HOW TELEVISION CAMERAS WORK.

So appalled was I by his foul words that I tried to drown them out by beating my hands together as vigorously as I could...

I'M EVERY WOMAN

Apparently, this thing allows millions of people to see exactly what you're doing...!

No it doesn't.

THE STORY SHOWS THE INTENSE PRESSURE WOMEN COME UNDER TO WITHDRAW COMPLAINTS OF THIS NATURE, EVEN WHEN THE INCIDENT IS BROADCAST TO A GLOBAL AUDIENCE. WHILE FIFA BARRED RUBIALES FROM CONTACTING HERMOSO, IT HASN'T STOPPED HIS FAMILY FROM RAMPING UP THE EMOTIONAL BLACKMAIL. NOR DID IT PREVENT THE RFEF FROM PUBLISHING A SERIES OF PHOTOS, TAKEN FROM BEHIND ONE OF STADIUM AUSTRALIA'S GRASSY KNOLLS, SHOWING HERMOSO LIFTING POOR OLD LUIS OFF HIS FEET, LIKE IT PROVES SOMETHING. WHO KNOWS WHAT OTHER DYNAMITE THEY'VE IN THEIR FILES...

THE INFERNO THAT CAUSED RUBIALES TO GIVE ATHENEA DEL CASTILLO A FIREMAN'S LIFT AROUND THE STADIUM IN A PERFECTLY NORMAL FASHION.

THE SPIDER THAT RAN UP THE TROUSER LEG OF THE FORMER HAMILTON ACE, CAUSING HIM TO AGGRESSIVELY GRAB AT HIS VIP AREA.

PHOTOGRAPHIC EVIDENCE THAT HERMOSO HAS A DEMONIC ROTATING HEAD, LIKE IN THE EXORCIST

NO WONDER MAMÁ LOCKED HERSELF IN A CHURCH. THE POWER OF CHRIST COMPELS YOU. THE POWER OF CHRIST COMPEL

AS CRISIS STRATEGIES GO, THREATENING LEGAL ACTION AGAINST HERMOSO WAS UP THERE WITH PUTTING OUT A FALSE STATEMENT ON HER BEHALF, BUT STILL THE RFEF CONTINUES TO DIG, GIVING THE IMPRESSION IT WAS BASING ITS DEFENCE ON THE TOXIC REPLIES BENEATH MATCH OF THE DAY'S FACEBOOK POSTS ON THE STORY.

My God, these are all gold!

"Boring." "YAWN" "Who cares?"

"Your continentals are more relaxed about workplace misconduct. Move on!"

"Wot about that time Gary Neville kissed Paul Scholes lol?"

BUT EVEN IT'D HAD ENOUGH BY MONDAY AND JOINED THE LEGION OF VOICES CALLING FOR HIM TO QUIT. FIFA HAS SUSPENDED RUBIALES, BUT THERE'S STILL NO WORD FROM UEFA. WHILE IT MAY BE SMART TO KEEP YOUR MOUTH COVERED WHEN LUIS IS ABOUT, ITS SILENCE IS DEAFENING. THE GAME IS UP FOR CAPTAIN GASLIGHT, AND WHILE THE RFEF ISN'T ONE DUDE, THIS WHOLE GRIM EPISODE HAS BEEN WIDELY PROCLAIMED AS SPANISH FOOTBALL'S #METOO MOMENT. SUDDENLY THOSE BIG SWINGING D'S LOOK LIKE SHRIVELLED EMPTY SUITS.

SE ACABÓ
10

Se Acabó   Se Acabó

2023-24:

ON A ROLL

'I've been to see the referee . . . one of his assistants was eating a sandwich at the time – I thought that was a complete lack of respect. Hopefully he enjoyed his sandwich while he was talking to a Premier League manager.'

– Chris Wilder, Sheffield United manager, 31 January 2024

As an example of football's inflated sense of self-importance, it was some top-tier satire. A million applause emojis, from a fan of cheese and pickle. If you were desperately reaching for a narrative theme to kick off this section, you could argue there was a culinary thread running through the 2023–24 season . . .

Tottenham's James Maddison spoke of a desire to be 'the main man' whenever he goes for a roast dinner with his family, which might explain why they always seem to have other plans; Chelsea's latest lightning rod Mauricio Pochettino claimed he had a bowl of lemons to absorb negative energy, which by the time he left Stamford Bridge had presumably swollen to the size of the Ford Cortinas that used to park behind the goal there; and Arsenal's Mikel Arteta won the league title of dignity by being hand-fed meat by the most powerful man in football, Salt Bae.

Like Mikel, we all kidded ourselves there was a title race (yeah, binning off the food thing now), until Manchester City won their game in hand against Tottenham – a result that seemed to break something in Spurs boss Ange Postecoglou – and leapfrogged Arsenal for top spot with one match remaining.

It was another season dominated by the weekly vortex of VAR-related bullshit, and Arteta's post-match outburst that followed a controversial defeat at Newcastle in November was a classic of the genre. However, he could sleep well knowing it probably wouldn't make much difference come the end of the season. Ah.

Even the famously unflappable Nottingham Forest owner Evangelos Marinakis seemed to succumb to paranoia as his club spent their second season back in the Premier League experiencing a public nervous breakdown. This culminated in the loan signing of former Premier League referee Mark Clattenburg from the BBC's *Gladiators* as a kind of match-official Watchman, and their social media account wailing, 'The VAR's a Luton fan!' after a defeat at Everton that didn't appear to benefit The Hatters in any way, BUT THAT'S WHAT THEY WANT YOU TO THINK.

Along with Everton, Forest were docked points for breaching profit and sustainability rules. Lacking the financial resources and political heft of a nation state, neither club was able to bombard the Premier League with legal writs. In other news, Manchester City's inevitable title win was their fourth in a row, which set a new English record (suck it, 1920s Huddersfield Town!). They also became the first club to land two titles while under investigation for historical financial breaches, but were denied the Double-Double with a shock defeat in the FA Cup final to Manchester United (remember them?!).

United had been buoyed by the mid-season arrival of Sir Jim Ratcliffe and his INEOS, high-performance LinkedIn mindset, which included the Brexiteer tax exile demanding that remote staff return to the office, because irony is dead.

While Big Jim was a fun addition to the extended Premier League universe (unless you worked for him), it was a season that robbed us of two main characters. Jürgen Klopp announced he would be leaving Liverpool at the end of the season, and having wearily accepted nothing could be done to improve Crystal Palace's fortunes, Roy Hodgson also stepped away, meaning we could only imagine his face when his replacement, Oliver Glasner, transformed them into the Croydon Globetrotters.

With an expanded Champions League and new Club World Cup on the horizon, the Premier League's big boys successfully lobbied to have FA Cup replays scrapped, even for the rounds before they enter the competition. It was a season when the greed, self-interest and hypocrisy of the Premier League's most powerful made you wonder whether you'd be happier switching to a hobby that requires fewer moral compromises (is there a market for topical cartoons about the donkey-molesting scene?). But then, from the mists of gloom, a ray of light: a manager complains about someone eating a sandwich in his presence, and you realise you're hooked for life.

However, like every year, the season began with some wildly inaccurate predictions . . .

THE AWFUL REALISATION OF THE WAY FOOTBALL IS HEADING AND THE GROWING ACCEPTANCE THAT YOU CAN ONLY LIVE OFF PUNS ABOUT NINETIES INDIE BANDS FOR SO LONG, MEANS IT'S TIME TO CONNECT WITH A YOUNGER AUDIENCE AND DEVELOP A TEENAGE FAN CLUB (HEY, OLD HABITS DIE HARD) WITH...

THE PREMIER LEAGUE
MATCHDAY FOUR HIGHLIGHTS
FOR TRANSFER WEIRDOS

LET'S START AT STAMFORD BRIDGE WHERE CHAMPIONS OF TRANSFERS CHELSEA CONTINUED THEIR SUPERB FORM, DESTROYING NOTTINGHAM FOREST BY OUTSPENDING THEM BY £315.5M. AS WELL AS AMORTISING A LOAD OF NEW UNITS, THE CLEARLAKE CAPITAL HEADHUNTERS ALSO OFFLOADED A TONNE OF DEADWOOD, INCLUDING THOSE SUBSIDISED COACH TRAVELLERS WHO WERE DRAINING THE ENTERPRISE BY AS MUCH AS 11.5 MILLIONTHS OF A MOISÉS CAICEDO AND WHOSE FIFA STATS *SUCK*.

0 ASSET VALUE

SUBSIDISED BUS LIABILITY

47	INSTA FOLLOWERS	56	YEARS SUPPORT
0	YOUTUBE SUBSCRIBERS	70	PACE (MOTORWAY)
10	SPENDING POWER (£)	4	MARKETABILITY

AT THE OTHER END OF THE DONE DEAL TABLE THERE WAS A RELEGATION SIX-POINTER BETWEEN SHEFFIELD UNITED - OWNED BY SAUDI ARABIA'S ONLY THRIFTY PRINCE - AND BANTER TITANS EVERTON. HONOURS WERE EVEN AS EVERTON WERE INITIALLY LIFTED BY JOGGING ON NEAL MAUPAY, ONLY TO BE PEGGED BACK BY THE KNOWLEDGE OF HOW THIS STORY NOW INEVITABLY ENDS.

LIVERPOOL EARNED THREE POINTS WITH SOME EXCELLENT DEFENDING, CLEVERLY PUTTING MO SALAH'S PHONE ON FLIGHT MODE TO STOP HIM SEEING THE LATEST WILD OFFERS FROM THE SAUDI PRO LEAGUE (£150M PLUS ADD-ONS: A STEGOSAURUS AND A GEL POUCH CONTAINING THE ELIXIR OF LIFE). HOWEVER, SOMEONE AT THE SPL SEEMS INTENT ON COLLECTING ALL THE MEMBERS OF LIVERPOOL'S 2019 CHAMPIONS LEAGUE-WINNING SQUAD LIKE THEY'RE POKÉMON, RIGHT KIDS?

BALLON D'OR 2024

If you'd told me when I rejoined Brentford on loan that I'd end up as the Premier League's top scorer and would captain France to glory at the Euros, I'd have accused you of constructing an unlikely scenario for comedic purposes!

SADIO : GOT   BOBBY : GOT   GINI : GOT
Standard Chartered
FABS : GOT   HENDO : GOT   MO : NEEEEED

NEWCASTLE FAMOUSLY HAVE NO LINKS TO THE SAUDI STATE, AND THEY TRAVELLED TO BRIGHTON WEARING A SAUDI ARABIA KIT WHILE THEIR HOME GROUND IS PREPARED FOR HOSTING TWO SAUDI ARABIA FRIENDLIES. BUT NOT EVEN THEIR SUMMER OF GOOD BUSINESS COULD MATCH BRIGHTON'S FINISHING (SIGNING ANSU FATI ON DEADLINE DAY) AND THEY WERE UNDONE BY THE QUALITY OF ALBION'S LATEST RANDO FOOTBALL MANAGER REGENS.

TOTTENHAM SCORED FIVE TRIVIAL GOALS AT TURF MOOR, BUT HAD NO ANSWER TO THE ABSOLUTE QUALITY OF BURNLEY'S TRANSFER ANNOUNCEMENT VIDEOS. CLASSIC ALK CAPITAL-BALL! BIG ANGE HAS ENJOYED A HAPPY START TO LIFE AT SPURS - JUST LOOK AT THAT NET SPEND! - BUT HAVING FAILED TO MATCH A TIK-TOK FEATURING ZEKI AMDOUNI AND THE TELETUBBIES, THE AUSTRALIAN FACED ANOTHER GRILLING FROM THE FOURTH ESTATE.

'STEVE' VALDERRAMA!   'EVAN' FERGUSON   'JAMES' MILNER

OMG. NEEEED!

AMERICAN CREDIT CARD

Have you heard of a singer called Robbie Williams?

Have you ever seen snow?

Or a teletubby?

Do all the phones in Australia look like hamburgers or is it just the one in the surf club?

Mate.

I'll put yes.

ARSENAL EMERGED VICTORIOUS FROM THEIR CLASH WITH MANCHESTER UNITED, WHO WERE UNDONE BY THE OPTICS OF NOT SELLING HARRY MAGUIRE, WITH NO OTHER CLUB APPARENTLY WILLING TO RAISE THE REQUISITE NUMBER OF CRY-LAUGHING EMOJIS TO SIGN THE DARLING OF THE NO-CONTEXT BULLYING AGGREGATOR ACCOUNTS. HOWEVER, ARSENAL'S WIN WAS MIRED IN CONTROVERSY, WITH SOME ARGUING IT SHOULDN'T HAVE STOOD AFTER MIKEL ARTETA'S POST-MATCH IMPRESSION OF SWISS TONI (ASK YOUR PARENTS)

You see, Kai, settling in at a new club is like making love to a beautiful woman. First you need to find the fastest route to the training ground, then you have to dribble round the cones, and before you know it, you're enjoying a loan spell in Leipzig.

THE PREMIER LEAGUE NOW BREAKS UNTIL THE TRANSFER WINDOW REOPENS IN JANUARY, BUT IF YOU'RE LEFT FEELING BEREFT AT THE LACK OF GOSSIP AND WONDERING IF THERE'S ANY POINT TO A LIFE FREE OF HECTORING JOURNOS ONLINE FOR UPDATES ON TREVOH CHALOBAH'S POTENTIAL LOAN MOVE THEN FRET NOT, BECAUSE WE CAN ALWAYS FILL THE VOID WITH OUR SECOND FAVOURITE OBSESSION:

SLAGGING OFF ♡ REFEREES! ♡

JUST CHECK OUT THIS GUY'S FIFA STATS...!

0 POPULARITY

PGMOL

WEBB

78	APOLOGIES	100	BLAME FOR EVERYTHING THAT EVER WENT WRONG FOR YOU
24	VISITS TO DE ZERBI		
90	PACE (WHEN DE ZERBI'S GOT THE HOB-NOBS IN)	0	SHAMPOO ADS

You've drained your bank account to buy the new shirt.

You've returned it, having spotted a glaring factual error in the shadow pattern...

It says we won the Makita International Trophy twice, but we actually won it *thrice*, shopkeep.

You've worn your thumb down to a nub, scrolling for news of transfer deals...

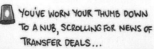

Nothing on LinkedIn. Tumbleweed on Mastodon. Better stalk Fabrizio Romano on Friends Reunited.

You've waved farewell to a club legend as he embarks upon a new adventure in a magical faraway kingdom where he'll continue to advocate for LGBTG+ rights.
(Lolly, gold, bling, treasure, quids +)

Hah! Hendo's gonna feel pretty silly when he realises he forgot his rainbow laces!

The battle lines have been drawn between age-old rivals...

HEDGE FUND PLAYTHING

THEOCRACY PR PROJECT

The wait is finally over, because

THE 2023-24 PREMIER LEAGUE SEASON IS UPON US!

WHAT CAN WE EXPECT FROM THE NEW SEASON? WELL, SOME THINGS ARE CERTAIN:

Manchester City will lull everyone into a false sense of security until January, when Pep makes some groundbreaking tactical tweak and lays the division to waste.

Guys, I got this new hoodie and -KABOOM!- we won 16 on the bounce.

We'll be told at least three times that David Moyes MUST WIN HIS NEXT GAME or face dire consequences.

And we can look forward to regular, astonished reports that Luton's ground looks like it was hosting non-league football less than a decade ago. Sure, they've bulldozed the conservatory showroom that ran the length of one side, but Kenilworth Road remains inversely attractive to manager Rob Edwards. It's the architectural equivalent of the portrait of Dorian Gray.

I mean, for God's sake.

Even Watford fans want to smell him

ASYMMETRICAL HOVEL

Evenly spaced stubble follicles

Hasn't even got a fromagerie, lads

You have to go through someone's living room to ge

Inevitably, there will be some VAR controversy, most likely involving Roberto De Zerbi.

CHECKING POSSIBLE VISIT FROM HOWARD WEBB
VAR

sigh.

And we can expect a completely mad story from the real world to penetrate the Premier League bubble, almost certainly impacting Everton.

I am but a mere custodian of this football club, but I will crush all who try to stop me from getting Everton back where they belong.

Speaking of ownership, the highly edifying Manchester United takeover saga will rumble on until all three parties are still negotiating as they board the billionaire climate apocalypse escape shuttle.

Only one spot left, brother; but who should we let join us in the Lunar VIP bubble?

Lord knows, but whoever we pick is sitting next to Elon...

THERE'S ALSO PLENTY OF NEW STUFF TO LOOK FORWARD TO.
FOR EXAMPLE, IT WILL BE FASCINATING TO SEE HOW MAURICIO POCHETTINO
ADAPTS TO LIFE UNDER TACTICS TODD AT CHELSEA.

NEW PLAYERS HAVE ALSO ARRIVED, AND THERE IS A PALPABLE SENSE OF
ANTICIPATION AS WE ALL AWAIT THE NEXT ROUND OF IMAGES OF NEWCASTLE'S
UNIMPRESSED EXCHANGE STUDENT, SANDRO TONALI!

EXCITEMENT MOUNTS AT TOTTENHAM TOO, WHERE THE KING OF AUSTRALIA, ANGE
POSTECOGLOU, HAS BEEN HIRED TO LEAD THEIR ANNUAL CULTURAL REVOLUTION. IF HIS
TRACK RECORD IS ANY INDICATION, WE CAN SOON EXPECT SPURS TO FALL UNDER
ANGE'S CULTISH SPELL.

BUT HE'S NOT THE ONLY FRESH FACE IN THE DUGOUTS. THERE'S A HIP YOUNG
GUNSLINGER OVER AT CRYSTAL PALACE WHO WILL HAVE SPENT THE SUMMER
RESEARCHING A RADICAL NEW STYLE...

CONGRATULATIONS
IF YOU CORRECTLY
PREDICTED THE
ULTIMATE BATTLE
FOR WORLD SUPREMACY
WOULD TAKE PLACE AT
THE VITALITY STADIUM,
THE ARRIVAL OF
ANDONI IRAOLA AT
BOURNEMOUTH
HERALDING THE
ENDGAME OF THE
FOOTBALL CULTURE
WARS: PROPER
FOOTBALL MEN
VERSUS TACTICS
BLOGGERS. WHOEVER
WINS... WE LOSE.

IF YOUR TEAM HASN'T BEEN MENTIONED HERE, TAKE IT AS AN OPPORTUNITY TO
EXERCISE YOUR PARANOIA DUCTS BEFORE THE BIG KICK-OFF. YOU'RE WELCOME.
IT'S MOSTLY NOTHING PERSONAL, IT'S JUST THAT THE LAW NOW STIPULATES THAT
SPACE BE MADE FOR A COMPULSORY SALUTE TO THE PREMIER LEAGUE'S
UNOFFICIAL 21ST CLUB, BLOODY ~~SALFORD~~...

O, Sweet refrain.

NEIL WARNOCK HAS LEFT HIS JOB AS HUDDERSFIELD BOSS, BUT THE NATION'S SWEETHEART IS ALREADY THINKING ABOUT HIS NEXT JOB...

What next, gaffer?

I don't know, Ronnie lad, I've been thinking...

I'm not surprised. When people hear the name Neil Warnock, they immediately think of sober, self-reflection.

Exactly. Lately I've been wondering if I still want to be leaping around on the touchline at Roy Hodgson's age. I need to go out with some dignity, you know?

Yep.

Maybe it's time to try something different. Perhaps I'll do one of those travel shows where I can navigate the country in a steam train. I've still got some red trousers from my Scarborough days...

We're in London now, aren't we?

I've got a load of box sets to get through too. Can you believe I've never watched The Wire? And I never finished writing that novel...

Is it about football, boss?

I'd say it's more of an erotic space romp. I've only got as far as designing the cover, but it's spicy stuff, I can tell you.

CAPTAIN COLIN
DEEP MOON EXPLORER

KENNY

"And since we're talking sci-fi fantasy, I reckon the time is right to cash in on the crypto craze and launch me own NFT..."

Hell, I can do whatever I bloody well please. A life-drawing class...

Stand-up.

I tell you, these jokes are so controversial you won't be able to tell 'em by the time the bloomin' transfer window re-opens (pause for applause).

Or perhaps it's time to get out and enjoy the natural world my generation has done so much to preserve. To feel the sun on me massive face, the breeze in me Morty Smith hairline...

As you get older, you develop a deeper connection with nature — hills and trees and fields and that sh*te. It's almost as if it's calling to you...

Bloody marvellous.

PING!

Breaking news
Mid-sized Championship club fires manager

SHARONNN!

NEWS THAT THE UK AND IRELAND WILL HOST EURO '28 GIVES US ALL SOMETHING TO LOOK FORWARD TO. PICTURE IT NOW, AN OPENING CEREMONY FEATURING REWORKED COVERS OF SUELLA-SANCTIONED BANGERS AT WEMBLEY AS A PRELUDE TO INEVITABLE ENGLAND GLORY — THE OTHER NATIONS' TEAMS HAVING BEEN DENIED ENTRY AND SENT TO PLAY A SECONDARY TOURNAMENT ON A DISEASED DETENTION BARGE – HARD LUCK, WALES!

Love's got the world in motion and I know what we can do. Immediately close all the borders, stop the woke scum getting through.

IN A SEPARATE BOOST FOR ULEZ-HATERS CRAVING THE SWEET RELEASE OF CLIMATE OBLIVION, FIFA HAS ANNOUNCED THE 2030 WORLD CUP WILL BE PLAYED ACROSS THREE CONTINENTS, CREATING A CARBON FOOTPRINT BIGGER THAN GIANNI'S STAN SMITHS AND SWELLING ITS COFFERS LIKE THE RIVER THAT NOW RAGES THROUGH YOUR HIGH STREET. FOR ALL THE GENERIC FIFASPEAK ABOUT EQUALITY, YOU HAVE TO ACCEPT THE APOCALYPSE WILL BE A GREAT LEVELLER, AND THINK OF THE SELFIE OPPORTUNITIES A DEAD PLANET WILL CREATE!

FOOTBALL UNITES THE WORLD!

EARTH
4.6 BN BC – 20??

BUT HELPING TO HASTEN MASS HUMAN EXTINCTION HAS THE ADDED BENEFIT OF HANDING SAUDI ARABIA A FREE SHOT AT HOSTING THE 2034 WORLD CUP. GOOOOOAAAAAAAL! IT'S THE KIND OF BRAZENLY COSY ARRANGEMENT THAT ALMOST MAKES YOU NOSTALGIC FOR THE CARTOONISH, OLD-SCHOOL, MAYOR QUIMBY-STYLE CORRUPTION OF THE PREVIOUS FIFA REGIME. MAYBE INFANTINO'S GURNING, ROBOT BUTLER ACT WOULD BE MORE PALATABLE IF HE DROVE A MOBILITY SCOOTER AND HAD A TRUMP TOWER APARTMENT FULL OF CATS.

Today I feel... itchy.

FIF

THE SAUDI REGIME IS CERTAINLY GETTING ITS MONEY'S WORTH FROM ITS NEWLY-ACQUIRED FOOTBALL AMBASSADORS, WITH ITS UNCONTESTED BID ENDORSED BY VARIOUS SOCCER SUPERSTARS, MAKING YOU FEEL AS WARM AND FUZZY AS THEIR GENTLE PUPPET HIDES.

The Prince has loads of shiny horses and I saw the shiny horses and I was allowed to touch one of the shiny horses and it felt shiny and smelled like shit... and hay.

We do not let this drip!

STILL, EVERYONE'S GOT A PRICE ON THEIR HEAD [ISSUES COME AND TEST MY MORAL RESOLVE PLEA]. ULTIMATELY, IT'S UP TO THE INDIVIDUAL TO INTERROGATE THE PLUSHLY FURNISHED ROOMS OF THEIR OWN CONSCIENCE WHEN JUSTIFYING THEIR CHOICES TO ACCEPT THE SPORTSWASHING LAUNDRY TOKENS.

I had a lot of conversations with the LGBTQ+ people when I was over there and they said they'd been treated perfectly fine and enjoyed the games and felt it was the safest World 'Cup they've had for a long time –

Be honest.

I am!

Who did you speak to in Qatar?

Um. Loads of people... The spice markets were–

No, no, no, no, no. Which people did you speak to? Specifically, who?

OK, so, the people the rulers allowed us to, but–

Thank you!

HOWEVER, FIFA WALKS THE WALK WHEN IT COMES TO CORPORATE PLATITUDES ABOUT FAIR PLAY AND HAS GIVEN AUSTRALIA A WHOLE 25 DAYS TO DECIDE WHETHER IT'S GOING TO BLOW MILLIONS ON A DOOMED BID. WHILE THE ENDORSEMENT OF IMPORTED STARS LIKE JACK RODWELL MAY NOT HAVE AS MUCH SWAY AS NEYMAR, AUSTRALIA HAS ONE ACE IT COULD PLAY.

I meant questions about the game, mate, but sure... Moore, Connery, Craig, Lazenby –yes, Lazenby– Brosnan, Dalton...

Tell the Crown Prince the deal's off. He's a reasonable guy, he'll understand...

Gulp.

THERE HAS BEEN TALK OF AUSTRALIA TEAMING UP WITH INDONESIA AND NEW ZEALAND ON A JOINT, ILL-FATED BID. AT LEAST NEW ZEALAND WILL GET ITS CHANCE TO HOST A MEN'S WORLD CUP WHEN THE ONLY SURVIVING HUMANS ARE THE TECH BROS AND PLUTOCRATS HOLED UP IN THEIR DOOMSDAY BUNKERS IN THE LAND OF THE LONG WHITE CLOUD.

I've improved the ball. Now it can move in four directions. What's the matter; too radical for you?

Ugh. Maybe I shouldn't have banished my robot butler. If only there was something I could do.

WORLD CUP

Eternal Sunshine of the Sportless Mind

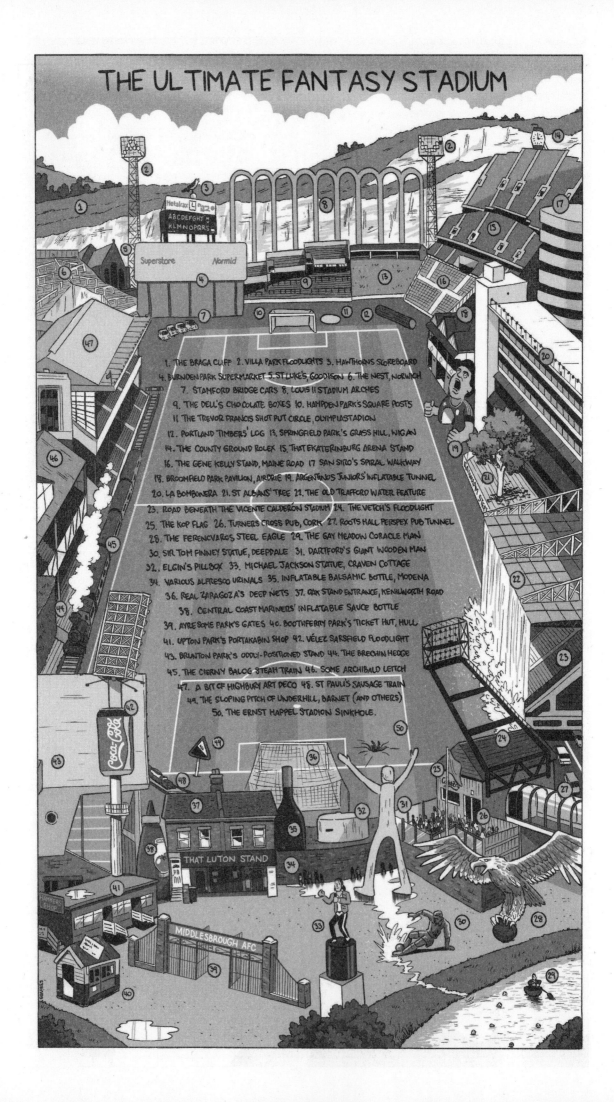

THE ULTIMATE FANTASY STADIUM

1. THE BRAGA CLIFF 2. VILLA PARK FLOODLIGHTS 3. HAWTHORNS SCOREBOARD
4. BURNDEN PARK SUPERMARKET 5. ST LUKE'S, GOODISON 6. THE NEST, NORWICH
7. STAMFORD BRIDGE CARS 8. LOUIS II STADIUM ARCHES
9. THE DELL'S CHOCOLATE BOXES 10. HAMPDEN PARK'S SQUARE POSTS
11. THE TREVOR FRANCIS SHOT PUT CIRCLE, OLYMPIASTADION
12. PORTLAND 'TIMBERS' LOG 13. SPRINGFIELD PARK'S GRASS HILL, WIGAN
14. THE COUNTY GROUND ROLEX 15. THAT EKATERINBURG ARENA STAND
16. THE GENE KELLY STAND, MAINE ROAD 17. SAN SIRO'S SPIRAL WALKWAY
18. BROOMFIELD PARK PAVILION, AIRDRIE 19. ARGENTINOS JUNIORS' INFLATABLE TUNNEL
20. LA BOMBONERA 21. ST ALBANS' TREE 22. THE OLD TRAFFORD WATER FEATURE
23. ROAD BENEATH THE VICENTE CALDERÓN STADIUM 24. THE VETCH'S FLOODLIGHT
25. THE KOP FLAG 26. TURNERS CROSS PUB, CORK 27. ROOTS HALL PERSPEX PUB TUNNEL
28. THE FERENCVAROS STEEL EAGLE 29. THE GAY MEADOW CORACLE MAN
30. SIR TOM FINNEY STATUE, DEEPDALE 31. DARTFORD'S GIANT WOODEN MAN
32. ELGIN'S PILLBOX 33. MICHAEL JACKSON STATUE, CRAVEN COTTAGE
34. VARIOUS ALFRESCO URINALS 35. INFLATABLE BALSAMIC BOTTLE, MODENA
36. REAL ZARAGOZA'S DEEP NETS 37. OAK STAND ENTRANCE, KENILWORTH ROAD
38. CENTRAL COAST MARINERS' INFLATABLE SAUCE BOTTLE
39. AYRESOME PARK'S GATES 40. BOOTHFERRY PARK'S TICKET HUT, HULL
41. UPTON PARK'S PORTAKABIN SHOP 42. VÉLEZ SARSFIELD FLOODLIGHT
43. BRUNTON PARK'S ODDLY-POSITIONED STAND 44. THE BRECHIN HEDGE
45. THE CIERNY BALOG STEAM TRAIN 46. SOME ARCHIBALD LEITCH
47. A BIT OF HIGHBURY ART DECO 48. ST PAULI'S SAUSAGE TRAIN
49. THE SLOPING PITCH OF UNDERHILL, BARNET (AND OTHERS)
50. THE ERNST HAPPEL STADION SINKHOLE.

THE PACKED CHRISTMAS SCHEDULE IS NEARLY UPON US, AND FOR THOSE WHO WANT TO SUCCEED THIS SEASON, PREPARATION IS EVERYTHING – IT IS *IMPERATIVE* YOU GET TO THE RADIO TIMES WITH YOUR HIGHLIGHTER PEN FIRST.

25 DECEMBER IS THE ONLY DAY WHEN THERE'S NO LIVE FOOTBALL ON THE BOX, BUT YOU CAN DISTRACT YOURSELF WITH THESE CHOICE TV CUTS…

5am BBC One High Performance Christmas Presents
Jake Humphrey pays a motivational visit to his local hospital, giving patients the gift of a CEO mindset.

8am BBC Two Songs of Waheys
The choir of St Banterlads travel to the cathedral of a city it considers less salubrious than its own, and sings a selection of carols mocking the economic circumstances of its ho-ho-hosts.

1pm BBC One Top of the Pops
A one-off return, featuring some of your favourite festive hits from a time when you understood the charts. Included is a song growled with a voice of purest shovelled road grit that would have been the Christmas No 1 if those snakes at the Official UK Top 40 hadn't deducted it 10 downloads.

3pm BBC One, BBC Two ITV
The King
1990s full-back Phil King's Christmas message to the nation and the Commonwealth

3.10pm BBC Two
Some Aardman film about a passive-aggressive plasticine reindeer who saves Christmas.

7.30pm ITV The Core
Christmas special (they've green-screened some tinsel) of the year's hit game show, hosted by Michael Owen.

8pm BBC Two Maupay Unwise
Another chance to enjoy Neal Maupay and Emi Martinez's classic comedy performance at the Gtech Community Palladium, first aired in December 2023. Features guest appearances from Unai 'Dick' Emery, and Angela Rippon as Thomas Frank.

9.45pm BBC One Bleak London-based Soap Opera
A misunderstanding over lunch leads to an hour of shouting and tears to round off your Christmas evening.

IT WAS A GOAL AS PREDETERMINED AS JAMIE CARRAGHER'S CHOICE OF MAN OF THE MATCH; BRENTFORD'S RETURNING HERO, IVAN TONEY, MANIFESTING A FREE-KICK AROUND THE NOTTINGHAM FOREST 'WALL' AND INTO THE NET, RYAN YATES HAVING BEEN FLUNG OUT OF ITS WAY BY DESTINY ALONE.

The narrative, I'm powerless to resist it!

That's a new one.

TONEY'S TRIUMPHANT RETURN AFTER AN EIGHT-MONTH BAN FOR BETTING OFFENCES IS THE COMEBACK STORY OF THE SEASON. IS IT EVEN THE MOST REMARKABLE IN BRENTFORD'S HISTORY?

I wouldn't bet on it.

AT THE VERY LEAST, IT'S A TALE THAT GIVES HOPE TO ANY FOOTBALLER WHO MAY HAVE SELF-SABOTAGED THEIR CAREER...

Stevie, we hebben een serieus probleem.

GIVEN THE REASON FOR TONEY'S EXTENDED ABSENCE, AND HIS PERSONAL STRUGGLES WITH GAMBLING ADDICTION, IT'S FORTUNATE THERE WERE NO JARRING REMINDERS OF THE GRIP THE GAMING INDUSTRY HAS ON ENGLISH FOOTBALL. THE MATCH WAS EVEN PLAYED AT BRENTFORD, WHO'D PROBABLY STILL BE KNOCKING ABOUT IN THE SKYBET LOW ROLLERS' LEAGUES IF NOT FOR THEIR OWNER WHO MADE HIS COIN IN THE BETTING INDUSTRY. JUST AS WELL THE JEDI MASTER IVAN CAN SCORE GOALS WITH HIS EYES CLOSED.

THE BUZZ ABOUT TONEY'S RETURN WAS PERHAPS SLIGHTLY UNDERMINED BY HIS CANDID COMMENTS ABOUT WANTING TO MOVE TO A BIGGER CLUB, IF THERE IS SUCH A THING. SOME SAW THIS AS DISRESPECTFUL TO A CLUB THAT STUCK BY A PLAYER THEY VALUE AT £100M AND WHOSE GOALS COULD HELP THEM STAY IN THE PREMIER LEAGUE. AT THIS POINT, HE COULD PRETTY MUCH SAY OR DO WHAT HE WANTS.

Look, gaffer, a spilled shipping container full of Salon Selectives.

Ivan, I can't see any...

That's Ludo!

You moved your counters!

Did I? Or is it merely that I actualised success through positive thought and self-belief?

Oh this is bullsh—

Very good, well done, Ivan. No one really knows the rules anyway.

NOTTINGHAM FOREST WEREN'T ENTIRELY ENCHANTED BY THE FAIRYTALE AND HAVE WRITTEN TO THE PREMIER LEAGUE TO ASK WHY TONEY'S GOAL WAS ALLOWED TO STAND AFTER HE'D MOVED THE BALL TO A MORE ADVANTAGEOUS SPOT _AND_ BESMIRCHED THE SANCTITY OF THE SQUIRTY VANISHING FOAM.

What's the point of rules if they aren't applied rigorously?!

So... a club should be punished if, say, it falls foul of our profit and sustainability rules by missing the deadline for selling a player...?

You're allowed a yard either side of it...

BRENTFORD'S 3-2 WIN EASED THEIR RELEGATION FEARS, LIFTING THEM ABOVE CRYSTAL PALACE, WHOSE FANS SEEM UNHAPPY, DESPITE ALSO SHARING FIVE GOALS WITH ARSENAL. HONESTLY, WHAT MORE DO THEY WANT?!

Wasted potential. On and off the pitch. Weak decisions. Taking us backwards. Visit Rwanda.

Raymond, it's the track list from side one of my favourite Mogwai long player! The fans just get me! And to think I was considering leaving! Not now! Not ever!

Ugh, how humiliating for him.

Less prattle, more cattle.

WHERE WERE YOU WHEN YOU HEARD THE NEWS? I WAS WALKING MY DOGS AND SAW A YOUNG WOMAN STOP, STARE AT HER PHONE, MITTENS SHOOTING TO HER MOUTH...

It's Jörg Schmadtke, Liverpool's sporting director, he's... leaving!

EVERYONE IN EARSHOT RUMMAGED IN THEIR POCKETS TO FIND PHONES, TO STOP AND STARE.

Elite development coach Vitor Matos too?!

The world seemed nicer, better, easier navigable with his conker hair shining.

IN OTHER NEWS, HAVING TRANSFORMED LIVERPOOL'S FORTUNES AND WON EVERYTHING POSSIBLE, JÜRGEN KLOPP HAS ANNOUNCED HE'S DEPARTING AT THE END OF THE SEASON - A BOMBSHELL THAT WOULD HAVE REPERCUSSIONS BEYOND FOOTBALL.

Richard Osman's written a limerick, so we need to do another rebrand.

AFTER EIGHT MOSTLY GLORIOUS YEARS, THE DEMANDS OF BERATING FOURTH OFFICIALS WHILE DRESSED LIKE A CHARACTER FROM FARGO HAVE FINALLY CAUGHT UP WITH HIM, NOT TO MENTION THE TOLL OF DOING BATTLE WITH HIS GREATEST COACHING RIVAL:

KLOPP HAS GIVEN EVERYTHING: TROPHIES, SUCCESS, THE SLAPSTICK COMEDY OF TWANGING HIS HAMMY WHILE SCREAM-GLOATING AT JOHN BROOKS. HE POPULARISED THE SNOOD AND CAME WITHIN A WHISKER OF NOT BEING RATTLED BY AN EVERTON BALLBOY'S SARCASTIC APPLAUSE. AND NOW, HE LEAVES WITH ONE FINAL GIFT: A NEW MEME FORMAT FOR MANAGERIAL DEPARTURES.

I have joined the club.

I am leaving the friggin' club.

SOME LIVERPOOL / PERSPECTIVE FANS HAVE LIKENED THE NEWS TO A DEATH IN THE FAMILY. JUST BECAUSE HIS WEDDING RING FELL OFF, IT DOESN'T MEAN HE'S A GHOST. KLOPP MADE HIS DECISION BACK IN NOVEMBER, AND THERE WERE PERHAPS SIGNS OF HIS GROWING WEARINESS WHEN HE REACTED TO CONDUCTING A PRESS CONFERENCE NEAR SOME HAPPY TOULOUSE FANS LIKE A NEIGHBOUR TRYING TO SHUT DOWN A HOUSE PARTY.

My boys have got a 12:30 start in two weeks, but yeah, keep screaming "Woo" for no reason. Super helpful.

Sucking the balloons rather than blowing into them. This is clearly a really well organised event!

THE CLUB'S HIERARCHY NOW FACES THE TASK OF HIRING A REPLACEMENT WHO GETS LIVERPOOL, THE OBVIOUS CANDIDATE BEING THE MAN WHO INSPIRED THEM TO A FAMOUS VICTORY IN THE 2005 CHAMPIONS LEAGUE FINAL, BUT IF HE WON'T LEAVE LEVERKUSEN THERE ARE OTHER OPTIONS...

I've ruined the new contract! Oh, Stevie, you're such a klutz! I guess it's invalid now, right? Damn, and I was loving it here at...

Al-Ettifaq.

Right. Oh well, "We go again", as I always say. I'll be seeing you around...

Sit down.

LIVERPOOL ARE SAID TO BE USING A DATA-DRIVEN PROCESS TO INFORM THE RECRUITMENT PROCESS AND ONE CAN ONLY HOPE THEY ARE PLOTTING THE CANDIDATES AGAINST THE BANTER MATRIX TO SEE WHO CAN DELIVER THE MAXIMUM CARTOON CONTENT.

WTF?!
RAGE
YAWN
WILL ANNOY OTHER PREM CLUBS
WILL ANNOY EVERTON
LFC LEGENDS ZONE
MOU
WAZ
LAMPS
ROY
DON CARLO
RAFA
RODGERS
ALONSO
ANGE
EMERY
FRANK
DE ZERBI
STEVIE
FANS WALK FROM PUB TO GROUND IN PROTEST
MEH
MEH ← BANTZ → LOL

WITH EVERYTHING STILL TO PLAY FOR THIS SEASON, KLOPP IS DETERMINED HEAVY-METAL FOOTBALL DOESN'T MAKE WAY FOR A FOUR-MONTH ACOUSTIC COVER OF A CAST SONG - A POSSIBILITY THAT COULD MAYBE HAVE JUST BEEN AVOIDED BY ANNOUNCING HIS DECISION IN MAY. THE CLUB'S TOP BRASS WILL ALREADY BE MAKING PREPARATIONS FOR A TYPICALLY UNDERSTATED FAREWELL PARTY AFTER LIVERPOOL'S FINAL PREMIER LEAGUE MATCH OF THE SEASON AT ANFIELD. AS WELL AS THE OBLIGATORY RENDITION OF WOLVES FANS PRETENDING MANCHESTER CITY ARE LOSING, WE CAN EXPECT A FEW SURPRISES...

What do you think, Jürgen? A hundred school kids dressed like you, singing "Walk Away". The dental bills alone will impact José's transfer budget next season, but it's worth it.

Wait a second...

Who swapped them for 100 sarcastic Everton ballboys?!

Yeah, well done.

Lol.

Boom.

A DAY IN THE LIFE OF CHRIS WILDER

AKA THE EARL OF SANDWICH

THE PREMIER LEAGUE'S MOST HUMBLE MANAGER

"Knill awakens me with a single quail egg and the day's newspapers with the league table redacted. I treat him with dignity, even though he's not a Premier League manager..."

Ah, my Groom of the Stool, and not before bloody time!

I keep telling you, that's not in my job description, gaffer.

"Regardless of his insolence, I permit Knill to robe me in the finery that befits my lofty status."

The monogrammed duck down puffer tunic and the onyx tracksuit pantaloons today, I think, Knill.

Sigh

"My carriage awaits. The Mercedes E-class offers the best VFM in the crowded executive chariot field. With plush Premier League dugout racing car seats and a two-horsepower engine, it really is an impressive bit of kit."

PREMIER LEAGUE MANAGER

"Despite what your do-gooders would have you believe, the common folk - who will never know the grandeur of being interviewed in a corner bejewelled with crypto logos - respect life's natural order. The love for their betters is palpable as they skip to the latest Sheffield United fixture, their simple hearts bursting with joyful anticipation."

Can't believe we're leaving the pub for this.

S'only for half an hour.

"To duty. A morale-lifting inspection of the staff..."

And what do you do?

Seriously?

"Before some ceremonial ribbon cutting to get proceedings underway."

I hereby pronounce this defence...open!

SHEFFIELD STEEL

15

20

"After the customary defeat, I perform an ancient ritual that can be traced all the way back to the days of Dame Bassett... sorry... Dave Bassett. A visit to the match officials' cupboard for a whinge about the global conspiracy to stymie the ambitions of Sheffield United ... but what freshly-made hell is this ?!"

A sandwich? A succulent, pre-packed sandwich?! Not two metres away from a PREMIER LEAGUE MANAGER?!

munch... swallow

Barely.

"Anarchy! Sacrilege! Egg and cress! There hasn't been such contempt for aristocratic protocol since Cradle of Filth were booked for the Royal Variety Performance. Where is the respect? I invented the overlapping centre-back! To add insult to injury, no one seems to be taking this obscenity seriously."

Don't get a COB on, there's no agenda against your CLUB!

They lost again but he's still his Mother's Pride!

Maybe he should have used his SUBS! Like the sandwich!

Knill! Get back here, man.

"If you can't honour the man, honour the bench coat! Oh, one supposes one shouldn't be surprised - the erosion of deference can be witnessed everywhere. Arteta being interrogated by the Flying (down the wing) Squad; Pochettino clinging on to power; and look how they massacred my Roy - Crystal Palace courting his replacement while he still holds the role."

After an extensive recruitment process that involved both begging and pleading, I'm delighted to introduce the only person willing to become the new manager of Crystal Palace FC...

Mr Roy Hodgson!

"However, having successfully retained my dignity, I return to my quarters. After administering Knill with the thrashing of his life, I hand him the quill and parchment and dictate a letter to the snake, Webb, H. I shall have my restitution, for I am a Premier League Manager and no mortal can take that away from me for at least three months!"

All finished. Or, as you could say: that's a... wrap!

Like the wrap.

Knill, I swear to God...

FOOTBALL HAS EXPERIENCED RAPID CHANGE IN RECENT YEARS, BUT SOME CONSTANTS REMAIN. FANS CAN STILL BE FOUND HUDDLING AROUND THEIR WIRELESS DEVICES, DISCOVERING THE LATEST RESULTS IN RECRUITMENT. THIS WEEK'S BIG HUMAN RESOURCES STORY REVOLVES AROUND THE POTENTIAL TRANSFER OF ARGUABLY THE GREATEST TALENT OF HIS GENERATION: DAN ASHWORTH

'THE TRANSFER WHISPERER' HAS TOLD NEWCASTLE HE WANTS TO LEAVE HIS ROLE AS SPORTING DIRECTOR AMID INTEREST FROM MANCHESTER UNITED, WHO ARE KEEN TO MAINTAIN THEIR SPOTLESS RECORD WHEN IT COMES TO BIG-MONEY SIGNINGS. NEWCASTLE HAVE CURLED THEIR LITTLE FINGER TO THE CORNER OF THEIR MOUTH AND DEMANDED 20 MILLION POUNDS FOR THE SERVICES OF ASHWORTH, WHO HAS ALREADY DEMONSTRATED HIS ACUMEN FOR STRATEGY BY LANDING THAT MOST COVETED OF PRIZES...

Fully paid gardening leave!

ALTHOUGH NEWCASTLE HAVE REPORTEDLY BLOCKED ASHWORTH'S ACCESS TO HIS COMPUTER, THEY'LL BE WORRIED HE'LL REVEAL THE SECRETS OF THE DEATH STAR'S FOOTBALL TEAM TO A RIVAL.

Hah, bloody hell, Tindall brushes with Tipp-Ex!

THE CREATION OF SPECIALIST ROLES HAS HAD A HUGE IMPACT ON THE MODERN GAME. ARSENAL HAVE BEEN IN SIZZLING FORM SINCE MIKEL ARTETA BEGAN PICKING THE BRAINS OF THEIR NEW NUTRITIONIST, AND VICE VERSA.

Burnley's a difficult place to come and they've been very competitive in their big games.

... AND NOTTINGHAM FOREST HAVE HIRED CELEBRITY REFEREE, MARK 'CLATT'S ENTERTAINMENT' CLATTENBURG, TO PROVIDE EXPERT INSIGHT.

Nitro's command of the pugil stick is *world class*. Beware of leotard chafe when building up speed for the travelator. Clatt-wooga!

I said we should have hired John Anderson.

ASHWORTH'S MOVE HAS THE POTENTIAL TO BE MESSIER THAN CRYSTAL PALACE'S REMOVAL OF ROY HODGSON, A PROCESS THAT DRAGGED ON LONGER THAN A BANNER IN THE HOLMESDALE END. RECENT PALACE MATCHES HAVE BEEN PLAYED TO A BACKDROP OF SUPPORTER DISCONTENT, WITH FREQUENT CUTAWAYS TO STEVE PARISH AND MARK BRIGHT PUFFING THEIR CHEEKS IN EXASPERATION.

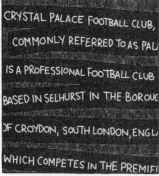

CRYSTAL PALACE FOOTBALL CLUB, COMMONLY REFERRED TO AS PAL IS A PROFESSIONAL FOOTBALL CLUB BASED IN SELHURST IN THE BOROUC OF CROYDON, SOUTH LONDON, ENGL WHICH COMPETES IN THE PREMIE

I ain't reading all that. I'm happy for u tho. Or sorry that happened.

AFTER WEEKS OF SPECULATION, ROY WAS FINALLY MUTUALLY CONSENTED ON MONDAY, POSSIBLY BRINGING TO AN END A LONG AND MOSTLY DISTINGUISHED CAREER. NO DOUBT TO HIM IT WILL FEEL LIKE ONLY YESTERDAY HE WAS ZIPPING THROUGH THE STREETS OF MILAN ON A VESPA, THE WARM AIR BLOWING THROUGH HIS SOFT BROWN HAIR.

FOOTBALL MOVES ON QUICKLY, AND AS IF TO HIGHLIGHT THE COACHING CYCLE OF LIFE, PALACE'S DRAW WITH EVERTON SAW A BRIEF SHOT OF TACTICAL ANALYSIS BEING PROVIDED BY A WHIZZ-KID SO YOUNG HE MAY HAVE ONLY JUST DESCENDED FROM THE CLOACA OF THE CLUB'S EAGLE MASCOT.

Cowabunga!

PALACE ISSUED A GRATEFUL FAREWELL STATEMENT TO A GREAT SERVANT WHO COULD HAVE BEEN SPENDING HIS AUTUMN YEARS EXPLORING THE METROPOLITAN WATERWAYS OF EUROPE'S ANCIENT CITIES, RATHER THAN BEING SUBJECTED TO A PAINFULLY PUBLIC EXIT. HOWEVER, THE GAME STOPS FOR NO ONE AND PALACE NOW ENTER THE ERA OF OLIVER GLASNER, WHO MIGHT PROVE TO BE MORE DEMANDING THAN HODGSON.

No one brought the Extra Strong Pfefferminzbonbons? Not even a frikkin' *Wagon Wheel*? Oh, I am very much thinking this is the amateur hour, yes?

Whoosh!

— Mark

Pls cm bck ;-)

Come on Raymond, we can still make the river cruise, old friend...

IN A STORY THAT WILL DO AS MUCH GOOD FOR YOUR BRAIN HEALTH AS HAVING A CIGAR BURNT THROUGH YOUR EYEBALL, NIKE'S NEW ENGLAND SHIRT HAS CAUSED QUITE A CONFECTED STIR. THE COLLAR OF THE TOP INCLUDES A "PLAYFUL UPDATE" OF THE ST GEORGE CROSS, USING THE TONE PALETTE OF JOEY BARTON'S FACE WHEN TRYING TO SUMMON THE SELF-AWARENESS TO FATHOM WHY HE DOESN'T GET MUCH WORK THESE DAYS.

IT WAS AN EPISODE THAT HIGHLIGHTED ENGLAND'S BEST CHARACTERISTICS: RABID NATIONALISM, MISDIRECTED FURY, A WILFUL IGNORANCE OF HISTORY (THE 2012 SHIRT DESIGN, FOR WHICH PETER SAVILLE WILL BE RETROSPECTIVELY THROWN INTO THE TOWER). OBVIOUSLY, IT'S FINE FOR A TORY MP TO SMEAR THE ST GEORGE CROSS ON HIS SWEATY FACE FOR THE LIKES, AND FOR INGERLUND FANS TO MODIFY THE DESIGN WITH TEXT ABOUT LADS BEING ON TOUR, BUT FOR NIKE TO DESECRATE THE ITALIAN BANNER NAMED AFTER A GREEK SAINT WAS AN AFFRONT TO THOSE WHO ARE ALWAYS AT FULL-MAST FOR THE FLAG.

THE GOOD NEWS IS THAT COLLARS CAN NOW BE ADDED TO THE GROWING LIST OF WOKE THINGS THAT ARE DESTROYING FOOTBALL, INCLUDING, BUT NOT LIMITED TO:

OF COURSE THE CALL TO BOYCOTT NIKE PRODUCTS IS BEING CHAMPIONED BY THE PEPERAMI MAN WHO USED TO BE MARRIED TO BILLIE PIPER, AND OF COURSE HE'S WEARING A PAIR OF NIKE TRAINERS WHILE DOING IT. HOWEVER, THE PRICE OF THE KIT ALREADY LIMITS THE NUMBER OF PEOPLE WHO'LL BE ABLE TO WEAR IT...

YEAH, THAT'LL BE IT, CHAMP. THE INTERNATIONAL BREAK MEANT JOEY COULD TAKE SOME TIME OUT FROM BULLYING FEMALE PUNDITS AND COMMENTATORS ONLINE TO GET HOT UNDER THE COLLAR ABOUT ANOTHER NON-ISSUE, AND WAS SOON JOINED BY AN ANGRY CHORUS OF THE USUAL PUB BORES: LEE ANDERSON, NIGEL FARAGE, PETER SHILTON. THE ACTUAL PRIME MINISTER STUCK HIS SIZE FOURS IN TOO, BECAUSE IT'S NOT LIKE THE WORLD IS ENDING OR ANYTHING LOL. NEVER ONE TO MISS A CHANCE TO DESPERATELY SEEK THE APPROVAL OF PEOPLE WHO'D NEVER VOTE FOR HIM, KEIR STARMER WEIGHED IN TOO, MAKING YOU WONDER WHERE HE'S TAKING HIS LEAD FROM...

AN FA SPOKESPERSON SIGHED THAT THE MULTICOLOUR FLAG IS MERELY A TRIBUTE TO THE TRAINING GEAR WORN BY THE WORLD CUP-WINNING TEAM OF 1966 - A TIME MANY PEOPLE WOULD APPARENTLY LIKE TO RETURN TO, WHEN CHEERFUL BOBBIES COULD IMPRISON YOU FOR BEING GAY AND LIFE WAS JUST A BIT BLOODY SIMPLER...

SHOULD THE FA AND NIKE REVERT TO THE TRADITIONAL FLAG, EVERYONE'S LIVES WOULD IMMEDIATELY IMPROVE - IN THE SAME WAY THEY DID WHEN THE PASSPORTS CHANGED COLOUR - ALLOWING US ALL TO MOVE ON TO THE NEXT CULTURE WAR DISTRACTION...

THE WEEKEND'S FA CUP SEMI-FINALS WERE PLAYED TO A BACKDROP OF WIDESPREAD INDIGNATION, FOLLOWING THE FA'S ANNOUNCEMENT THAT REPLAYS WOULD BE SCRAPPED FROM THE FIRST ROUND ONWARDS, REMOVING THE CHANCE OF FINANCIALLY TRANSFORMATIVE PAYDAYS FOR CLUBS WHO CAN'T EASE THEIR DEBTS BY JUST SELLING SOME HOTELS TO THEMSELVES. MANY FANS FELT THE CHANGES WERE MADE WITHOUT ALL OF THE COMPETITION'S 732 COMPETING CLUBS IN MIND...

DESPITE AN ONGOING BEEF ABOUT THE EXTENT TO WHICH THE PLEBEIAN LEAGUES WERE CONSULTED, THE FA PROUDLY CLAIMS THE CHANGES WILL STRENGTHEN THE ONLY THING IT HAS LEFT OF ANY VALUE, LIKE HOW ELON MUSK'S BIG-BRAIN IDEAS HAVE STRENGTHENED TWITTER! THE PREMIER LEAGUE WAS FAMOUSLY FORMED WITH THE PRIMARY INTENTION OF KEEPING ALL THE CHEDDAR FOR ITSELF, BUT HAS KINDLY AGREED TO DONATE £33M (ROUGHLY ONE NICOLAS JACKSON) TO GRASSROOTS CLUBS, UNDOUBTEDLY WITH SOME CAVEATS...

ON SATURDAY, MANCHESTER CITY REACHED ANOTHER FA CUP FINAL, WHICH WAS ALL THEY BLOODY NEEDED, BUT PRESENTS AN OPPORTUNITY MOST CLUBS COULD ONLY DREAM OF: ~~DOING THE DOUBLE~~ BITCHING ABOUT YOUR WORKLOAD ON NATIONAL TELEVISION. IT WAS A MOMENT OF TOP, TOP ROOM-READING FROM PEP, AND A SUBJECT HE'S BEEN WANGING ON ABOUT FOR A WHILE...

COMPLAINTS ABOUT *THE SCHEDULE* DIDN'T GARNER MUCH SYMPATHY FROM PEOPLE WHO WORK GRUELLING HOURS IN JOBS WITH TANGIBLE BENEFITS TO SOCIETY (NURSES, SOCIAL WORKERS, CARTOONISTS, ETC), NOT TO MENTION THE GRASSROOTS PLAYERS WHO HAVE TO JUGGLE A CONGESTED FOOTBALL CALENDAR WITH FULL-TIME EMPLOYMENT. THANKFULLY, THE FA HAS THOUGHT OF THAT BY CHANGING THE DEFINITION OF THE WEEKEND AS SOMETHING THAT RUNS FROM FRIDAY TO WEDNESDAY.

THERE WERE SHAMEFUL SCENES IN THE OTHER SEMI-FINAL, WHERE COVENTRY CITY FORCED *THE PREMIER LEAGUE'S SEVENTH BEST TEAM* TO PLAY ANOTHER 30 MINUTES OF FOOTBALL, SO WELL DONE TO ANTONY FOR MOCKING THE CHAMPIONSHIP PLAYERS WHO WERE DENIED ONE OF THE FA CUP'S MOST GLORIOUS COMEBACK VICTORIES BY THE WIDTH OF A COAT OF DYE ON HAJI WRIGHT'S LEFT BOOT. WHILE OFFSIDE IS A BINARY CALL, AND THE 'V' IN VAR DOESN'T STAND FOR 'VIBES', IT TAKES A SPECIAL BREED OF NARK TO DENY COVENTRY THEIR MOMENT OF JOY AND ROB US ALL OF ONE OF THE FUNNIEST THINGS TO EVER HAPPEN.

WHILE IT'S UNQUESTIONABLY AWFUL, AT LEAST SOME PEOPLE ARE ABLE TO KEEP A HEALTHY SENSE OF PERSPECTIVE ABOUT VAR...

THERE HASN'T BEEN SUCH A SENSE OF INJUSTICE SINCE NFFC RELEASED THEIR SEASON-TICKET PRICES FOR 2024-25. VAR WAS ONE OF THE MUCH-DEMANDED MEASURES INTRODUCED TO FIX FOOTBALL, AND EVERYONE SEEMS TO HAVE THEIR OWN THEORIES ON HOW TO IMPROVE THE GAME: *TURN LEAGUE ONE INTO A TALENT HUB FOR PRECOCIOUS PREMIER LEAGUE BOYS! SCRAP THE CARABAO CUP! OR AT LEAST LET LOWER-LEAGUE CLUBS DECIDE WHICH OFFSHORE GROWTH MARKET SHOULD HOST THE TIES!* HERE'S ONE TO THROW INTO THE MIX, PRESENTED IN THE STYLE OF A BOOMING WEMBLEY PRE-MATCH PYRO SPECTACULAR:

FOR THE FIRST TIME SINCE THE REIGN OF THE TACTICS TRUCK, IPSWICH TOWN ARE BACK IN THE BIG TIME – THE ASCENT OF THE TRACTOR BOYS IN NO WAY STRENGTHENING THE NOTION THAT THE PREMIER LEAGUE IS THE REAL FARMERS' LEAGUE. THEIR ELEVATION MADE HEADLINES AROUND THE WORLD, AND WAS GREETED WARMLY BY ALL ASIDE FROM DELIA PARTISANS AND FANS OF THEIR PROMOTION RIVALS...

KIERAN MCKENNA'S BOYS WILL NOW EMBARK UPON A GREAT ADVENTURE, WITH THE WIDE-EYED ENTHUSIASM OF REPLACEMENTS MARCHING HEADLONG INTO A MEAT GRINDER.

MCKENNA TOOK OVER IN 2021, WITH IPSWICH 12TH IN LEAGUE ONE. THEIR CONSECUTIVE PROMOTIONS HAVE MADE A MOCKERY OF THE ACCEPTED WISDOM THAT ESCAPING THE CHAMPIONSHIP IS EVEN HARDER THAN DITCHING A TV SUBSCRIPTION.

HOWEVER, IPSWICH WILL BE WELL AWARE OF THE HIGHER STANDARDS DEMANDED IN THE PREMIER LEAGUE, AS DEMONSTRATED LAST WEEK WHEN THE CHIEF OF FOOTBALL OPERATIONS, SIR JIMBO, REACTED ANGRILY TO THE SCRUFFY STATE OF THE YOUTH CHANGING ROOMS AND IT DEPARTMENT AT MCKENNA'S ALMA MATER, MANCHESTER UNITED.

... AND EVEN THE MOST POSITIVE OF NEW ARRIVALS CAN BE QUICKLY GROUND DOWN.

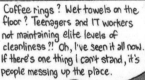

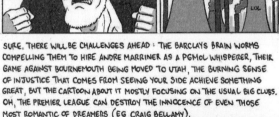
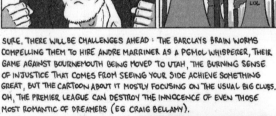

SURE, THERE WILL BE CHALLENGES AHEAD: THE BARCLAYS BRAIN WORMS COMPELLING THEM TO HIRE ANDRE MARRINER AS A PGMOL WHISPERER, THEIR GAME AGAINST BOURNEMOUTH BEING MOVED TO UTAH, THE BURNING SENSE OF INJUSTICE THAT COMES FROM SEEING YOUR SIDE ACHIEVE SOMETHING GREAT, BUT THE CARTOON ABOUT IT MOSTLY FOCUSING ON THE USUAL BIG CLUBS. OH, THE PREMIER LEAGUE CAN DESTROY THE INNOCENCE OF EVEN THOSE MOST ROMANTIC OF DREAMERS (EG CRAIG BELLAMY).

BUT QUITE RIGHTLY, NO ONE CARED ABOUT THAT AS THEY RACED ON TO THE PORTMAN ROAD PITCH ON SATURDAY. THESE ARE THE MOMENTS YOU LIVE FOR AS A FAN, THE ONES YOU MIGHT ONLY EXPERIENCE A HANDFUL OF TIMES. THE JOY, THE RELIEF, THE BLOODY-HELL-WE-ACTUALLY-DID-IT-NESS OF IT ALL. A BURSTING PRIDE IN THE TEAM, THE TOWN, AND THE YOUNG MANAGER, THE SECURITY OF KNOWING THAT ONE WHO EVER PUBLICLY DECLARES LOVE FOR A CLUB IS EVER COAXED AWAY BEFORE THE OPEN-TOP BUS HAS COOLED DOWN.

LIKE A NOVELTY ACT THAT ACHIEVES FOUR CONSECUTIVE CHRISTMAS NO 1s, MINUS THE CHARITY ANGLE, MANCHESTER CITY (AKA ETIHADBABY) ARE CHAMPIONS AGAIN! THEIR DOMINATION IS ALMOST ENOUGH TO HAVE YOU PINING FOR THE CYNICAL NOUGHTIES PRE-EMINENCE OF SIMON COWELL'S CHELSEA, BUT THERE WAS SOME SENSE OF JEOPARDY ON SUNDAY AS WE ALL WAITED TO SEE HOW JACK GREALISH WOULD INJURE HIMSELF DURING THE POST-MATCH CELEBRATIONS.

HOWEVER, THERE WAS NO SENSE CITY FANS WERE GOING THROUGH THE MOTIONS WITH THEIR ANNUAL PITCH INVASION, EXPERIENCING THE JOY OF ANYONE LIVING THEIR BEST CAUTIONARY TALE. VICTORY WAS SECURED WITH A WIN AGAINST WEST HAM, AND WHILE THE CITY MACHINE WILL TRUNDLE ON LIKE AN INFINITE RONDO, THIS SEASON MARKS THE END OF AN ERA, WITH PEP LATER SPEAKING TEARFULLY ABOUT HIS GREAT, DEPARTING RIVAL...

ARSENAL RAN CITY CLOSE, AND MAY EVEN HAVE GOT CLOSER IF THE PREMIER LEAGUE HAD GOT ROUND TO CONCLUDING ITS INVESTIGATION INTO CITY'S 115 ALLEGED FINANCIAL OOPSIES. WITH THAT IN MIND, RODRI'S POST-MATCH CRITICISM OF THE GUNNERS MUST HAVE STUCK IN MIKEL ARTETA'S THROAT LIKE ONE OF SALT BAE'S CREMATIONS.

CITY ALSO FACE THE NIGHTMARE SCENARIO OF HAVING TO PLAY ANOTHER THEORETICALLY COMPETITIVE FOOTBALL MATCH ON SATURDAY! IT'S A FATE TOTTENHAM AND NEWCASTLE CLEVERLY DODGED BY OPTING OUT OF THE LATTER STAGES OF ANY CUP COMPETITIONS, ALLOWING THEIR PLAYERS TO GET SOME WELL-EARNED REST ABOARD THE LUXURY AIRLINER TAKING THEM TO A CARBON-UNFRIENDLY FRIENDLY ON THE OTHER SIDE OF A DYING PLANET. THANK GOD THEY SCRAPPED THOSE CUP REPLAYS, EH?

THERE WERE A COUPLE OF SURPRISES THIS SEASON. ASTON VILLA CRACKED THE TOP FOUR AND THE BLUE, BILLION-POUND BANTZ LORDS WHO FINISHED 12TH LAST YEAR QUALIFIED FOR EUROPE TOO. ON THAT BASIS, YOU'D ASSUME POCH'S JOB WOULD BE SAFE, BUT THAT'S NOT THE CHELSEA WAY. JUST HOW BADLY DID LAST WEEK'S DINNER WITH TACTICS TODD GO?

HOWEVER, THE SEASON'S FINAL WORD BELONGS TO A TRUE LEGEND, THE ADVANCE WARNING OF WHOSE DEPARTURE DID LITTLE TO LESSEN THE EMOTIONAL IMPACT; A MAN WHOSE LEGACY STRETCHES BEYOND FOOTBALL, EARNING THE BEGRUDGING RESPECT OF THE NON-RED HALF OF THE RIVER CITY WHERE HIS FACE BEAMS DOWN FROM MURALS. THE BATTLES NOW OVER, PERHAPS THE OLD WARRIOR ALLOWED HIMSELF ONE LAST SOLITARY STROLL ON TO THE PITCH THAT HOSTED THOSE FAMOUS EUROPEAN NIGHTS, AND IN THE SILENCE OF THE OLD STADIUM CONTEMPLATED ALL HE HAD ACHIEVED...

IT WAS A MEETING WHERE THE OUTCOME SEEMED SO OBVIOUS IT COULD HAVE JUST BEEN DONE OVER ZOOM, BUT WE ALL KNOW HOW SIR JIM FEELS ABOUT THAT KIND OF THING, SO EVERYONE TRAIPSED DOWN TO LONDON FOR ANOTHER ROUTINE WIN FOR MANCHESTER CITY AGAINST MANCHESTER UNITED. HOWEVER, ERIK TEN HAG IS A GRADUATE OF THE EXALTED AJAX SCHOOL AND ITS TEACHINGS (WIN THE FA CUP FOR UNITED, THEN GET DE SACK) AND MASTERMINDED A FAMOUS VICTORY FOR THE LEAST LIKELY OF UNDERDOGS. WHAT HAPPENED?

I won.

Also, Jimbo wants to know why you're not in the office.

TACTICALLY, TEN HAG GOT IT SPOT ON. THE FAMOUS MIDFIELD DOUGHNUT FORMATION TIGHTENED, THE DEFENCE SOMEHOW LOOKED MORE SOLID *WITHOUT* CASEMIRO (!), AND THEIR ATTACKING PLAY WAS SO FLUID THAT EVEN JOSKO GVARDIOL WAS BRIEFLY INSPIRED TO JOIN IN. TEN HAG HAS BEEN CRITICISED FOR SOME OF HIS SIGNINGS, BUT SOFYAN AMRABAT HAD HIS BEST GAME IN A UNITED SHIRT AND ANTONY WAS USED SUPERBLY.

AS PEP LAUNCHED THE INQUEST INTO WHEN SOMETHING WOULD FINALLY GO RIGHT FOR CITY...

Why didn't you stop the game when you saw I wasn't wearing my enchanted cardie of inordinate expense and magic?!

JIM RATCLIFFE POURED PETRO-CHEMICAL PRODUCTS ON TO THE FLAMES OF SPECULATION ABOUT TEN HAG'S FUTURE BY NOT MENTIONING HIM DIRECTLY IN HIS POST-MATCH CONGRATULATIONS.

... Fred the Red ... Rock of Gibraltar... The Carriage and Wagon Department at the Lancashire and Yorkshire Rail Depot at Newton Heath... and of course... The Head of Football Operations!

TEN HAG ACQUITTED HIMSELF ADMIRABLY WHEN ASKED ABOUT HIS JOB AFTER THE GAME, BUT IT MADE FOR AWKWARD VIEWING, LIKE WATCHING A CONDEMNED MAN IN THE TOWER FORCED TO CONTEMPLATE HIS FUTURE — A VIBE ACCENTUATED BY THE PRESENCE OF ROYALTY.

Mr Bean. Funny.

STILL, TEN HAG IS DUTCH AND THEREFORE FAMILIAR WITH BRUTALLY TOUGH INTERVIEWS. REMEMBER THAT ONE JORDAN HENDERSON DID THE OTHER WEEK? HOO BOY.

Do you feel you're a disappointment? Like, on a *molecular* level? HEY! Don't look at them. They can't help you now. It's just you and me, "Hendo"...

WITH CALLOUS DISREGARD FOR CARTOONISTS' PRINT DEADLINES, THE UNITED HIERARCHY ARE YET TO ANNOUNCE THEIR DECISION, BUT SEVERAL CANDIDATES HAVE BEEN LINKED TO TEN HAG'S JOB. THE LATEST IS ROBERTO DE ZERBI, WHO ALREADY GOT UNITED WINNING IN HIS LAST GAME AS BRIGHTON BOSS! OTHER CONTENDERS INCLUDE THE WIDELY-COURTED KIERAN MCKENNA...

It's an invitation to Sir Dave Brailsford's leadership symposium brunch, with guest keynote thought leader, Sir Dave Brailsford.

MAURICIO "POCH" POCHETTINO — CLEARLAKE CAPITAL FC'S OUTGOING SANITATION COMMISSIONER...

It's so gratifying to leave you wallowing in the mess you've made. You're screwed. Thank you. Bye.

AND THOMAS TUCHEL, WHOSE REPUTATION FOR 'MANAGING UP' WOULD BE EMBRACED WARMLY BY THE INEOS LADS...

A leadership symposium brunch without tapioca pancakes with caramelised pear? What sick stunt are you trying to pull here, Brailsford?!

GARETH SOUTHGATE WAS LINKED, BUT IT'S DOUBTFUL HE'S COOL AND RELEVANT ENOUGH FOR A CLUB THAT STEPPED OUT AT WEMBLEY WEARING PRESENTATION JACKETS THAT REFERENCED *THE STONE ROSES* — A BAND EVEN JONNY EVANS MIGHT BE TOO YOUNG TO REMEMBER. HOWEVER, IT'S HARD TO THINK OF AN ENVIRONMENT BETTER SUITED TO SOUTHGATE'S AQUA PARK GOOD TIME VIBES...

IN A TIME WHEN BAYERN MUNICH SWOOP FOR THE MANAGER WHO LED BURNLEY TO 19TH, ANYTHING'S POSSIBLE: MOYES 2.0, MOURINHO (*PLEASE GOD*), EVEN THE NUCLEAR KLOPPTION. MAYBE THEY WILL EVEN GO ROGUE AND HIRE A RELATIVE UNKNOWN WHO'S RECENTLY CAUSED A HUGE SHOCK, BEFORE HE INEVITABLY KNOCKS UNITED OUT OF THE EUROPA LEAGUE WITH, SAY, SEVILLA, IN A COUPLE OF YEARS' TIME.

They say he doesn't wear socks, Sir Jim.

Oh come on! A Breaking Bad reference? In 2024?! Seriously!

INEOS

MEN'S EUROS 2024:
THE (S)PAIN BARRIER

Euphemistically, Euro 2024 was described as a tournament of 'moments', rather than one of 'entertainment'. While this wasn't always great for viewers, it was tremendously helpful for TV editors, who only had to decide which Coldplay song to choose for their end-of-tournament montages.

The clear star of the competition was Own Goal, who secured the Golden Boot with ten strikes, single-handedly reviving the dormant football-gaffe DVD market. However, the long-term effects of the relentlessly congested football calendar were evident in the performances of some of Europe's other big names. Harry Kane, for example, played like he was experiencing a month-long stress migraine. Kylian Mbappé also endured a difficult Euro, suffering a broken nose in France's opener against Red Bull Austria and being forced to wear a vision-restricting protective mask. On the bright side, this meant he was able to see less of Didier Deschamps' France, because *mon Dieu*.

By contrast, Cristiano Ronaldo enjoyed a superb tournament, consistently being the most trending topic on multiple social media platforms whenever Portugal played. A natural leader, his performances exuded the energy of the PE teacher in *Kes*. Time and again, he resisted the calls of his better-placed subordinates, selflessly shooting from all angles to ensure as many spectators as possible were able to take home a match ball as a priceless souvenir. I must confess, I wept with him when Slovenia's Jan Oblak saved his penalty in extra time of their second-round tie, because I knew I wouldn't be able to draw anything as funny.

In a lovely nod to Italia 90 nostalgists, England didn't play well until the semi-final. Despite getting worse with every game, they muddled through. Their status as the most baffling team of the tournament was confirmed with a flawless penalty shoot-out win against Switzerland. *What was happening?*

Gareth Southgate placed his trust in his players to make the most of their individual talents when it mattered, and his greatest success as England manager was to remove the sense of fear associated with playing for the national side (apart from after the team score a goal). When they weren't doomsday-prepping in their own penalty area, the England lads provided plenty of content for the highlights package: Jude Bellingham's match-saving overhead kick against Slovakia; Bukayo Saka's curling finish to neutralise Switzerland; Ollie Watkins's touch and finish to avenge Graham Taylor in the semi-final against the Netherlands; Lewis Dunk building a LEGO Hogwarts castle at the training base; and Cole Palmer's equaliser in the final, which cut across the Berlin turf with the precision of a barber's scissors gliding across his weird fringe.

For all the criticism of their performances, it is established knowledge that teams don't lift international trophies by winning every game and playing brilliantly throughout, which made it extra awkward when Spain did exactly that. Coach Luis de la Fuente – a man who emphatically doesn't look like a laugh – hit upon a novel winning formula: picking a well-balanced team of skilled players, all operating in their best positions. Literal child sensation Lamine Yamal lit up Europe, delivering the goal of the tournament and the existential gift of making us all ponder what we've done with our lives. Yes, at seventeen years old he has talent, wealth and stardom, but is he on the path to barely scraping through Sociology *and* History A levels from Swindon's second-most highly regarded sixth-form college? I somehow doubt it.

The final was to be Southgate's swansong, and his resignation a couple of days later heralded a brief ceasefire in the culture war that's raged in group chats since his appointment in 2016. I'm writing this a week afterwards, and I still haven't found a way of replying diplomatically to the WhatsApp message from a loved one clamouring for Frank Lampard to get the job.

If it was an exhausting tournament for the players, spare a thought for our brave and tireless cartoonists, mining the tournament for precious comedy gems. The whole internet scrapping over the same content sends you into strange areas in an attempt for originality, which is why one of the following strips contains a lengthy bit about an advertising board for 'The No1 NEV maker'. The harsh nature of international football cartooning means that Anthony Gordon falling off his bike gets two references, while the superb attacking football Georgia served up doesn't even get one.

RIGHT, THERE'S A LOT TO GET THROUGH, SO LET'S GET STRAIGHT DOWN TO—
*BLOODY HELL, ALBANIA HAVE SCORED AGAINST ITALY! THAT'S THROWN
A FRANKFURTER IN THEIR CARBONARA*, THIS COULD BE ONE OF THE
ALL-TIME SHOCKS, OH WAIT, ITALY ARE WINNING 2-1. IT WORKED OUT FINE
FOR THE HOLDERS, BUT IT WOULDN'T BE THE ONLY FRIGHT LUCIANO SPALLETTI
WOULD EXPERIENCE ON THE OPENING WEEKEND OF EURO 2024...

Now to enjoy Poland versus
WHAT THE HELL?!

How did they clone me?
And why am I dressed like
John McCririck?!

MICHAL PROBIERZ POL

NO PARTY CAN GET STARTED WITHOUT ENGLAND, AND THEIR 1-0 WIN
AGAINST SERBIA EXCITED DOOMERS AND FANTASISTS ALIKE. JUDE
BELLINGHAM WAS ENGLAND'S STAR PERFORMER AND A THEME OF THE
EARLY GAMES HAS BEEN THE IMPRESSIVE DISPLAYS BY PLAYERS YOUNGER THAN
SOME ITEMS OF YOUR UNDERWEAR. JAMAL MUSIALA SHONE FOR GERMANY,
THAT LITTLE LAD N'GOLO KANTÉ BOSSED IT FOR FRANCE, AND SPAIN'S ACTUAL
CHILD STARLET LAMINE YAMAL SEEMED DETERMINED TO RUIN SOME OLD
BLOKES' SATURDAY FOOTBALL BY RUNNING ABOUT.

He looks
keen.

Oh this is
all we
need!

I really wish
I hadn't had
that second
currywurst
on the
train.

AS A TRIBUTE TO BELLINGHAM, ENGLAND'S SECOND-HALF PERFORMANCE WAS
AS RAGGED AS HIS HOL(E)Y SOCKS. MUCH DEBATE CENTRED ON TRENT
ALEXANDER-ARNOLD'S MIDFIELD ROLE, WHICH HE'S HAVING TO LEARN ON
THE JOB WHILE WATCHING YOUTUBE VIDEOS. IT MAY SEEM ODD TO TEST
THIS OUT **NOW**, BUT GARETH SOUTHGATE HAS FAITH HE'S UP TO
THE TASK...

I've seen the evidence Trent can
provide a defensive shield, Dutch.

What evidence?

That fashion shoot he did when
he dressed like a nightclub
bouncer.

Oh.

THE BENCHMARK FOR
EXPECTATION MANAGEMENT
WAS SET BY SCOTLAND
AGAINST GERMANY IN THE
OPENING GAME, WHICH
THEY EXPERTLY KEPT TO
0-0 (SHOTS, SHOTS ON TARGET).
THERE WERE SOME
POSITIVES TO TAKE FROM
THE 5-1 DEFEAT: THAT KID
GETTING HIS HAIR RUFFLED
AFTER SWEARING ON SKY
NEWS; THAT FAN FLASHING
HIS MATE'S MANNSCHAFT
ON GERMAN TV; AND THEY'LL
ALWAYS HAVE ROBERTSON
AND TIERNEY WINNING
THAT GOAL-KICK OFF
MUSIALA EARLY DOORS.

GOOAAL (KICK)
03:19

I haven't felt this good
since we left to definitely
win the World Cup in 1978.

HUNGARY DISAPPOINTED IN THEIR
DEFEAT TO SWITZERLAND BUT
MAY PRESENT MORE OF A
CHALLENGE TO GERMANY,
ESPECIALLY IF MARTIN ÁDÁM CAN
GET SOMEONE TO COVER HIS SHIFT
AT THE MICROBREWERY.

Classic
DARK
HORSE

AS ALWAYS, PLAYERS WILL BE
TRYING TO CATCH THE EYE FOR BIG,
POST-TOURNAMENT MOVES,
INCLUDING THE SCORER OF THE
NETHERLANDS' WINNER AGAINST
POLAND: WOUT WEGHORST!

Ashworth, put
those secateurs down,
I've just found our
new no 9...

FRANCE'S HARD-FOUGHT
1-0 WIN AGAINST AUSTRIA
COULD COME AT A COST
TO BOTH TEAMS...

I like the thrust of
this Austrian lot. Put me
in touch with that coach
of theirs, will you?

This
frikkin'
place, man...

KYLIAN MBAPPÉ MAY FACE A SPELL ON
THE SIDELINES AFTER A COLLISION
THAT LEFT HIS BUSTED NOSE
FOLLOWING THE EXACT CURVATURE
OF HIS SECOND-HALF MISS.

AIE!

SLOVAKIA PRODUCED A
SURPRISE RESULT FOR ANYONE
UNFAMILIAR WITH THE
INTERNATIONAL FOOTBALL TEAM
OF BELGIUM. THE RED DEVILS'
EXPLORATION OF NEW AREAS
OF BANTZ EVEN INCLUDED
TECHNOLOGY FROM OTHER SPORTS,
WITH SNICKO RULING OUT
ROMELU LUKAKU'S LATE
EQUALISER FOR A HANDBALL
IN THE BUILDUP. BELGIUM'S
CHANGE KIT FOR EURO '24 IS
FAMOUSLY MODELLED ON
TINTIN'S OUTFIT—MAYBE HE
SHOULD BE DIRECTLY
ENGAGED TO DISCOVER THE
SOURCE OF LUKAKU'S APPARENT
JINX AT INTERNATIONAL
TOURNAMENTS...

Cursed Golden Glove of chippy,
spurned goalkeeper...
I wish to make all the
football headlines!

Mystery
solved.

THIBAUT
COURTOIS

THERE WAS A GREAT MOMENT FOR THE
ROMANTICS TOO, WITH CHRISTIAN
ERIKSEN SCORING FOR DENMARK,
THREE YEARS AFTER SUFFERING A
CARDIAC ARREST AT THE LAST
EUROS FINALS.

Does he?!

No, I don't know if it's too
late to plant agapanthus!

HOWEVER, UKRAINE WERE
EMPHATICALLY DENIED AN
EMOTIONAL VICTORY BY
ROMANIA, WHOSE THEFT OF
THE NARRATIVE APPEARS TO
HAVE SET OFF AT LEAST ONE
DYE PACK.

DON'T COME HOME TOO S—
OH, YOU'RE BACK, YOUR TEA'S STILL WARM. YES, SCOTLAND ARE OUT OF THE EUROS, ELIMINATED BY A LATE HUNGARY GOAL WHEN THEY WERE JUST SECONDS AWAY FROM THE PROMISED LAND OF WAITING A FEW MORE DAYS TO DISCOVER TWO POINTS WOULDN'T HAVE BEEN ENOUGH TO SEND THEM THROUGH ANYWAY. STEVE CLARKE WAS PARTICULARLY AGGRIEVED THAT THE REFEREE FROM *ARGENTINA* HADN'T AWARDED HIS SIDE A PENALTY. HONESTLY, YOU SPEND 38 YEARS CELEBRATING DIEGO MARADONA AND *THIS* IS HOW THEY REPAY YOU ?!

EARLY EVIDENCE SUGGESTS ENGLAND ARE ALSO IN GERMANY FOR A ~~GOOD~~ TIME, NOT FOR A LONG TIME, AS THEY ENJOY THEIR TRADITIONAL GROUP STAGE EXISTENTIAL CRISIS. AT LEAST WE'VE PROBABLY SEEN THE LAST OF *THE ALEXANDER-ARNOLD EXPERIMENT*, WHICH SOUNDS LIKE A PROG ROCK GROUP IN WHICH THE BASSIST IS GIVEN RESPONSIBILITY FOR A COMPLEX 90-MINUTE MOOG SOLO WITH LITTLE TIME TO PREPARE.

ENGLAND'S PLAYERS HAVE BEEN SURPRISED BY THE CRITICISM OF THEIR PERFORMANCES, PERHAPS UNDER THE ILLUSION NONE OF US HAD SEEN THEM. THE LATEST TO FACE THE MEDIA WAS THE BRONZE STATUE OF HARRY KANE, WHO HAS BEEN RELEASED FROM THE BROOM CUPBOARD AT WALTHAM FOREST COUNCIL TO LEAD THE FRONT LINE, MAKING YOU WONDER HOW BAVARIA'S REAL FAVOURITE SON IS SPENDING HIS SUMMER.

NO MATTER WHAT ELSE HAPPENS AT EURO '24, NOTHING WILL MATCH THE SHOCK OF SEEING CRISTIANO RONALDO PASS TO BRUNO FERNANDES WITH THE GOAL AT HIS MERCY AGAINST TURKEY.

THAT'S UNTIL YOU REALISE IT MEANT HE CLAIMED THE ALL-TIME RECORD FOR THE MOST ASSISTS AT THE EUROS, LEAVING YOU TO WONDER WHAT OTHER ACHIEVEMENTS HE HAS IN HIS SIGHTS...

THE GAME ALSO WITNESSED SEVERAL PITCH INVASIONS FROM CHILDREN OF ALL AGES, KEEN TO HAVE THEIR PHOTO TAKEN IN THE AURA OF THE INFLUENCER-AMBASSADOR OF SAUDI ARABIA, WESTFALENSTADION TRANSFORMED INTO THE PHYSICAL EMBODIMENT OF THE MOST VAPID SECTION OF TWITTER FOR THE AFTERNOON.

ITALY ARE THROUGH TO THE NEXT ROUND BY THE SKIN OF A MOZZARELLA BALL AFTER A LAST-GASP MATTIA ZACCAGNI EQUALISER AGAINST CROATIA. THE AZZURRI SEEMED DOOMED WHEN THEY FELL BEHIND TO A LUKA MODRIC GOAL, MOMENTS AFTER THE HEROIC GIANLUIGI DONNARUMMA HAD SAVED HIS PENALTY AND PULLED OFF ANOTHER VITAL SAVE...

IT WAS A CRUEL END FOR MODRIC, WHOSE GOAL MADE HIM THE OLDEST PLAYER TO SCORE IN A EUROS FINALS MATCH, TO THE ASTONISHMENT OF VIEWERS EVERYWHERE...

ALL THAT REMAINED WAS FOR THE OBLIGATORY HOLLOW-EYED PHOTOGRAPH WITH THE PLAYER OF THE MATCH AWARD, ONE OF THE GREAT ADDITIONS TO RECENT INTERNATIONAL TOURNAMENTS. BUT IF THERE'S ONE THING WE KNOW ABOUT MODRIC, IT'S THAT HE NEVER GIVES UP, AND CROATIA COULD YET PROGRESS IF OTHER RESULTS GO THEIR WAY. IT AIN'T OVER TILL THE OOMPAH BAND PARPS, LUKA !

AS BANTZ GOES, IT HAD A SPECTACULAR SIDE BENEFIT — JUDE BELLINGHAM SCORING A 95TH-MINUTE EQUALISER AGAINST SLOVAKIA, WITH ENGLAND'S FIRST SHOT ON TARGET, WHILE MAKING REFERENCE TO ANTHONY GORDON'S ELECTRIC BICYCLE ACCIDENT.

Why me?!

Who else?!

We're truly honking!

THE FANS HAD BEEN DRIFTING AWAY, THE SCAPEGOATS BEING CHOSEN (*THOSE WOKE COLLARS!*) AND SOMEWHERE, GRAHAM POTTER WAS BROWSING THE M&S WEBSITE FOR CLASSIC SUMMER KNITS. BUT NOW, THE CRITICS HAD BEEN *COMPREHENSIVELY SILENCED!* EVEN BETTER WAS TO FOLLOW WITH A WINNING GOAL IN THE FIRST MINUTE OF EXTRA-TIME FROM THE CAPTAIN (TOM-ESQUE) HARRY KANE, WHO, LIKE THE REST OF THE TEAM, IS PLAYING LIKE HE'S CARRYING A LOT ON HIS SHOULDERS...

THIS WAS SUPPOSED TO BE **THE EASY SIDE OF THE DRAW** (AS EVIDENCED BY ENGLAND'S PRESENCE IN IT), BUT FRANCESCO CALZONA'S TEAM REFUSED TO FOLD AND WERE SECONDS AWAY FROM PULLING OFF THE LEAST SHOCKING SHOCK OF THE TOURNAMENT. HOWEVER, ENGLAND MADE IT THROUGH, AND IF THEY MAINTAIN THIS LEVEL OF PERFORMANCE, THEIR PATH BECOMES CLEAR...

DÜSSELDORF

BIRMINGHAM AIRPORT

Arrivals

A NICE HOLIDAY

What level of travel insurance should I get for a staycation?

IT WAS A ROUGH FEW MINUTES FOR SLOVAKIA, BUT NOTHING COMPARED TO THOSE ENCOUNTERED BY DENMARK'S JOACHIM ANDERSEN AGAINST GERMANY. THANKFULLY, THE USE OF TECHNOLOGY THAT HAS SO ENHANCED THE FOOTBALL EXPERIENCE ALLOWS US TO TRACK HIS EMOTIONS.

I'VE SCORED! WE'RE GOING TO DO IT! SPIRIT OF '92! I'LL GET MY OWN LEGO FIGURE FOR THIS!

DON'T THINK ANYONE NOTICED.

UH-OH, THAT BRUSHED MY FINGERS.

NOPE, THEY SAW NOTHING ESCAPES THE EAGLE EYE OF *STUART ATTWELL!*

HOORAY FOR THE RULES BEING EFFICIENTLY APPLIED! GOOD PROCESS, GUYS. OH, AND A BOOKING TOO! *THANK YOU, MR OLIVER!*

OH, DELANEY WAS A CUTICLE OFFSIDE. NICE ONE, SASQUATCH.

HAVERTZ SCORES THE PENALTY.

FRANCE'S 1-0 WIN AGAINST BELGIUM WAS SO BORING YOU WOULD HAVE FORGIVEN KYLIAN MBAPPÉ IF HE'D DRAWN EYES ON HIS MASK.

ZZZZZZZ

GIVEN THE POLITICAL SITUATION IN FRANCE, PERHAPS IT WOULD BE FOR THE BEST IF THEIR TALENTED MULTICULTURAL TEAM REFOUND THEIR MOJO AND WON THE TOURNAMENT, THE ARC DE TRIOMPHE AGAIN ILLUMINATED WITH THE IMAGE OF ONE OF THEIR HEROES...

VERTONGHEN'S KNEE

ALL OF THIS WAS A MERE WARM UP FOR THE MAIN EVENT OF **THE RON SHOW** VERSUS MISCELLANEA. IN AN ACT OF SOLIDARITY WITH ENGLAND, PORTUGAL DREW A BLANK AGAINST SLOVENIA, DESPITE BEING LED BY AN INFLUENCER WHOSE ACT NOW SEEMS TO MOSTLY CONSIST OF HOWLING AT THE SKY — I SHOW LITTLE SPEED. HIS SELECTION OF SHOTS, HEADERS AND FREE-KICKS MAY HAVE SEEMED INEFFECTIVE, UNTIL YOU LOOKED AT THE BIGGER PICTURE:

Mr Ronaldo, what do you think about letting someone else have a turn...?

What?

RON

Nothing, nothing...

RONALDO

7

Yeah, that's what I thought.

I tried...!

RONALDO WASN'T THE ONLY ONE WITH TEARS ROLLING DOWN HIS FACE WHEN JAN OBLAK SAVED HIS EXTRA-TIME PENALTY — IT WAS OBJECTIVELY HILARIOUS. ALTHOUGH DEFENSIVELY SUPERB, SLOVENIA'S PROFLIGACY IN FRONT OF GOAL LED YOU TO SUSPECT THEY'D SOMEHOW CONTRIVE TO BE OFFSIDE DURING THE PENALTY SHOOTOUT, BUT ULTIMATELY THEY WERE DENIED BY THE SHEER WILL OF ONE MAN, AND TODAY WE SPELL REDEMPTION R-O-N.

⚽ EURO CURIO ⚽ DIOGO COSTA SAVED THREE PENALTIES AND A ONE-ON-ONE IN THE 115TH MINUTE BLAH, BLAH, BLAH.

LIKE THE FOOTBALL EQUIVALENT OF HOMER SIMPSON'S MISSHAPEN BARBECUE PIT CREATING A BUZZ IN THE SPRINGFIELD ART SCENE, GARETH SOUTHGATE'S WEIRD AND WONKY ENGLAND TEAM ARE THROUGH TO THE LAST FOUR OF EUROPE'S PREMIER COMPETITION, AFTER A PERFORMANCE PIECE AGAINST SWITZERLAND THAT LEFT THE BBC'S CULTURE PUNDITS DROOLING...

HAVING SEEN THE BEEB'S ELECTION COVERAGE, IT WAS AT LEAST A RELIEF THEY STUCK WITH THE MAIN STORY, RATHER THAN CUTTING AWAY TO FOOTAGE OF THE NEWLY-ELECTED NIGHTMARE FOR CLACTON.

ALTHOUGH IT MIGHT HAVE BEEN FUN TO HAVE SEEN HIS REAL-TIME REACTION TO THE NEWS HE'S ACTUALLY EXPECTED TO GO BACK TO CLACTON OCCASIONALLY.

ENGLAND PROGRESSED DESPITE BEING SECOND-BEST FOR LONG PERIODS. SWISS COACH MURAT YAKIN MAY VAGUELY RESEMBLE A CHARACTER FROM THE MARVEL CINEMATIC UNIVERSE, BUT ON THE DAY HE WAS NO MATCH FOR THE SURREAL SPONTANEITY OF CAPTAIN CAUTIOUS.

FOR ALL HIS FLAWS, SOUTHGATE HAS CHANGED THE ENGLAND MINDSET AND KNOWS HOW TO INSPIRE HIS PLAYERS, AS SHOWN IN A FLAWLESS, HISTORY-DEFYING PENALTY SHOOTOUT.

JORDAN PICKFORD CRUCIALLY SAVED THE SPOT-KICK OF MANUEL AKANJI, WHO MAY HAVE BEEN TIRED FROM CARRYING HARRY KANE IN HIS POCKET ALL EVENING AND SPORTINGLY PROVIDING GARETH WITH SOME FREE TACTICAL ADVICE.

IVAN TONEY DIDN'T EVEN LOOK AT THE BALL AS HE STUCK HIS AWAY. TO PUT HIS SKILL INTO PERSPECTIVE, HERE'S WHAT HAPPENS WHEN YOU TRY TO DEPICT THE MOMENT WITHOUT LOOKING AT THE PEN:

AND BUKAYO SAKA. WOW. AFTER WHAT HE ENDURED IN 2021, EVERYONE IN THE DÜSSELDORF ARENA BREATHED A SIGH OF RELIEF AS HE CALMLY FOUND THE NET.

PLAYERS FROM BOTH SIDES WERE QUICK TO CONSOLE AKANJI, AS WAS THE CASE THE PREVIOUS EVENING WHEN PORTUGAL LOST ON PENALTIES TO FRANCE - THE UNFORTUNATE JOÃO FÉLIX SURROUNDED BY HIS TEAM, CRISTIANO RONALDO BY HIS...

THE QUARTER-FINALS LEFT YOU FEELING LIKE NOTHING COULD STOP ENGLAND AND FRANCE FROM BORING THEIR WAY TO THE CENTRE OF THE TOURNAMENT WALL CHART, LIKE IT'S THE CHANNEL TUNNEL EXCAVATION...

PERHAPS FRANCE WOULD HAVE BEEN LIVELIER IF KYLIAN MBAPPÉ WASN'T BEING CALLED UPON TO AVERT ANOTHER NATIONAL CRISIS.

HAVING ENDED THE PENALTY CURSE FOREVER, ENGLAND NOW HAVE A CHANCE TO EXACT SOME REVENGE ON RONALD KOEMAN FOR ROTTERDAM '93:

JOHN STONES GETS AWAY WITH FOULING MEMPHIS DEPAY'S HEADBAND WHEN THROUGH ON GOAL...

...THEN FLICKS A FREE-KICK INTO THE TOP CORNER.

DOES HE NIET LEUK THAT.

HELLO DARKNESS, MY OLD FRIEND. IT'S NOT COMING HOME AGAIN.

BECAUSE A KNOWLEDGE SLOWLY CREEPING: TONIGHT WE'LL SEE NO ROSS KEMP SHRIEKING. AND THE VISION THAT WAS PLANTED IN MY BRAIN, STILL REMAINS: THE ANAL FLARES ... ARE SILENCED.

IN EXHAUSTION THE PLAYERS WERE MIRED...

WHICH NO DOUBT MEANS LEAGUE TWO SHOULD BE RETIRED...

IT WAS WORSE THAN ED SHEERAN PLAYING HIS GUITAR FOR THE BOYS. THE OUTSIDE NOISE.

AND IN THE BERLIN NIGHT WE SAW, TEN THOUSAND ENGLAND FANS OR MORE, PEOPLE SUDDENLY BELIEVING:

BUT IT ALL PROVIDES CONTENT FOR THE BEEB'S NEXT MONTAGE REEL. RIGHT IN THE FEELS.

AT LEAST THEY DEFIED THEIR XG, WITH AN ALL-BANGERS POLICY...

THOUGH THEIR TROPHY COUNT IS STUCK ON ONE, WE'LL ALWAYS HAVE THAT MANIC JOHN STONES RUN...

...BUT THE ENDING RUINED THE START OF THE KILLERS' SET, AN ENTRANCE MET... WITH SILENCE.

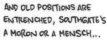

AND OLD POSITIONS ARE ENTRENCHED, SOUTHGATE'S A MORON OR A MENSCH...

IT WILL ALL BE BETTER ONCE THE NEXT GUY GETS THE CALL, HAIL POTTERBALL...

AS GARETH SOUTHGATE CLEANS OUT HIS OFFICE AT ST GEORGE'S PARK, HE'S ASSISTED AS EVER BY STEVE HOLLAND...

Hah, remember this, Dutch?

Ah, great days. I've found where we left Loftus-Cheek too!

Sigh... Euro 2020... That was the one that got away, Steve. We did OK overall though, didn't we?

My G, which other manager of the England men's team came so close to three cups?!

Hmm...

We beat Spain when it counted, in the Nations League, and gave the fans a team to be proud of. More importantly, you changed the culture. You made people want to play for England again... Apart from Ben White, the recalcitrant, caramel spray-tanned...

Breathe.

PUFF

AAA

I just wanted to treat people with respect and dignity. It shows how far we've fallen as a society when that was regarded by some as a radical Marxist position...

How am I doing, Boss?

TEN GERMAN SOCIOLOGISTS

You might have had more control of the means of production if Stones didn't keep rolling it back to Pickford to leather upfield, son.

Just think, none of this may have happened if Big Sam hadn't got a bit loose-lipped in that sting operation...

Oh, go on then...

Ahem. Anyway... keep or shred?

HOW TO BEAT THE PENALTY CURSE

Oh, keep. The next guy might need that. Who do you think they'll go for?

Hmm. Luis de la Carsley knows where the teabags are kept, but Lampard's shown an aptitude for failing up. It's hard to resist the tractor beam of Howe and Tindall, but Newcastle's owners have issued a hands-off warning.

Are you doing a bit?!

Yeah.

What'll you do until you inevitably come back to haunt England with eg Belgium?

Oh there's probably a role in the cabinet as a Vibes Tsar, and there's always the LinkedIn, CEO-mindset, after-pickleball, motivational circuit. This being football, the obvious choice would be to break everyone's heart by joining Al-Nassr, but I think maybe I'll dip my toe into the old Podcast Wars...

the Outside Noise
WITH GARETH SOUTHGATE

There's no denying it, this week's Match of the Day was shi !

THE Outside Noise

Come on, let's get out of here, old friend. There's a lovely old English oak tree that reminds me of Harry's performances in Germany that I want to take one last look at.

We did stink in the group stage, though, eh boss?

Mate, until the semis I thought it was the drains!

Oh come on...

OBITUARIES AND TRIBUTES

These are always the cartoons that give me the most stress. The fear of getting the tone wrong can be almost debilitating – the most important factor in a person's death obviously being how the internet reacts to my cartoon about them. How do you condense a life into a few small drawings? People are complex, weird, contradictory, especially those who spent most of their life in the public eye – imagine what being Pelé would do to your head. I strive to avoid mawkishness (not always successfully) and to think about what the subject of the cartoon meant to me personally or the people's lives they touched. Often, I'll try to keep text to a minimum, to avoid repeating well-trodden facts or stories people will have already read in obituaries.

One example would be the cartoon in this section paying tribute to Bobby Charlton, whose story was the most remarkable in English football history. For someone to survive a plane crash that claimed the lives of so many friends and colleagues, and recover to not only play football again, but become the best in the world, is beyond the comprehension of someone who has barely left the house for a year after being bitten by a dog.

Charlton's death in October 2023 resulted in so much great writing about his life and career. I couldn't match that, so I decided to use his own words, set against a series of drawings depicting memories from his life, interspersed with images from the Munich air disaster. The thickening snowfall also provided a visual metaphor for a mind gradually and cruelly clouded by dementia, until the picture finally fills white as his story reaches its end.

A few months after its publication, I organised to have a few copies of the cartoon printed. I sent the file to my local printer, and a few days later, I received a phone call: 'You've sent us this cartoon, but you've left the last square blank by mistake.' So much for poignancy.

Some of the tribute cartoons are more personal. Alan McLoughlin was a player who meant a lot to me as a Swindon Town fan, having met him at the start of both our footballing careers, his arguably more successful than my own, which remained firmly imaginary.

Pete Aitken became a friend over many years of attending Sydney FC matches. We enjoyed some great nights, and many more mundane ones (it's rarely mentioned how routinely unmemorable most football matches are). Despite being roughly thirty years our senior, Pete drank our little group under the table on more than one occasion. He'd pretty much quit alcohol by the time he got sick, and was a much calmer presence for it, but was never afraid to call someone out if they were acting a tit in our seating bay. He loved a laugh, loved a chat, loved breaking my balls about Brexit – something I never thought I'd miss, but here we are.

WHERE TO START?

AS YOU'LL KNOW BY NOW, FIVE PEOPLE LOST THEIR LIVES IN A HELICOPTER CRASH OUTSIDE LEICESTER'S KING POWER STADIUM ON SATURDAY EVENING. AMONG THE DEAD WAS LEICESTER'S OWNER, VICHAI SRIVADDHANAPRABHA.

VICHAI BOUGHT LEICESTER FOR £39M IN 2010, AND WHEN THEY WERE PROMOTED TO THE PREMIER LEAGUE IN 2014, HE SPOKE OF FINISHING IN THE TOP FIVE WITHIN THREE SEASONS. FRANKLY, THIS WAS AS OUTLANDISH AS SAYING, WELL...

Leicester will finish in the top five within three seasons!

Are you an ostrich?

AS WELL AS UNDERSTANDING THE IMPORTANCE OF FANS TO A FOOTBALL CLUB, AND ITS PLACE IN THE CORE OF A COMMUNITY, HE ALSO ENJOYED STRONG RELATIONSHIPS WITH MANY OF LEICESTER'S PLAYERS. DURING THAT AMAZING TITLE SEASON, HE EVEN FLEW IN BUDDHIST MONKS TO HELP OUT.

Three things cannot be long hidden: the sun, the moon, and the truth.

Whoaaaa... Danny Drinkwater's always saying that.

I am, yeah.

...TO BIG ONES, LIKE DONATING MILLIONS TO A LOCAL CHILDREN'S HOSPITAL.

HIS DONATIONS EVEN HELPED TO FUND THE REBURIAL OF RICHARD III.

He wanted a cast like Vardy's.

We get this a lot.

Chat quit, fix arm.

u wot.

UNLIKE MANY OWNERS, VICHAI SEEMED TO BE MOTIVATED BY A GENUINE LOVE OF FOOTBALL. HE WASN'T AT LEICESTER TO SIPHON PROFIT OR STRIP ASSETS. NOR WAS HE THERE TO MARKET AN OPPRESSIVE REGIME OR TRAMPLE ON THE CLUB'S HERITAGE. IN FACT, HE WAS QUITE DIFFERENT FROM THE KIND OF WRONG 'UN WHO USUALLY TURNS UP AT YOUR FAVOURITE TEAM.

The consortium of tripods from War of the Worlds will get us back into League One!

Yoink!

IT TURNED OUT TO BE AN UNDERSTATEMENT, AS IN 2016 THEY PRODUCED ONE OF THE BIGGEST SHOCKS IN BRITISH SPORT HISTORY BY WINNING THE FLIPPIN' PREMIER LEAGUE! IT WAS A GLORIOUSLY POSITIVE STORY IN AN OFTEN BLEAK YEAR. LOOKING BACK NOW, YOU FIND YOURSELF WONDERING IF IT EVER REALLY HAPPENED.

Mate.

I know.

FEW OF US OUTSIDE OF LEICESTER KNEW MUCH ABOUT HIM, ASIDE FROM HIS ROLE AS THE CLUB'S CHAIRMAN. BUT IN THE DAYS SINCE THE TRAGEDY, WE HAVE LEARNED OF HIS GENEROSITY AND ACTS OF PHILANTHROPY THAT EARNED HIM A PERMANENT PLACE IN THE HEARTS OF THE CITY'S RESIDENTS:

FROM SMALL GESTURES, LIKE BUYING FANS FOOD, SCARVES, DRINKS, OR SEASON TICKETS...

AS THE CLUB MOURNS, THEIR CUP TIE WITH SOUTHAMPTON HAS BEEN POSTPONED. AFTER ALL, IT'S ONLY FOOTBALL. BUT EVENTUALLY, THE GRIEVING PLAYERS WILL TAKE TO THE FIELD AGAIN AND THE FANS WILL CELEBRATE ONCE MORE; THEIR CLUB IN A FAR HEALTHIER STATE THANKS TO THE INVOLVEMENT OF VICHAI SRIVADDHANAPRABHA.

SQUIRES

ALAN McLOUGHLIN, WHO PASSED AWAY LAST WEEK, WAS MY FIRST FOOTBALL HERO...

HE'D NOT LONG JOINED SWINDON TOWN IN 1986 WHEN HE PRESENTED ME WITH A CERTIFICATE FOR THE SUCCESSFUL COMPLETION OF A HALF-TERM SOCCER SKILLS COURSE THAT WOULD HAVE TESTED EVEN THE MOST PRODIGIOUS OF TALENTS. FROM THAT MOMENT ONWARDS, HE WAS MY FAVOURITE PLAYER.

SUPER SKILLS
This is to certify that
SQUIRES
Slowly dribbled round some cones and scuffed a shot towards an empty goal

Wow.

SIGNED ON A FREE TRANSFER FROM MANCHESTER UNITED, THE KID FROM MOSS SIDE DEALT WITH THE CULTURE SHOCK OF FINDING HIMSELF IN THE BADLANDS OF NORTH WILTSHIRE, BUT THE SMALL, INDUSTRIOUS MIDFIELDER DIDN'T QUITE FIT WITH LOU MACARI'S FOOTBALL ETHOS.

'MACCA' WENT OUT ON LOAN TO TORQUAY, PLAYING IN *THAT* GAME...

... AND REMAINED ON THE FRINGES OF THE SWINDON SQUAD UNTIL OSSIE ARDILES TOOK OVER AS MANAGER IN 1989. ARDILES CHANGED THE STYLE AND PLAYED McLOUGHLIN AT THE TIP OF A MIDFIELD DIAMOND, WHERE HE SPARKLED APPROPRIATELY. NOW FREE TO EXPRESS HIMSELF, MACCA'S TRANSFORMATION WAS ASTONISHING. HE PLAYED 61 GAMES THAT SEASON, BARELY MISSING A PASS. HIS 17 GOALS INCLUDED A WINNER IN THE PLAY-OFF FINAL AGAINST SUNDERLAND; A JEWELLER'S EYEPIECE REQUIRED TO SPOT THE DEFLECTION HIS SHOT TOOK OFF GARY BENNETT.

TEN DAYS LATER, SWINDON WERE DEMOTED TWO DIVISIONS (LATER REDUCED TO ONE ON APPEAL) BY THE FOOTBALL AUTHORITIES FOR FINANCIAL SHENANIGANS. BY THEN McLOUGHLIN WAS IN ITALY WITH IRELAND'S WORLD CUP SQUAD.

Players and fans punished for the actions of individuals at board level? I've heard it all now!

THE PAIN FELT BY THE SWINDON FANS WAS SLIGHTLY LESSENED BY THE PRIDE IN ALAN MAC. ONE OF OUR LITTLE TRIBE, THERE ON THE GREATEST STAGE, BLOCKING PETER SHILTON'S VIEW OF KEVIN SHEEDY'S EQUALISER FROM AN OFFSIDE POSITION.

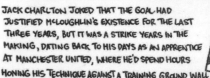

Good job I'm not the kind of bloke to bang on about this sort of thing.

IT WAS WHILE WEARING THE IRELAND SHIRT THAT McLOUGHLIN SCORED THE GOAL FOR WHICH HE'S BEST REMEMBERED: A SUPERBLY TAKEN LEFT-FOOT VOLLEY THAT CUT THROUGH A SEA OF LIMBS (MOST OF THEM SEEMINGLY ATTACHED TO NIALL QUINN) TO SECURE QUALIFICATION FOR USA '94 ON A POISONOUS NIGHT AT WINDSOR PARK.

JACK CHARLTON JOKED THAT THE GOAL HAD JUSTIFIED McLOUGHLIN'S EXISTENCE FOR THE LAST THREE YEARS, BUT IT WAS A STRIKE YEARS IN THE MAKING, DATING BACK TO HIS DAYS AS AN APPRENTICE AT MANCHESTER UNITED, WHERE HE'D SPEND HOURS HONING HIS TECHNIQUE AGAINST A TRAINING GROUND WALL.

BY THEN, McLOUGHLIN HAD JOINED PORTSMOUTH, WHERE HE WAS BUSY MAKING HIMSELF A CLUB LEGEND. IT WAS ALWAYS A BITTERSWEET MOMENT SEEING HIS NAME ON THE OPPOSITION TEAM SHEET.

Ah great, we get to see Macca play again.

We're definitely going to lose!

AFTER RETIRING FROM PLAYING, HE MOVED IN TO COACHING WITH POMPEY AND LATER BACK AT SWINDON. THE LAST WEEK HAS BEEN NOTABLE FOR THE HEARTFELT EULOGIES FROM THE YOUNG PLAYERS WHOSE LIVES HE TOUCHED.

PORTSMOUTH FC
PROFESSIONAL CONTRACT
AMC
Wow.

McLOUGHLIN WAS OF COURSE MORE THAN JUST AN EXCEPTIONAL FOOTBALLER AND BRILLIANT COACH. HE WAS A WARM, INTELLIGENT, FUNNY, BRAVE MAN WHO UNDERSTOOD THE IMPORTANCE OF A FOOTBALL CLUB TO A COMMUNITY. IT IS BECAUSE OF HIS QUALITIES AS A HUMAN THAT HIS LOSS IS FELT SO DEEPLY AMONG THE FANS OF THE CLUBS HE PLAYED FOR, AND IN THE NATION HE SO PROUDLY REPRESENTED. AS FOOTBALL HEROES GO, I COULDN'T HAVE PICKED A BETTER ONE THAN ALAN McLOUGHLIN.

USUALLY, WHEN THERE'S NEWS ABOUT STATUES IN THE WEST COUNTRY, IT'S BECAUSE A CULTURE WAR HAS ERUPTED OVER A MONUMENT TO A CONTROVERSIAL HISTORICAL FIGURE (HONESTLY, WHERE DOES IT ALL END IF WE ALLOW THE WOKE RADICAL LEFT TO DEMOLISH THE STATUE OF THE FOUNDER OF SLAVES-2-U?!). BUT SOON A STATUE WILL BE UNVEILED IN PLYMOUTH TO AN INSPIRATIONAL PERSON NO ONE CAN OBJECT TO (THEY WILL):

JACK LESLIE

LESLIE SPENT 14 SEASONS AT HOME PARK BETWEEN 1921 AND 1934, DURING WHICH TIME HE WAS ONE OF ONLY TWO BLACK PROFESSIONAL FOOTBALLERS PLAYING IN ENGLAND. HE BANGED IN 133 LEAGUE GOALS IN 384 APPEARANCES FOR PLYMOUTH, ALSO CAPTAINING THEM TO PROMOTION. BUT WITH NO FILM FOOTAGE, WE'RE FORCED TO FORM A PICTURE FROM CONTEMPORARY REPORTS AND WEIRD OLD CARTOON WITH DATED CULTURAL REFERENCES BAFFLING TO ALL BUT A RAPIDLY VANISHING GROUP OF ELDERLY PEOPLE – IMAGINE THAT!

"CATFLAP BANJO DE-HUMIDIFIER, MRS PARSNIPS!"

"BREATHTAKING RACIAL EPITHET!"

BORN IN CANNING TOWN, HIS PLAYING CAREER STARTED AT BARKING TOWN, FOR WHOM HE SCORED OVER 250 GOALS, CATCHING THE EYE OF THE ARGYLE SCOUTS. HAVING LEFT LONDON, A LESSER CHARACTER WOULD HAVE BEEN DAZZLED BY THE BRIGHT LIGHTS OF PLYMOUTH, BUT LESLIE MANAGED TO KEEP HIS FEET ON THE GROUND.

RED HOT PASTIES

SCRUMPY

SCOOZES

ALTHOUGH PLAYING IN THE THIRD DIVISION, HIS PERFORMANCES EARNED THE INSIDE-LEFT A DESERVED CALL-UP TO THE ENGLAND SQUAD AS A RESERVE FOR AN INTERNATIONAL AGAINST IRELAND IN OCTOBER 1925. EVERYONE AT THE CLUB AND IN THE TOWN WAS DELIGHTED AND PROUD TO SEE JACK'S NAME PRINTED THERE IN BLACK AND WHITE IN THE NEWSPAPER.

HOWEVER, THAT WAS THE LAST ANYONE HEARD OF IT. THE SELECTORS NEVER CONTACTED HIM AND HIS NAME MYSTERIOUSLY VANISHED FROM THE NEXT PUBLISHED SQUAD LIST. THE CONTROVERSY WAS REPORTED LOCALLY AND NATIONALLY, WITH THE WIDELY-HELD BELIEF THAT HIS OMISSION WAS DUE TO THE COLOUR OF HIS SKIN. AS LESLIE SAID IN LATER LIFE: "THEY MUST HAVE FORGOT I WAS A COLOURED BOY".

The scouts say this Leslie chap is a tremendously exciting talent.

Yes, and he'll go down in history as the first person of his ethnicity to play for England!

Come now, it's no big deal; I'm sure we've picked wurzels before.

Sweet mother of...

BUT JACK STILL MADE HIS MARK ON THE INTERNATIONAL SCENE DURING PLYMOUTH'S TOUR OF SOUTH AMERICA IN 1924. AS WELL AS BEATING ARGENTINA, ARGYLE ALSO SAW OFF THE FUTURE OLYMPIC AND WORLD CHAMPIONS URUGUAY, 4-0, WITH LESLIE SCORING.

IT TOOK UNTIL 1978 FOR A BLACK FOOTBALLER TO REPRESENT ENGLAND AT THE SENIOR LEVEL. WHEN VIV ANDERSON MADE HIS INTERNATIONAL DEBUT, JACK WAS WORKING AS A 'BOOT BOY' AT WEST HAM, WHERE HE WAS REMEMBERED FONDLY BY PLAYERS WHO WERE UNAWARE OF HIS ACHIEVEMENTS.

HE MAY HAVE BEEN TOO MODEST TO TALK ABOUT HIS ACCOMPLISHMENTS, BUT NOW THERE WILL BE A PERMANENT MEMORIAL TO A TRUE FOOTBALL PIONEER.

THE KID WHO WOULD BE KING

PELÉ, THE BOY FROM BAURU WHO ROSE FROM POVERTY TO BECOME THE GREATEST FOOTBALLER IN THE WORLD, HAS DIED. A PLAYER DECADES AHEAD OF HIS TIME, PELÉ APPEARED OTHER-WORLDLY IN COMPARISON TO HIS CONTEMPORARIES. IT WAS AS IF HIS PARENTS FOUND HIM IN THE GLOWING CRATER OF A METEORITE. HIS GREATEST HITS ARE SEARED INTO OUR CONSCIOUSNESS LIKE A BEATLES MELODY OR FOOTAGE OF THE MOON LANDING. PELÉ'S AMAZING LIFE WOULD HAVE BEEN BEYOND EVEN THE WILDEST FANTASIES OF THE KID WHO SHINED SHOES OUTSIDE HIS LOCAL FOOTBALL GROUND...

TWO GOALS TO HELP WIN THE 1958 WORLD CUP WHEN BARELY OUT OF HIS SHOE-SHINE GEAR

EMOTIONAL SCENES ENSUE...

THE SOMBRERO

O great

A SECOND WORLD CUP IN 1962 AND GLOBAL FAME THANKS TO AN ENDLESS WORLD TOUR.

RECORDING HIS THOUSANDTH CAREER GOAL IN 1969.

PELÉ (AND SANTOS)

COMING SOON TO A TOWN NEAR YOU — NO MATTER WHERE YOU LIVE!

Can I have a day off now, please?

And miss Crawley in November?! Are you mad?

OF COURSE, SCORING GOALS WAS LOADS EASIER BACK THEN,

AS PELÉ DISCOVERED AT THE 1966 WORLD CUP.

THE EFFERVESCENT SPACE-AGED FOOTBALL OF 1970 — PELÉ'S MASTERPIECE.

THE SHOT...

... THE DUMMY...

...THE LAY-OFF

THE FINAL FRONTIER: AMERICA

THE NASL ... NEW YORK ... HOLLYWOOD!

John Wark?!

Don't stare, kid.

THE POST-RETIREMENT COMMERCIAL ACTIVITY, A NECESSITY OF HIS FINANCIAL PROBLEMS AND THE LINGERING PSYCHOLOGICAL SHADOW OF CHILDHOOD POVERTY — A TRAUMA THAT NEVER FULLY LEAVES YOU.

Is this all I've got?!

AND AT THE FINAL WHISTLE, TRIBUTES FROM AROUND THE WORLD AND THOUSANDS LINING THE STREETS TO PAY THEIR LAST RESPECTS TO A KING WHO EARNED HIS CROWN THROUGH INCOMPARABLE TALENT AND SHEER DETERMINATION. NOT BAD FOR A KID WHO LEARNED TO PLAY THE GAME WITH AN IMPROVISED FOOTBALL...

MY FRIEND PETE DIED RECENTLY.

IF YOU'RE A REGULAR FOOTBALL ATTENDEE, YOU PROBABLY HAVE A PETE IN YOUR LIFE. THEY'RE THE PERSON WHOSE SEASON TICKET HAS BEEN RANDOMLY ALLOCATED NEXT TO YOURS, WHO YOU END UP SPENDING MORE TIME WITH THAN MEMBERS OF YOUR OWN FAMILY. IT'S LIKELY YOU'RE SOMEONE ELSE'S PETE. SOMETIMES, PETES ARE A NIGHTMARE AND YOU HAVE TO MOVE SEATS TO AVOID THEM, BUT THIS PETE WAS A GOOD PETE.

HONESTLY, AT FIRST IT WAS A BIT OF A SHOCK TO FIND THE USUALLY VACANT SEAT AT THE END OF OUR ROW SUDDENLY FILLED BY A LOUD, CRAZY-HAIRED, SEMI-RETIRED CANADIAN TAXI DRIVER WHO HAD A HABIT OF PUNCHING YOU IN THE ARM TO INITIATE A CONVERSATION...

DID YA SEE THAT ?!

Oh this won't do.

AND MAYBE - JUST MAYBE - THERE WERE TIMES WHEN HE ALSO FOUND IT LESS THAN ENCHANTING TO BE SAT ALONGSIDE OUR SMALL GROUP OF ENGLISH IMMIGRANTS WHO SPENT MOST OF THE GAME WANGING ON ABOUT THE LEAGUE TWO PROMOTION RACE OR THE CONSTITUENT ELEMENTS OF THE PERFECT BREAKFAST BUFFET, BUT THIS IS HIGHLY UNLIKELY.

What about your baked beans?

They fulfill a decorative function, but no one would really miss them if they weren't there. They're basically the Crawley Town of the breakfast spread.

Oh I gotta call the membership office...

UNTIL HE FELL ILL, PETE WAS VIRTUALLY EVER-PRESENT. HIS SENSE OF LOYALTY ILLUSTRATED BY THE FACT HE HAD THE SAME MICROWAVE FOR 20+ YEARS. LET'S FACE IT, SOME WEEKS STAYING AT HOME AND WATCHING THAT OVEN WOULD HAVE PROVIDED MORE ENTERTAINMENT THAN THE A-LEAGUE, BUT HE KEPT COMING BACK. IN A TRUER SENSE, HIS DEPENDABILITY WAS SHOWN IN THE WAY HE VISITED AN OLD MATE TO WATCH THE SUPER BOWL EACH YEAR, EVEN THOUGH A NEUROLOGICAL CONDITION HAD LONG SINCE ROBBED HIM OF THE ABILITY TO RECOGNISE PETE.

AS IS COMMON WITH MANY MALE RELATIONSHIPS, WE DIDN'T KNOW MUCH ABOUT EACH OTHER'S LIVES OUTSIDE THE CONFINES OF FOOTBALL. I DID KNOW THAT HE WAS IMMENSELY PROUD OF HIS DAUGHTERS AND GRANDCHILDREN. THE ONLY THING THAT SEEMED TO GIVE HIM AS MUCH PRIDE WAS HIS ABILITY TO SNEAK A BOTTLE OF WINE PAST THE STADIUM SECURITY EACH WEEK - A FACT HE WOULD SHARE WITH OUR GROUP IN HUSHED TONES, AS IF RECOUNTING THE PLOT OF A SPY THRILLER.

You see, to the bored security guard, it looks like an ordinary flask. But that's not soup inside, it's... wine!

Fruity.

ELITE FOOTBALL HASN'T EXACTLY COVERED ITSELF IN GLORY IN RECENT TIMES, BUT THE GAME'S POWER TO BRING PEOPLE TOGETHER REMAINS UNDIMINISHED. FOOTBALL ISN'T ABOUT COEFFICIENTS OR NON-FUNGIBLE TOKENS. IT'S NOT EVEN REALLY ABOUT THE FOOTBALL. IT'S ABOUT THOSE HUMAN CONNECTIONS, SOMETIMES WITH GREAT PEOPLE YOU'D NEVER HAVE OTHERWISE MET. CHEERS PETE, SEE YOU NEXT TIME...

SQUIRES

ACKNOWLEDGEMENTS

All the cartoons in this book were, of course, published by the *Guardian*, and I owe a huge debt of gratitude to the team there, especially James Dart, Will Woodward and Gregg Bakowski, whose Tuesday mornings frequently involve him acting as the middleman in negotiations between me and the lawyers. My gratitude also to those very same legal eagles for keeping me out of debtors' prison – even someone with over 400 followers on Mastodon can't afford a lengthy court battle with ███████████. A hat-tip also to Mike Hytner at *Guardian Australia* for printing my A-League cartoons and providing friendship services above and beyond his job description.

As ever, I must thank my partner Sarah for her patience and support, and my friends and family for tolerating me missing yet another social event because I'm sat at my desk. Guys, I promise I'll try to make your next wedding, if it doesn't clash with a major-tournament group game.

Enormous thanks also to my agent David Luxton, and to Mo Hafeez and the good people at Faber.

Finally, thanks to a total stranger called 'Bluey', who came to my rescue when a stray pit bull terrier misidentified me as a chew toy in early 2024. Without his brave intervention, I wouldn't be typing this now. And yes, I am aware that my hero shares the name of an Australian cartoon dog, because even my near-death experiences must include daft puns.